THE STRUCTURE OF
INORGANIC RADICALS

*An Application of Electron Spin Resonance
to the Study of Molecular Structure*

BY

P. W. ATKINS

Fellow of Lincoln College, Oxford

AND

M. C. R. SYMONS

Professor of Physical Chemistry, The University of Leicester

ELSEVIER PUBLISHING COMPANY

AMSTERDAM - LONDON - NEW YORK

1967

ELSEVIER PUBLISHING COMPANY
335 JAN VAN GALENSTRAAT, P.O. BOX 211, AMSTERDAM

AMERICAN ELSEVIER PUBLISHING COMPANY, INC.
52 VANDERBILT AVENUE, NEW YORK, N.Y. 10017

ELSEVIER PUBLISHING COMPANY LIMITED
RIPPLESIDE COMMERCIAL ESTATE, BARKING, ESSEX

LIBRARY OF CONGRESS CATALOG CARD NUMBER 66-20555

WITH 74 ILLUSTRATIONS AND 57 TABLES

PRINTED IN THE NETHERLANDS

Preface

In two senses this book is intended to serve a dual purpose. On the one hand, whilst it is concerned with the trapping and detection of radicals it also dwells extensively on details of electronic structure.

On the other, whilst it aims primarily at a description of the underlying physical phenomena in a fairly down-to-earth manner, at the same time, the more rigorous mathematical basis is outlined in the Appendices.

We hope that this approach is a useful one, and that we have not fallen into too many pitfalls in treading this particular path.

We have tried to avoid giving the impression that all the problems are solved: there has, surely, been a step forward, but it seems to us that there is still a very great deal to be accomplished in this field.

The book was evolved at Leicester University, largely during the period 1961–1964. We are glad to record our debt to all those who have collaborated with us, or who have otherwise contributed to our understanding of the subject. We are especially indebted to Ron Catterall and David Tinling for their assistance in editing the text.

At some stage in the production of a book the manuscript must be made legible: for the typing of the manuscript in its entirety we are greatly indebted to Mrs. Judith Atkins.

Leicester and Oxford,   M. C. R. SYMONS
July, 1966   P. W. ATKINS

Contents

Chapter 1

Introduction

In this Chapter, after a survey of the contents of successive Chapters and the Appendices, we dwell briefly on the historical background of the work under consideration, paying particular attention to the impact of electron spin resonance. The way in which this technique is linked to various others is then outlined.

1.1 SURVEY

Our plan is to indicate how, by studying the detailed results of the electron spin resonance spectra of simple radicals, one can build a solidly based picture of the electronic structure, not only of these radicals but more generally of the related diamagnetic molecules from which the radicals can be derived by electron gain or loss.

The radicals are classified according to the number of atoms in the basic types. Thus under triatomic radicals we deal first with single BAB species either linear or bent. We include many more complex species however in which the "ligand" atoms B have become groups, but which can conveniently be considered in terms of those "parent" species.

Tetratomic radicals, in our classification, are those in which a central atom A is bonded to three ligand atoms B, and again B may be a group rather than an atom. Similarly, AB_4 radicals have A linked to four B atoms or groups.

Each of these Chapters is subdivided into one section entitled STRUCTURAL ASPECTS and one entitled EXPERIMENTAL RESULTS. The former is designed to give an indication of current ideas of electronic structures of the classes of molecules under consideration, independently of the results that have been obtained (but probably prejudiced by them nevertheless). It continues by indicating the expected features of the electron spin resonance spectra for such radicals. This is included partly because many workers in the field have had to use just such an approach in order to arrive at a correct identification of a radical. In other words the argument has a cyclic element in it: this aspect of identification is referred to in many subsequent sections.

Some more specific aspects of the contents of individual Chapters are now discussed.

(a) Details of Chapters

In Chapter 2 a brief introduction to the technique of electron spin resonance will be found. This is included for those readers who are unfamiliar with this method, and special emphasis is given to the way in which the resulting parameters can be used to derive structural information about the radicals.

Chapter 3 covers the other important items of background information, namely, the ways in which radicals are usually prepared and trapped. Many of the techniques are sufficiently novel and unusual to warrant this generalised treatment.

Our first Chapter on specific species (Chapter 4) is concerned with the simplest of all radicals: trapped or solvated electrons. In one sense these electron "centres" are simple, but from another viewpoint they are extremely complicated and the results more difficult to interpret than those for polyatomic radicals. This is so, because the nature of the trapping medium is all important in determining the properties of the centre.

The medium also plays a part, though to a smaller extent, in determining the magnetic properties of trapped atoms, which form the subject matter of Chapter 5. Current theories for the role of the medium are first outlined, and the results for hydrogen atoms, alkali metal atoms, silver atoms, and atoms or ions of groups V, VI and VII of the Periodic Table are outlined. Silver atoms are included because of the contrast the results make with those for the alkali metals, and because of the link they provide with transition metal complexes.

In Chapter 6 we at last reach the topic of radicals in the normally accepted sense. Here diatomic radicals are considered, and the Chapter is divided into two, the first half being concerned with basic theory and the second with specific examples. These are listed in the Index, so there is no need to enumerate them here.

Chapters 7, 8, and 9 extend this treatment to tri-, tetra- and penta-atomic radicals in turn, with the addition of detailed results for a wide variety of structurally similar species. In Chapter 9 special reference is made to the question of pair-wise trapping of radicals in solids, since the phenomenon is especially well-defined for SO_5^- radicals in photolysed persulphates. Also included in Chapter 9 is a brief comparison between results for thirty-three electron AB_4 radicals and those for d^1-transition metal tetroxides. This is particularly concerned with the relative importance of atomic d-orbitals in such structurally similar species.

Chapter 10 represents an attempt to rationalise the quantity of information in the preceding chapters. Some generalisations are drawn, and specific results are emphasised. Some of the areas where incompletely solved problems exist are touched on and possible future developments are suggested.[*]

In Appendix 1 the language of Group Theory is outlined and in Appendix 2 a more formal derivation of the equations appropriate to the electron spin resonance experiment is given. This leads to Appendix 3 which is specifically concerned with the difficult task of estimating g-values for polyatomic radicals. Appendix 4 is an elaboration of the way in which data for electron spin resonance can be used to calculate spin densities in radicals and hence, in some instances, their shape. This is an extension of the discussion given in Chapter 2.

Finally, in Appendix 5, the more mundane but very important task of interpreting electron spin resonance spectra is discussed for the possible benefit of new workers in the field.

1.2 HISTORICAL REVIEW

Two aspects of this work are sufficiently novel to warrant a brief historical introduction. These are the technique of electron spin resonance and the phenomenon of radical stabilisation by trapping.

(a) Electron spin resonance

The basic experiment was first performed in Russia by Zavoisky[1] and at Oxford by Bleaney and his co-workers[2] just after the Second World War. The natural choice of paramagnetic material was a transition metal complex, and these were sufficiently numerous to be a fertile area for physicists for many years. A few sporadic studies of inorganic radicals such as NO_2[3,4] were undertaken during this period, but when the technique was inherited by chemists in the 1950's, attention was turned, in the main, to the topic of organic π-radicals.

* *Note added in proof.* Some of these aspects are covered in greater depth in an article by H. Bower, M. C. R. Symons and D. Tinling in *Radical Ions,* edited by Dr. Larry Kevan, published by Wiley–Interscience, 1967.

Starting with stable radicals, such as Ph_3C and 1,1-diphenyl 2-picryl hydrazyl, it was soon recognised that a wide range of radical anions could be prepared by alkali metal or electrochemical reduction of the corresponding aromatic compounds, and the results proved to be of very great use to theoretical workers in this field [5, 6]. Indeed, such studies still continue, and have been supplemented by the equally interesting field of radical cations formed from similar aromatic molecules by oxidation, often in sulphuric acid [5, 6].

A development of great importance was the discovery, originally due to LEWIS and LIPKIN [7] but revived in the mid 1950's, that normally very unstable radicals could be stabilised for indefinite periods simply by their preparation in a rigid medium [5, 8]. These developments, which will be discussed in the next section, came at a time when the technique of electron spin resonance was just passing into a second phase, in which various refinements were introduced to increase the sensitivity and resolving power of the instruments enormously. Trapped radicals in very low concentration could then be detected, but identification was hampered by an inability, in many instances, to interpret the complex envelope spectra obtained from powders or glasses.

Irradiated single crystals of glycine and other organic molecules had been studied but the very complex, anisotropic spectra remained uninterpreted for several years until Gosh and Whiffen correctly unravelled part of the complex spectrum from irradiated glycine crystals [9]. This was followed by several studies of simpler organic radicals in irradiated single crystals and now the picture is fairly clear for a wide range of radicals.

At the same time, solid state physicists were turning their attention to the study of radiation damage of inorganic solids using this technique. Previously, ultraviolet spectroscopy had been one of their main weapons and so the damage centres were often known as "colour-centres". The way in which the presence of these centres modified the electrical properties of solids had long been a major interest, and hence they are commonly discussed in terms of band-theory.

The results from electron spin resonance studies constituted a triumphant confirmation of the anion vacancy theory of F-centres (§ 4.1a) but in many other cases these studies either failed entirely or the results were not in accord with the then accepted models. An outstanding example of the latter was the study of the V_K-centre in potassium chloride [10]. This centre, which we discuss in detail in § 6.2d(ii) proved to consist of an electron associated with two equivalent chlorine atoms. It was soon realised that this, and other electron deficit centres were better described as small molecules rather than as "hole-traps" in a continuous medium[11].

It is now realised that a wide variety of paramagnetic centres formed in inorganic crystals by high energy radiation are satisfactorily described as isolated radicals with the unpaired electron closely confined to a relatively small molecular orbital. Certainly the crystal lattice must govern the properties of these radicals to some extent, but in all instances for which direct comparisons have been made, such environmental effects seem to be small.

Two of the main links which established this fact were the radicals NO_2 and ClO_2. These are amongst the very few stable inorganic radicals and hence their electron spin resonance spectra could be measured without ambiguity of identification, and the results compared with those for centres formed by irradiation. For ClO_2 the issue was clear. Thus results for this molecule in frozen sulphuric acid were closely similar to those for a centre which could be formed in various chlorates and perchlorates by exposure to γ-rays[12,13] (§ 7.2b (i)). Early studies of NO_2 were unfortunately clouded by a series of mistakes. These, which are outlined in § 7.2a (i), were eventually appreciated and the link with results for various centres in irradiated nitrates, nitrites and alkali halide crystals doped with these oxyions was established[14,15].

A great deal of work has now been done in this field: many new species have been characterised and studied, and the purpose of this book is to outline the results and to discuss their significance.

(b) Radical formation and trapping

There must be a wide variety of studies which, by intent or chance, with or without comprehension, have involved the stabilisation of reactive species by trapping. One such overt study already mentioned was that of Lewis and Lipkin[7]. Certainly the phenomenon, which is in essence extremely simple, relying as it does upon the fact that solids commonly confer immobility upon molecules contained within themselves, was appreciated by Rice and his colleagues[16] and was used extensively by Pimentel et al.[17] to isolate stable molecules such as that of water, in order to measure their spectra in the absence of strongly interacting neighbours.

The various techniques which have been used to stabilise radicals by trapping in solid matrices are reviewed in Chapter 3. The whole subject received an impetus in 1957 from the National Bureau of Standards in Washington D.C. Their concerted study of radical trapping, which brought many workers together, and which extended to a wide range of other laboratories, was conceived apparently because of the probability that new rocket fuels might result. Although this aim was not realised the venture was of great use to pure science, and, although the group was disbanded three years after its inception the international meetings which it sponsored are still an important biennial landmark for workers in the field. The work of this group has been summarised recently by Bass and Broida[8].

Since then the impetus has been retained and new methods developed. Most of the radicals described in this book have been stabilised by one or other of these methods, and we hope to show that a combination of the techniques of electron spin resonance and radical trapping represents a very powerful weapon for probing the electronic structure of molecules. For this reason, we do not intend to elaborate in detail the results of studies involving other techniques. This neglect does not represent an attempt to belittle these, but it is felt that our aim is best furthered by this limitation.

1.3 OTHER TECHNIQUES

Other techniques that have been used in the study of inorganic radicals include the following.

(a) Ultraviolet spectroscopy

This is a particularly important technique for studying the structure of molecules that can be prepared in the gas-phase, and much of our knowledge of their electronic structure stems from the interpretation of the vibration rotation fine-structure observed under high resolution[18-20]. Among the molecules that have been studied by this method are a variety of simple radicals, including, of course, NO_2 and ClO_2. Despite this it appears that the problems and ambiguities of interpretation are numerous, and although many of the radicals discussed in this book could have been studied by ultraviolet spectroscopy in the solid state (which is often nearly as sensitive a method as electron spin resonance) it is doubtful that clear-cut identifications could have been reached using only this method.

(b) Infrared and Raman spectroscopy

These techniques are usually of only indirect use for studies of electronic structure. Also, from the viewpoint of studying trapped or transient radicals they suffer from having relatively low sensitivity.

(c) Nuclear magnetic resonance

The same comment about sensitivity applies here also, therefore few studies of inorganic radicals with this technique have been undertaken. This is a pity, since the method is in many ways complementary to that of electron spin resonance. In particular it will reveal the signs of hyperfine coupling constants. Also signals can be detected by nuclear magnetic resonance under conditions where lines are too broad to detect by electron spin resonance. The application of this method to the study of solutions of metals in ammonia is discussed in Chapter 4.

(d) Microwave spectroscopy

In principle, this is an extremely powerful tool for the study of radicals in the gas-phase, as has been demonstrated by Radford[21] in his studies of the hydroxyl radical. A magnetic field is used to remove the degeneracy of the levels, and under favourable conditions both electric and magnetic dipole transitions can be detected. In this way both the isotropic and the anisotropic hyperfine coupling constants can be calculated. Analysis is difficult and as yet very few radicals have been studied using this technique. A recent study of NO_2 illustrates some of the difficulties[22].

References

1 Y. K. ZAVOISKY, *J. Phys. USSR*, 1945, *9*, 245.
2 See for example, the reviews by: B. BLEANEY AND K. W. H. STEVENS, *Rept. Progr. Phys.*, 1953, *16*, 108: K. D. BOWERS AND J. OWEN, *Rept. Prog. Phys.*, 1955, *18*, 304.
3 B. BLEANEY, W. HAYES AND P. M. LLEWELLYN, *Nature*, 1957, *179*, 140.
4 J. G. CASTLE AND R. BERINGER, *Phys. Rev.*, 1950, *80*, 114.
5 M. C. R. SYMONS, *Advan. Phys. Org. Chem.*, 1963, *1*, 284.
6 A. CARRINGTON, *Quart. Rev.*, 1963, *17*, 67.
7 G. N. LEWIS AND D. LIPKIN, *J. Am. Chem. Soc.*, 1942, *64*, 2801.
8 A. M. BASS AND H. P. BROIDA, *Formation and Trapping of Free Radicals*, Academic Press, 1960.
9 D. K. GHOSH AND D. H. WHIFFEN, *Mol. Phys.*, 1959, *2*, 285.
10 T. G. CASTNER AND W. KANZIG, *J. Phys. Chem. Solids*, 1957, *3*, 178.
11 M. C. R. SYMONS AND W. T. DOYLE, *Quart. Rev.*, 1960, *14*, 62.

12 P. W. ATKINS, J. A. BRIVATI, N. KEEN, M. C. R. SYMONS AND P. A. TREVALION, *J. Chem. Soc.*, 1962, 4785.
13 T. COLE, *Proc. Natl. Acad. Sci. U.S.*, 1962, *37*, 671.
14 H. ZELDES AND R. LIVINGSTON, *J. Chem. Phys.*, 1961, *35*, 563.
15 P. W. ATKINS AND M. C. R. SYMONS, *J. Chem. Soc.*, 1962, 4794.
16 F. O. RICE AND M. J. FREAMO, *J. Am. Chem. Soc.*, 1951, *73*, 5529.
17 E. D. BECKER AND G. C. PIMENTEL, *J. Chem. Phys.*, 1956, *25*, 224; E. WHITTLE, D. A. DOWS AND G. C. PIMENTEL, *J. Chem. Phys.*, 1954, *22*, 943.
18 R. S. MULLIKEN, *Rev. Mod. Phys.*, 1942, *14*, 204.
19 A. D. WALSH, *J. Chem. Soc.*, 1953, 2260 *et seq.*
20 *Discussions Faraday Soc.*, 1963, 35.
21 H. E. RADFORD, *Phys. Rev.*, 1961, *122*, 114.
22 G. R. BIRD, J. C. BAIRD, A. W. JACHE, J. A. HODGESON, R. F. CURL, A. C. KUNKLE, J. W. BRANSFORD, J. RASTRUP-ANDERSON AND J. ROSENTHAL, *J. Chem. Phys.*, 1964, *40*, 3378

Chapter 2

An introduction to electron spin resonance

This Chapter is intended to serve as an introduction to the principles and applications of electron spin resonance, showing, in particular, what information can be obtained from the spectra. Our intention is to give a highly qualitative outline so that the reader can first develop a feeling for the principles; once this is accomplished the mathematical details are much easier to understand and at that stage the ideas gained here can be treated with greater sophistication and precision. A more quantitative exposition of some of the points made in this Chapter is presented in the Appendices. A number of books on the principles of electron spin resonance has recently appeared, in particular, reference may be made to those of Pake[1], Slichter[2], and Al'tshuler and Kozyrev[3].

2.1 BASIC PRINCIPLES

Both theory and experiment have shown that an electron possesses intrinsic angular momentum which is known as its "spin". Because the electron is electrically charged and since there is a magnetic field associated with any moving charge, there is a magnetic field associated with the spinning electron. In other words an electron, by virtue of its intrinsic angular momentum, behaves as a tiny bar magnet.

In free space these magnets are aligned quite randomly, but in the presence of an externally applied magnetic field there will be a preferred direction. Quantum mechanics tells us that an electron has a spin quantum number of $\frac{1}{2}$ and that it can have only two orientations with respect to a given axis. Crudely, the electron can either spin clockwise at a particular rate or it can spin anti-clockwise at the same rate. In terms of the magnetic properties of an electron in an external field it can behave as a small bar magnet aligned effectively with the direction of the external field or against it.

A diagram, such as Fig. 2.1. can be used to illustrate the fact that the difference in energy between the two directions of spin (or orientation of the mag-

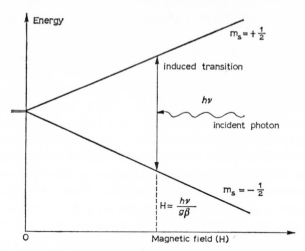

Fig. 2.1.   The effect of an external magnetic field upon the energy of an electron and
the transition induced by an electromagnetic field.

netic moment of the electron) depends on the strength of the external field:
it requires much more effort to hold a bar magnet opposed to a strong field
than it does to hold one opposed to a weaker field. It follows that if we could
contrive to reverse the electron spin then we would need to supply energy,
and that more energy would be needed in high than in low magnetic fields.

Basically, that is all that an electron spin resonance spectrum measures,
namely the energy required to reverse the spin of an electron in an externally
applied magnetic field. It is only necessary to bathe the electron in a reservoir
of energy. If this source of energy is a beam of radio waves having a single
frequency v (and, therefore, by Planck's relation, having a single energy hv),
there will be an exchange of energy between the electron spin and the radio-
frequency field such that the energy "resonates" between the two energy
systems, when the difference in energy between the two spin directions is
equal to the energy of the radio-frequency field. To give some idea of the
magnitudes involved, at a field of 3,000 gauss a frequency of about 9 kMcs
is required, corresponding to a wavelength of 3 cm. At this kind of field, it
is apparent that the radio-frequency waves required are in the microwave
region.

At this stage, we can see the general form of the apparatus needed in order
to observe an electron spin resonance spectrum: we require a sample containing unpaired electrons bathed in a microwave field and the whole placed

in a powerful magnetic field. Both the magnetic field and the microwave power must be monitored, in order that a properly calibrated spectrum be obtained. In passing, it may be pointed out that, for instrumental reasons, when a spectrum is recorded the microwave frequency is usually kept constant and the magnetic field varied. Since electron spin resonance spectrometers of very high sensitivity and resolving power are readily available commercially, no further details of instrumentation will be given here.

So far, this seems an expensive way to arrive at a rather dull result. But a glance at any of the spectra in the later pages of this book shows that they are of much greater complexity than our simple discussion allows. Looking at the spectra it is clear that there are three features which differ from spectrum to spectrum. The first is that resonances for a given microwave frequency do not always occur at the same magnetic field strength. Writing the resonance condition as

$$h\nu = g\beta H \tag{2.1}$$

(where ν is the microwave frequency, H the magnetic field strength and β the Bohr magneton), g may be taken as a parameter which governs the position of the resonance absorption. Secondly, it is rare for spectra to consist of only a single line. Extra lines *may* be due to other species with different g-values but there is also a mechanism which can give rise to a multiplet spectrum for a single species if it contains magnetic nuclei, and we show below how this can be distinguished from the former possibility. The third property of the spectrum is the width of the absorption lines. These three factors are discussed in turn.

2.2 *g*-VALUE VARIATION

Although the expected g-value for an electron with no angular momentum except that due to its spin is 2, the actual "free-spin" value is 2.0023. This is because a relativistic correction applies. Since other factors in which we will be interested cause deviations of comparable magnitude this correction is important.

An electron, however, may also have orbital angular momentum, with an associated magnetic moment. For atoms, linear molecules with an unpaired π-electron, and other systems with orbitally degenerate ground states in the gas-phase, the spin and orbital momenta must be combined, and transitions will be observed between the various combined states. Much of the present book will be concerned with species of lower symmetry, not having orbitally degenerate ground states or with species which should have orbital degeneracy but are in environments which remove the degeneracy so that the ground state is effectively an orbital singlet.

In these circumstances, deviation of the g-value from 2.0023 (Δg) will be small, and, to a first approximation can be thought of as stemming from an additional small perturbing field arising from a very slight induced orbital motion. This adds to or subtracts from the external field giving a negative ($-\Delta g$) or positive ($+\Delta g$) shift.

These ideas can be illustrated by reference to the molecule NO_2 discussed in Chapter 7. Since none of the orbitals of this bent molecule can be degenerate, the ground state of the radical cannot possess any electronic orbital angular momentum. To see this, consider Fig. 2.2. which illustrates the divergence of the energies of the in-plane and out-of-plane orbitals on the nitrogen as the molecule bends.

The figure is just a portion of Walsh's correlation diagram (Fig. 7.2.) which we shall consider in greater detail later. In the linear state, the p_x and p_y atomic orbitals contribute to a doubly degenerate π-orbital; the unpaired electron therefore has unit angular momentum about the internuclear axis. When the molecule is bent (as it really is) the degeneracy of the π-orbitals is removed and the electron occupies the lower (a_1) orbital. Since it can only "go round" the molecular framework about the y-axis by excitation through the b_1 orbital the ground state of the molecule has no orbital angular momentum. If, however, the molecule is put in an external field, as it is in an electron spin resonance experiment, then the field tends to *drive* the orbital angular momentum, that is it induces momentum to an extent governed by

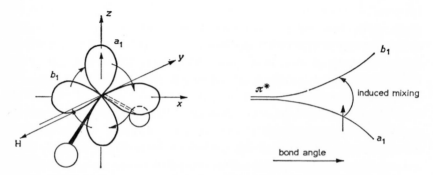

Fig. 2.2.   The effect of bending on the g-values of an AB_2 molecule.

the energy barrier (the difference in energy between the orbitals b_1 and a_1) which it must overcome in order to stimulate the orbital motion. An electron with orbital motion produces a magnetic field which is *opposed* to the applied field, that is there is a tendency to retain the original state of the system. Therefore, since the spin of the electron experiences the sum of the applied and induced fields (the sum, because the orbital moment couples with the spin through the spin–orbit coupling), a higher field will have to be used in order to reach resonance for a given microwave frequency. If the resonance condition is looked at it is seen that this implies a *g*-value of *less* than the free-spin value.

An alternative, yet equivalent, picture of the way in which a *g*-value different from that of the free spin arises is to consider the same situation but in reverse. That is, the spin and orbital momenta are coupled through the spin–orbit interaction in a free atom. In the present system, there is spin angular momentum and there is spin–orbit coupling; consequently, the spin tends to create a vestigial orbital angular momentum. The effectiveness of the spin in coupling to the magnetic field is thereby lowered and a higher field must be used in order to satisfy the resonance condition.

The *g*-shift should differ more from the free-spin value the greater the spin–orbit coupling constant of the relevant atoms of the molecule (this generally increases with increasing atomic number) and the smaller the energy difference between the states involved in the electron's progress about a particular axis.

If the unpaired electron occupied the upper orbital shown in Fig. 2.2 and the lower orbital contained two electrons, then the same situation would obtain if we considered the system as a single *hole* being urged round by the applied field; since the hole is positive relative to the electrons the field is increased, and consequently the resonance condition is fulfilled at lower applied fields. This will give a *g*-value greater than that of the free spin.

The illustration with NO_2 was concerned only with a migration about the *y*-axis. Obviously, if we applied the external field perpendicular to the plane of the molecule, then orbital motion would be induced about the *x*-axis but the orbital involved would now have to be the $p_y (b_2)$ orbital in order to provide a path around the *x*-axis. Since it is extremely unlikely that the b_1- and b_2-orbitals are degenerate, this must mean that the *g*-value in this direction is different from that in the *y*-direction. Similarly, the *g*-value in the *z*-direction is different from the other two. Thus we arrive at the result that the field at which resonance can be reached depends upon the orientation of

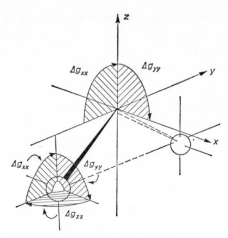

Fig. 2.3.   Orbital mixing in NO_2 that contributes to the g-tensor.

the radical to the applied field and that different radicals can have different g-values, each one of which may be either greater or smaller than the free-spin value of 2.0023. The anisotropy of the g-value and its dependence on direction suggests that we should write it as a tensor, and normally we shall record the principal values along the x-, y- and z-axes of the radical.

Fig. 2.3 illustrates the mixing involved on the nitrogen atom for all three g-values. (Δg_{zz} arises from mixing on the oxygen atoms because the p_z-orbital on nitrogen has zero component of angular momentum along z and so cannot couple with the field when it is in that direction.)

2.3 HYPERFINE INTERACTION

The hyperfine interaction is the mechanism which accounts for the multiplet character of some of the spectra referred to earlier. Many nuclei also have a "spin" associated with them and hence, because of their charge, are magnetic. In a molecule containing one or more magnetic nuclei the electron will experience not only the externally applied field, but also that from the magnetic nuclei. The nuclear magnetic moments are very small, but the unpaired electron is likely to approach them closely, and these hyperfine fields often reach strengths of several hundred gauss. The nuclear fields do not displace the spectrum but split it into a number of components centred about the position at which the resonance would have occurred had there been no hyperfine interaction. This happens because the orientation of the spin angular momentum is quantised.

(a) Multiplet spectrum from one nucleus

A nucleus of spin I has an associated magnetic quantum number m_I that can take all the values I, I−1, ..., −I. The presence of the external magnetic field also implies that some of these orientations are more favoured than others and therefore the more favoured states are expected to be more highly populated. However, since the nuclear moments are so small the energy differences between the orientations are also small, and so at normal temperatures the states are, for our present purposes, equally populated. For a nucleus of spin $\frac{1}{2}$ there are two orientations for the magnetic moment, one opposing and the other augmenting the external field. The unpaired electron then experiences the field $H \pm \delta H$, where δH is the field due to the nucleus. The situation is illustrated in Fig. 2.4.

As the field is increased from zero the resonance condition will be reached at the two field strengths at which the equation

$$hv = g\beta (H \pm \delta H) \tag{2.2}$$

is satisfied. Two lines will then be observed equally spaced about the position of the resonance in the absence of any hyperfine interaction*. It should be noted that only the transitions which do not involve a change in the nuclear magnetic quantum number are allowed, thus a type of Franck–Condon transition within the static nuclear spin framework has occurred. Also the high and low field transitions are of equal intensity; this is a consequence of the almost equal population of all the nuclear magnetic states m_I.

It is a simple extension to show that for a nucleus of spin I the spectrum will show a multiplet consisting of $2I+1$ lines of equal intensity.

(b) Multiplet spectrum from several nuclei

A more complex situation arises when the unpaired electron can interact with

---

* This is not strictly true—deviations from this simple situation are particularly noticeable when the hyperfine interaction is large (*ca.* 100 gauss). In these cases the curvature of the energy levels illustrated on the left hand side of Fig. 2.4. extends into the resonant region and must be taken into account in order to extract the spectral parameters. This is discussed more fully in Appendix 2.

References p. 33–34

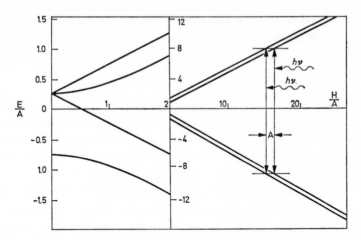

Fig. 2.4. Variation of the energy of an electron interacting with a spin $\frac{1}{2}$ nucleus in the presence of an external magnetic field.

more than one magnetic nucleus. If nucleus A has a spin of I_A then the unpaired electron experiences a field which is the vector sum of the field applied and the nuclear field. If there is another nucleus B present with spin I_B the field experienced is the sum of all three fields. Thus, if $I_A = \frac{3}{2}$ and $I_B = \frac{1}{2}$ the spectrum will consist of a quartet of doublets. This situation is depicted in Fig. 2.5.

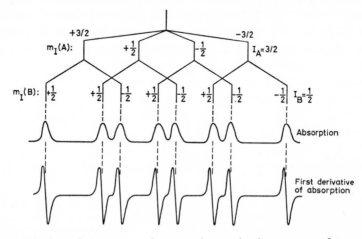

Fig. 2.5. The hyperfine spectrum from an electron in the presence of two nuclei, one with spin $^3/_2$ the other with spin $^1/_2$.

If all the nuclei are equivalent, particularly symmetric patterns are obtained. For example, six equivalent protons $(I=\frac{1}{2})$ give rise to a septet of lines with an intensity ratio distribution according to the binomial law $(1:6:15:20:15:6:1)$.

(c) Anisotropic (dipolar) interaction

We have employed the term "very close" in the preceding discussion and it is worthwhile reflecting upon what is meant by "close" and whether structural information can be obtained from the resulting hyperfine splitting.

The hyperfine splitting arises from the interaction of two dipoles; consequently it would be expected that the interaction should depend upon their mutual orientation. If we consider an electron in a p-orbital (Fig. 2.6.) we see that when the field is along the symmetry axis of the orbital the field at the electron due to the nucleus is in the same direction as the applied field, whereas when it is in a plane perpendicular to the symmetry axis it is opposed to the applied field. We may also recognise that the former is the Gauss A position for two dipoles, and that the latter is the Gauss B position; thus if the field at the electron due to the nucleus is β in the first position it will be $-\beta/2$ in each of the perpendicular positions. Thus if the radical were rotated in the yz plane with the field along z, the hyperfine splitting might be expected to change from 2β through zero to $-\beta$, that is the lines would change sides. This is not what happens in practice for we have neglected two important factors.

The first is that the above analysis is inaccurate inasmuch as it assumes that the nucleus is quantised strictly along the direction of the applied field,

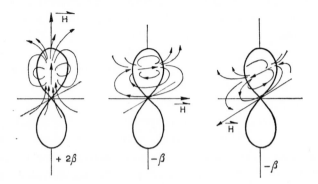

Fig. 2.6. The field at a nucleus due to an electron in a p-orbital.

a situation which is true only when the field is along the symmetry axis of the p-orbital. When the field is at an angle θ to this axis the actual field at the nucleus is the resultant of the applied field and the hyperfine field and the nucleus is quantised relative to this new axis. It may be shown that the tipping of the quantisation axis at the demand of the hyperfine field is sufficient to compensate for some of the reorientation pictured in Fig. 2.6. and instead of the dipolar interaction varying as $3 \cos^2 \theta - 1$ it really varies as $(3 \cos^2 \theta + 1)^{\frac{1}{2}}$ and so the hyperfine lines do not cross. When there is a strong hyperfine component always parallel to the applied field (that is, when there is a large isotropic component, for an account of which see the following section) then the quantisation of the nucleus is referred to the direction of the applied field, the compensatory reorientation of the nucleus does not occur, and the relatively small anisotropic splitting does follow a $3 \cos^2 \theta - 1$ law[4].

The presence of this isotropic coupling is the second reason for the absence of purely dipolar dependence of the splitting and to its explanation we now turn.

(d) Isotropic (contact) interaction

We should first note that because s-electrons are spherically disposed about the nucleus the dipolar interactions between them and the nucleus average to zero. The second point to note is that an ns-orbital is unique among atomic orbitals inasmuch as the wave-function is non-zero at the nucleus. This peculiarity gives rise to a hyperfine interaction which is known as the Fermi contact interaction and is isotropic. Consequently the observed hyperfine splitting, if the unpaired electron occupies an sp-hybrid on the magnetic nucleus, should consist of an anisotropic component superimposed upon an isotropic term. These can be extracted from the experimental data since the isotropic term $(A_{iso}^{(N)})$ is the mean value and subtraction of this from the experimental data gives the anisotropic term, **B**.

The manner in which the g- and hyperfine tensors can be extracted from the spectra of radicals in the solid phase is considered in Appendix 5.

In simple cases the principal directions (denoted by xx, yy, and zz subscripts) associated with the g-tensor (which is a parameter characteristic of the entire molecule) and the various hyperfine tensors $\mathbf{A}^{(N)}$ (which are parameters associated with the nuclei (N) concerned) are the same. In these cases, if the orientation of the radical in the host crystal is known or can reasonably be predicted, then the directions obtained for the magnetic axes can be compared with those for the radical. For example, in the case of NO_2 discussed above, the density axis of the $2p_z(N)$ orbital should lie along the bisector of the O–N–O angle. If the axes do not coincide then, even if the orientation of the radical in the host crystal is unknown the relative direction of the parameters can give useful information about the shape of the radical. This information may, however, be very difficult to extract from the spectra.

One problem in the unravelling of experimental information is that only the *magnitudes* of the principal values of the hyperfine tensors are obtained, not the *signs*. This is only a minor disadvantage in many instances, as is shown in several examples discussed in following chapters, but it can lead to unresolvable ambiguities. It would be easier if, as implied in this section, one could take the isotropic coupling as being positive. Certainly this must be so if the orbital on the magnetic nucleus concerned is an sp^n-hybrid. In fact, an isotropic term is almost invariably obtained, even when the electron is in a pure π-level, and in such cases $A_{iso}^{(N)}$ may be positive or negative. How this can come about is now considered in more detail.

(e) Inner shell polarisation

The paradox that p-electrons can give rise to an isotropic splitting is understandable when one realises that a quoted ground-state configuration is only a first approximation to the real configuration of the radical. There may be other configurations contributing to the true ground state (by "configuration interaction") which may be built from s orbitals. An example would be atomic nitrogen which, although it has a quoted $...2s^2\ 2p^3$, ^4S ground-state configuration, would be more accurately described by a mixture of this configuration with other ^4S states such as $...2s^1\ 2p^4$, ^4S. This latter configuration could be responsible for the observed isotropic splitting.

An alternative approach is to consider mechanisms whereby the filled s-levels are polarised by the half-filled p-orbital so that the α-spin orbital has a different radial function from that of the β-spin orbital. The resulting imbalance of spin-density at the nucleus produces an isotropic splitting.

The issue is complicated by the fact that spin-density on adjoining atoms can contribute to the overall isotropic splitting from the nucleus under consideration. For example, consider the nitric oxide molecule (NO). Here the unpaired electron is in a π-orbital which in the LCAO approximation is built from $2p$-levels on N and O. Isotropic hyperfine coupling to ^{14}N will arise in part from spin on nitrogen, as discussed above. For First and Second row elements this is known to be positive, but this is not necessarily always the case. (By "positive" one means that the "polarised" spin felt by the nucleus is parallel to the unpaired electron; negative spin-density arises when the polarisation mechanism leaves antiparallel spin at the nucleus.) There will, however, be appreciable spin-density on oxygen also and this give rise to a polarisation of the σ-bonding electrons as discussed for α-atom inter-actions in § 2.5a. This will give a negative contribution to $A_{iso}^{(N)}$ and hence the net isotropic coupling may be positive or negative.

We now go on to a consideration of the ways in which isotropic and aniso-tropic hyperfine coupling constants can give useful structural information.

2.4 MOLECULAR PARAMETERS

(a) Spin density distribution

We have seen that unpaired electrons in s-orbitals give rise to isotropic split-tings whilst electrons in p, d, ... orbitals give rise to anisotropic split-tings. We neglect all except the s- and p-orbital contributions for sim-plicity and consider the situation of a radical in which the unpaired electron occupies an orbital built from atomic orbitals which include an sp^n-hybrid on an atom with a non-zero nuclear spin. Suppose that this normalised molecular orbital is of the form

$$\psi = c_s\psi_s + c_p\psi_p + c_o\psi_o + c_{o'}\psi_{o'} + \cdots \tag{2.3}$$

where ψ_s and ψ_p are the s and p orbitals just discussed and ψ_o, $\psi_{o'}$, ... are all the other atomic obitals on the other atoms in the molecule. If overlap is neglected the amount of s-orbital involved is c_s^2 and the amount of p-orbital involved c_p^2. If we know that an s-orbital electron in the free atom gives an isotropic splitting of A_{iso}^* gauss and we observe an isotropic splitting of A_{iso} gauss then we can estimate the amount of unpaired electron in the s-orbital of the molecular orbital as

$$c_s^2 = A_{iso}/A_{iso}^* \tag{2.4}$$

Similarly, if there is an anisotropic splitting of B gauss, (where B is the maxi-mum value of the anisotropy) and we know that in the hypothetical atom, having unit occupancy of the particular p-orbital involved, the maximum value of the dipolar coupling is B* gauss, then the amount of electron in the

n	Isotope	Abundance (%)	Spin (I)	$\lvert\psi_{ns}(0)\rvert^2$ (a.u.)	$\langle r^{-3}\rangle_{np}$ (a.u.)	Isotropic coupling (A_{iso}) (gauss)	Anisotropic coupling (2β) (gauss)	λ (cm^{-1})	Reference
1	¹H	99.9844	1/2			508			22
	²H	0.0156	1			78			
2	⁶Li	7.43	1			39 (54)			23 (22)
	⁷Li	92.57	3/2	0.1673		105 (143)		0.2	23 (22)
	⁹Be	100	3/2	0.5704		130		1	23
	¹⁰B	18.83	3			242			
	¹¹B	81.17	3/2	1.408	0.775	725	38	11	23, 24
	¹³C	1.108	1/2	2.767	1.692	1,130	66	29	23, 24
	¹⁴N	99.635	1	4.770	3.101	552	34	76	23, 24
	¹⁵N	0.365	1/2			775	48		
	¹⁷O	0.037	5/2	7.638	4.974	1,660	104	151	23
	¹⁹F	100	1/2	11.966	7.546	17,200	1,084	270	23
3	²³Na	100	3/2			317		11	22
	²⁵Mg	10.05	5/2					20	
	²⁷Al	100	5/2	2.358	1.055	985	42	75	25
	²⁹Si	4.70	1/2	3.8069	2.0407	1,220	62	149	25
	³¹P	100	1/2	5.6251	3.3187	3,640	206	299	25
	³³S	0.74	3/2	7.9187	4.8140	975	56	382	25
	³⁵Cl	75.4	3/2	10.6435	6.7095	1,680	100	586	25
	³⁷Cl	24.6	3/2			1,395	84		25
4	³⁹K	93.08	3/2			83		38	22
	⁴¹K	6.91	3/2			45			
	⁴³Ca	0.13	7/2					105	
	⁶⁷Zn	4.12	5/2	4.5222		376	106	386	26
	⁶⁹Ga	60.2	3/2	6.9493	2.8665	2,675	134	551	26
	⁷¹Ga	39.8	3/2			3,400			
	⁷³Ge	7.61	9/2	9.5721	4.7848	535	26	940	26
	⁷⁵As	100	3/2	12.5606	6.9871	3,430	183	1,550	26
	⁷⁷Se	7.50	1/2	15.7791	9.2284	4,840	270	1,688	26
	⁷⁹Br	50.57	3/2	19.4127	11.8758	7,800	456	2,460	26
	⁸¹Br	49.43	3/2			8,400	564		26

* The values of $\lvert\psi_{ns}(0)\rvert^2$ and $\langle r^{-3}\rangle_{np}$ are those calculated by Morton, Rowlands and Whiffen [21] from the wave functions of the authors in the references.

p-orbital on the magnetic nucleus is

$$c_p^2 = B/B^* \qquad (2.5)$$

The free atom values A_{iso}^* and B^* are generally not known from experiment but they may in fact be calculated with moderate accuracy from self-consistent field wave functions. Typical values are given in Table 2.1.

We see, therefore, that if we know what splitting an entire electron will give with a nucleus when it is in either an ns- or an np-orbital on that nucleus we can estimate the actual occupancy of those orbitals and hence compare these with the calculated values of the coefficients of the molecular orbitals.

(b) Bond angles

Further information can be obtained from the hybridisation ratio $\lambda = c_p/c_s$. Coulson has shown[5] that if one assumes that the bonds formed from the hybridisation of s- and p-orbitals on an atom are orthogonal to each other, then it is possible to estimate the bond angle from the hybridisation ratio. Thus we now have a way not only of calculating the distribution of an unpaired electron in a radical but also, in some cases, of calculating bond angles. (We cannot calculate the bond angle by this method when the un-

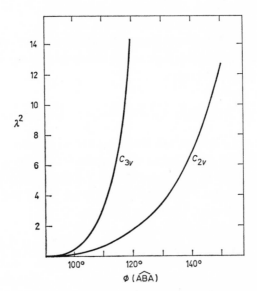

Fig. 2.7. Variation of bond angle with hybridisation ratio, λ.

paired electron is *not* in an sp^n-hybrid, that is when it is in a pure π-level.)

Formulae for the relationship between hybridisation ratio and bond angle are given in Appendix 4, but the graphical relationship is shown in Fig. 2.7.

We have accounted for some of the features of a spectrum and it is worthwhile reconsidering the information that we have been able to elicit so far. The g-values have revealed information about both the symmetry of the molecule and by a process of intelligent speculation a little about the relative energies of some orbitals in the molecule; a particularly useful function of g-values is that of identification of a radical by analogy with isoelectronic species whose g-values are known. The hyperfine interaction has been particularly informative inasmuch as the population of s- and p-orbitals on magnetic nuclei can be estimated and from this the electron distribution and (often) the bond angle determined. Once again, the hyperfine spectrum is useful diagnostically because the characteristic multiplet splitting of a magnetic nucleus is often readily recognisable.

2.5 HYPERFINE COUPLING TO α-ATOMS

Hyperfine structure also arises from atoms bonded directly to an atom bearing an unpaired electron. A simple example is the methyl radical: the problem is of special importance to organic chemists since it arises in all aromatic systems having an odd number of π-electrons. This aspect has been reviewed elsewhere[11]. The coupling can, as usual, be separated into dipolar (anisotropic) and contact (isotropic) parts.

(a) Anisotropic hyperfine coupling to α-atoms

For an electron in a p-orbital, this is of a similar magnitude and form to the coupling considered in § 2.3c but, if the electron is confined to one p-level it takes a different form, as illustrated in Fig. 2.8 for α-protons. The way in which the proton coupling varies with X–H bond length and with electronegativity of X is discussed further in Appendix 4.

(b) Isotropic hyperfine coupling to α-atoms

This discussion extends that given in § 2.3 and is of particular relevance to α-protons.

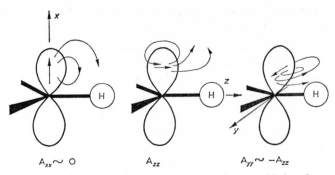

Fig. 2.8.   Dipolar interaction between an electron in a p-orbital and an α-proton.

The isotropic component of the α-atom interaction may be pictured in a number of ways, two of which we shall describe. For greater generality we shall develop the description further by considering the variation of the isotropic α-hydrogen splitting as the radical bends. To do so we consider the particular case of a seven valence-electron radical AH_3 (methyl or NH_3^+ for example). Two approaches to the problem are readily visualised.

(i) Polarisation mechanism[6, 7]

In a planar AH_3 radical A–H bonds are formed by spin-pairing of the electrons in the $H(1s)$ and A sp^2-hybridised orbitals, the unpaired electron being in the $2p_z$-orbital on A. For the isolated AH bond there is no *a priori* preference for a particular spin alignment. Introduction of the odd electron into the $A(2p_z)$-orbital gives rise to an energetically more favourable situation when the electron in the $A(sp^2)$-orbital is aligned parallel to the unpaired electron than when the electrons are antiparallel (Hund's principle). By the Pauli principle the electron formally in the $H(1s)$-orbital must be antiparallel to that in the sp^2-orbital and hence also antiparallel to the unpaired electron on A. Consequently there will be a net unbalance of spin at the proton and a negative spin-density will be observed (Fig. 2.9.).

When the angle between the unpaired electron's orbital and the A–H bond increases as the molecule is symmetrically bent s-character migrates from the $A(sp^2)$-orbitals to the $2p$-orbital until in a $90°$ molecule $(HAH = 90°)$ the unpaired electron is entirely s and the A–H bonds are pure p. At an intermediate stage both the A–H bonds and the unpaired electron's orbital are built from some s-character on A. Since the s-orbital then has a large magnitude in the vicinity of the nucleus, when the bonding electron is near the unpaired elec-

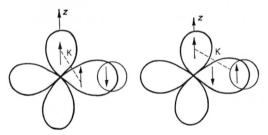

Fig. 2.9. Mechanism for the production of isotropic hyperfine interaction with an α-proton.

tron, both will have some s-character. In these circumstances these electrons tend to pair with their spins antiparallel, and since the remaining bonding electron (which is near the hydrogen) must still be antiparallel to the other, there will be a net positive spin-density at the proton.

On this model, therefore, as the molecule bends the originally negative spin-density will decrease to zero and then increase positively.

(ii) Configuration interaction mechanism[7]

The problem may be approached from the viewpoint of delocalised molecular orbitals; spin density now appears at the proton through the non-vanishing off-diagonal elements of the molecular orbital density matrix, in other words: configuration interaction. The general problem has been treated in the density matrix formalism by McWeeney and Sutcliffe[8] and applied to NH_2, but we shall present an exposition which has been given previously[7].

The ground state of a planar radical (symmetry group D_{3h}) with seven valence electrons is

$$(1a_1')^2 (2a_1')^2 (1e')^4 (1a_2'')^1, {}^2A_2''$$

The $1a_1'$ orbital is largely the $1s$-atomic orbital on A, $2a_1'$ and $1e'$ are AH bonding orbitals and $1a_2''$ is a non-bonding orbital centred on A and is predominantly an $A(2p)$-orbital. The z-axis is the C_3-axis.

The bent molecule has reduced symmetry and belongs to the group C_{3v} and the ground state has the orbital classification

$$(1a_1)^2 (2a_1)^2 (1e)^4 (3a_1)^1, {}^2A_1$$

The odd electron is now in the $3a_1$ orbital which has increasingly more $A(2s)$-character as the HAH angle approaches $90°$.

The proton interaction term depends on the mixing of excited states with the ground state, the permitted mixing being governed by symmetry require-ments. Since the symmetry of the orbital containing the unpaired electron changes from a_2 to a_1 on bending, the states involved in the two cases will differ.

For planar methyl Padgett and Krauss[9] and Higuchi and Aono[10] have shown by an LCAO–SCF molecular orbital calculation that the pertinent excitation is $3a_1' \leftarrow 2a_1'$ which is tantamount to a movement of charge out-wards from A to the ring of hydrogen atoms. To a first approximation the $1a_2''$ electron is unaffected by this migration. The electron in the $3a_1'$-orbital is predominantly near the hydrogens, and since it has a spin which is anti-parallel to the electron in the $2a_1'$-orbital and hence also to the electron in the $1a_2''$-orbital (because the $1a_2''$ and the $2a_1'$ electrons will tend to be aligned parallel to each other) a net negative spin-density will arise on the protons.

In the bent molecule a similar situation obtains except that, as described above, the symmetry of the orbital containing the odd electron is a_1. Excited states which can interact with the ground state must all have A_1 symmetry and include typically

$$(1a_1)^2 (2a_1)^1 (1e)^4 (3a_1)^2, {}^2A_1$$

Since the $3a_1$-orbital is already half-full, only an electron with a spin opposite to that of the unpaired electron can be promoted to it, consequently the elec-tron which remains in the lower level has the same spin as the previously unpaired electron. Since the $3a_1$-level is non-bonding it is more strictly con-fined to the central atom than any of the lower a_1-orbitals with which it inter-acts; consequently there will be a considerable positive spin density on the hydrogens. As the molecule bends, the s-character of the $3a_1$-orbital increases and so the level deepens in energy; interaction involving this level becomes more important and so the proton interaction becomes larger (more positive).

Thus the essential difference between the proton coupling for planar and bent radicals is that in the former interactions involving excitations from filled to unoccupied levels are involved because no interaction involving the a_2''-level is allowed, whereas under the descent in symmetry which occurs when the molecule bends such interactions are allowed because of the corre-lation $3a_1 \leftarrow 1a_2''$. Because this latter interaction does not depend on a polar-isation mechanism (as it does in D_{3h}) the interaction may be large and is positive.

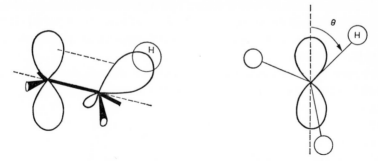

Fig. 2.10.   Model for hyperconjugative interaction with β-protons.

(c) Isotropic hyperfine coupling to β-atoms (hyperconjugation)

Since most of the inorganic radicals under consideration are relatively simple, a situation in which β or more remote atoms play an important part in hyperfine interaction is not often encountered. Coupling to β-protons is, however, a major aspect of the electron spin resonance spectra of many organic radicals[11] and the phenomenon of hyperconjugation which is thought to be responsible is of such general importance that the topic ought not to be neglected here. We give, therefore, a brief outline of the factors involved and some of the outstanding results obtained in the organic field. A more detailed account has been given recently[11].

The basic concept of hyperconjugation in a system such as that illustrated in Fig. 2.10 is that there is overlap between one or more of the σ(C–H) bonds and the p-orbital of the unpaired electron. This will result in some redistribution of electron spin on to the β-protons. It has been argued[12-14] that such an interaction ought to be at a maximum when the density axis of the p-orbital and the C–H bond are co-planar, and should be reduced to zero when the C–H bond lies in the radical plane, the interaction following a $\cos^2\theta$ law. There is now a considerable weight of evidence in favour of this postulate, especially from studies of radicals oriented in crystals.

The interaction is quite large and, in contrast with that for α-protons in π-radicals, it gives rise to positive spin-density at the proton. For a rotating methyl group such as that in the ethyl radical, the isotropic coupling is about +26 gauss, but for protons constrained to lie in a position of maximum overlap it would be twice this.

Coupling also varies with demand: the more positive the radical the greater the interaction. This is well illustrated by results for the cations of hexa-methylbenzene and durene[15].

There is considerable chemical evidence to show that hyperconjugation involving C–H bonds is considerably more important than that involving C–X bonds. Nevertheless, there is some indirect evidence that the phenome-non still occurs to a significant extent in, for example, C–C bonds.

2.6 RADICALS IN THE LIQUID AND SOLID STATE

Stationary radicals may be encountered either in single crystals or in glasses or polycrystalline powders. In each case, in order to obtain good resolution, they must be dilutely dispersed through the medium, otherwise the strong dipolar coupling between the electron spins causes a marked line-broadening.

(a) Radicals in single crystals

Provided that the radicals have preferred orientations in the host crystal the spectra will vary with the orientation of the crystal in the magnetic field in a manner which reflects the anisotropy in the g- and hyperfine tensors. If there are n magnetically distinguishable radicals in the unit cell in a general orientation of the crystal n sets of lines will be observed. The way in which the results can be processed to give the principal values and directions of the tensors is outlined in Appendix 5.

(b) Radicals in glasses

For a polycrystalline powder or glass (a rigid solution) the radicals are ran-domly oriented and the spectrum obtained is an envelope of all the possible spectra from the single crystal. Fortunately, only specific features appear and these can often be readily related to the principal values of the g- and hyper-fine tensors. Thus, under favourable circumstances it may not be necessary to study a single crystal. Details of the interpretation of such spectra are given in Appendix 5.

When a frozen solution is allowed to soften, the features narrow and shift in a characteristic manner, giving eventually the far simpler and more sym-metrical spectrum characteristic of the radicals in fluid solution.

(c) Radicals in solution

If the radical is rotating rapidly, as is generally the case for fluid solutions, its orientation relative to the applied field will have swept out all possible directions during the time of observation, and hence the dipolar interactions are averaged to zero (though they make a residual contribution to the width of component lines, § 2.7).

Thus spectra from fluid solutions reveal only A_{iso} and g_{av} for the radicals under observation, g_{av} being equal to $\frac{1}{3}(g_{xx}+g_{yy}+g_{zz})$.

2.7 LINE-WIDTHS AND RELAXATION

Although the lowest energy state for a collection of electron spins is with all of their magnetic moments aligned with the applied field, not all of the electrons will be in this state because thermal excitation will tend to distribute them into the higher levels; in the absence of the fluctuating microwave field there will be a preponderance of spins in the lower energy state but still a considerable proportion in the upper state. (It was the nearly equal distribution of nuclei among the various spin states that accounted for the equal intensity of hyperfine lines from a nucleus of spin I.) The presence of the radio-frequency field is just as likely to cause an electron to reverse its spin orientation from the upper level to the lower level (with emission of energy) as it is to cause stimulated absorption. Thus if the populations of the upper and lower levels were equal there would be no net absorption. At the beginning of an electron spin resonance experiment there is the afore-mentioned imbalance of populations, thus the absorption processes outweigh the emissive; consequently there is a tendency to equalise the populations and the absorption would be expected gradually to disappear. Usually this is not the case and the explanation must be that there is some mechanism which removes spins from the upper level and so tends to the condition of thermal equilibrium. Such mechanisms are referred to as relaxation processes. We shall say little about them here but will remark that two types of processes are important; these are known as the spin–lattice (T_1) and spin–spin (T_2) processes.

(a) Spin–lattice relaxation

The T_1 or spin–lattice relaxation process depends upon fluctuating magnetic fields close to the unpaired electron. Such fields may, for example, be due to

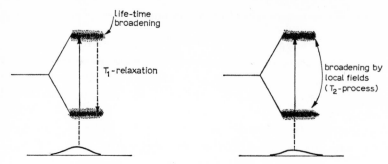

Fig. 2.11.   The relaxation processes T_1 and T_2.

lattice vibrations causing the oscillation of local electrically charged particles. Such fluctuating fields can couple with the spin magnetic moment of the electron and hence induce transitions. That is, the spin energy is dissipated as lattice phonons. Because of the induced emission the length of time which the particular spin spends in the upper state is reduced; by the uncertainty principle the energy of that state becomes less well defined and therefore the resonance line is broadened (Fig. 2.11.)*.

(b) Spin–spin relaxation

The T_2 or spin–spin process depends on local magnetic nuclei or unpaired electrons affecting the field at the unpaired electron. A random distribution of such fields will blur the energy levels of the unpaired electron and the line will be broadened by this mechanism also (Fig. 2.11.).

The T_2 process is also a relaxation process because the blurring of the energy levels is an equivalent to saying that the electron spin magnetic moments precess at different rates and therefore get out of phase: the total perpendicular component of magnetisation of the sample is therefore reduced towards the thermal equilibrium value (zero).

The line-widths are inversely proportional to the parameters T_1 and T_2 which describe the processes, thus short relaxation times (T_1, T_2) imply broad lines.

A great deal has already been written on the theory of relaxation processes[16-18] and we shall have more to say of them later (§ 7.2b(i)). In partic-

---

* The explanation in terms of the life-time effect is only an approximation to the real situation; see for example ref. 16.

ular, information concerning the interaction between a radical and its environment can be obtained.

Let us develop these points a little and simultaneously introduce the concept of correlation times. To do so we shall consider the theory due to McConnell[19] although the problem has been developed to considerable depth by several authors.

(c) Line-widths and correlation times

Consider a radical which has axially symmetric g- and hyperfine tensors and which can undergo restricted rotation in an environment. It is assumed that the orientation, Ω, of the species in the external field jumps from one value to another in a time which is negligible compared to the time for which it is stationary. The latter time is referred to as the "correlation time" and is denoted by τ_c. The behaviour envisaged is illustrated in Fig. 2.12.

During the jumps the species will experience a modulated magnetic field which will have components in the x-, y- and z-directions relative to the applied field which is assumed to lie along z. The amplitude of the modulation will be taken as Δ which, for the time being, will be left undefined but arises from the fluctuating nuclear hyperfine field and the anisotropy of the g-tensor. The modulation in the x- and y-directions is perpendicular to the applied field and so will tend to invert the electron spin and so reduce the life-time of the states; there is only one frequency of the modulating field which is particularly effective in this operation, namely the resonance frequency, ν_0.

The random fluctuation illustrated in Fig. 2.12 may be synthesized as a sum of sine and cosine terms; the component with the resonance frequency

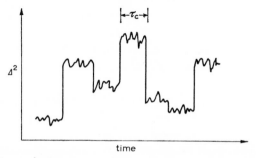

Fig. 2.12.   A random process, characterised by a correlation time τ_c.

References p. 33–34

will be active in the relaxation process and it can be shown[17] to give rise to a line-broadening directly proportional to $1/T_1$ where

$$1/T_1 \gtrsim \left(\frac{8\pi^2}{15}\right) \Delta^2 h^{-2} \tau_c (1 + 4\pi^2 v_0^2 \tau_c^2)^{-1} \tag{2.6}$$

The modulation parallel to the applied field cannot alter the net magnetisation of the sample, but it does affect the perpendicular component of the magnetisation vector as has already been described. All the components of the modulation frequency are effective in this, so that integration leads to a line-width proportional to $1/T_2'$. The line-width parameter T_2 is given approximately by

$$1/T_2 = 1/T_1 + 1/T_2' \tag{2.7}$$

and the line-width by

$$\Delta H_{MS} = 1/2\pi T_2 \tag{2.8}$$

The behaviour of T_1 and T_2' is illustrated in Fig. 2.13. which idealises the behaviour as τ_c increases. The inflexion points are readily determined by letting τ_c become very small or very large. It is seen that, in general, line-widths increase as the correlation time (which is often taken as being directly proportional to the macroscopic viscosity of the solution) increases. Specifically:

$$\Delta = (g_\parallel - g_\perp)\beta H + \beta(A_\parallel - A_\perp)m_I \tag{2.9}$$

When rotational motion is very rapid the spin samples a large number of

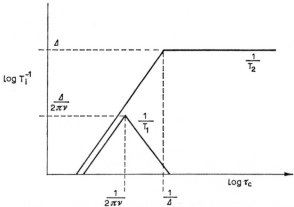

Fig. 2.13. The dependence of line-widths (αT^{-1}) on the correlation time for a relaxing random process.

fields in a short time and "motional narrowing" occurs because the broadening fields are averaged to zero and narrow lines are observed. An electronic analogue of this is when the radicals are so close together that the orbitals of the unpaired electrons overlap. The unpaired electrons are then distributed throughout the crystal and, once again, sample a large number of random fields in a time short compared to the observational time. A very narrow ("exchange narrowed") line results. In this case any nuclear hyperfine structure also disappears because the nuclear fields are also randomly sampled and so average to zero.

In the particular case of a radical in solution an electron exchange reaction of the type

$$A + A^- \rightleftharpoons A^- + A \qquad (2.10)$$

may occur. If this proceeds sufficiently rapidly the electron will experience random nuclear hyperfine fields and the observed hyperfine splitting will be zero; such an exchange process therefore results in the loss of the hyperfine spectrum. Analogous situations, including those in which the nuclei are exchanged are discussed in later chapters.

A further process which can broaden lines is when the wave function of the unpaired electron is distributed over a large number of magnetic nuclei but does not overlap with the wave functions of other unpaired electrons. For example, an electron may be trapped in a fluoride crystal, it may be highly confined but the tail of the wave function may extend through several neighbouring unit cells and there may be a small hyperfine splitting with a large number of nuclei ("superhyperfine interaction"). This splitting is generally unresolvable but it does lead to a broad line. Such a line is said to be inhomogeneously broadened but the process is not, of course, a relaxation.

The splitting from these multitudinous nuclei may be resolved if special methods involving double resonance are resorted to[20].

References

1 G. E. PAKE, *Paramagnetic Resonance*, Benjamin, 1962.
2 C. P. SLICHTER, *Principles of Magnetic Resonance*, Harper and Row, 1963.
3 S. A. AL'TSHULER AND B. M. KOZYREV, *Electron Paramagnetic Resonance*, Academic Press, 1963.
4 H. ZELDES, G. T. TRAMMELL AND R. LIVINGSTON, *J. Chem. Phys.*, 1960, *32*, 618.
5 C. A. COULSON, *Volume Commémoratif Victor Henri, Contributions à l'Etude de la Structure Moléculaire*, 1948, p. 15.

6 H. M. McConnell, *J. Chem. Phys.*, 1956, *24*, 762; *Ann. Rev. Phys. Chem.*, 1957, *8*, 105.
7 P. W. Atkins, N. Keen and M. C. R. Symons, *J. Chem. Soc.*, 1963, 250.
8 R. McWeeney and B. T. Sutcliffe, *Mol. Phys.*, 1963, *6*, 493.
9 A. Padgett and M. Krauss, *J. Chem. Phys.*, 1960, *32*, 189.
10 J. Higuchi and S. Aono, *J. Chem. Phys.*, 1960, *32*, 52.
11 M. C. R. Symons, *Advan. Phys. Org. Chem.*, 1963, *1*, 284.
12 A. D. McLachlan, *Mol. Phys.*, 1958, *1*, 233.
13 M. C. R. Symons, *J. Chem. Soc.*, 1959, 277.
14 H. M. McConnell, C. Heller, T. Cole and R. W. Fessenden, *J. Am. Chem. Soc.*, 1960, *82*, 766.
15 R. Hulme and M. C. R. Symons, *Proc. Chem. Soc.*, 1963, 241.
16 R. Kubo and K. Tomita, *J. Phys. Soc. Japan*, 1954, *9*, 888.
17 D. Kivelson, *J. Chem. Phys.*, 1960, *33*, 1094.
18 For further references see Ref. 2.
19 H. M. McConnell, *J. Chem. Phys.*, 1956, *25*, 709.
20 G. Feher, *Phys. Rev.*, 1959, *114*, 1219.
21 J. R. Morton, J. R. Rowlands and D. H. Whiffen, *Natl. Phys. Lab., Gr. Brit. Circ. No. BPR* 13.
22 N. Ramsey, *Nuclear Moments*, Wiley, 1953.
23 C. C. J. Roothaan and E. Clementi, University of Chicago.
24 D. Mayers, University of Oxford.
25 R. E. Watson and A. J. Freeman, *Phys. Rev.*, 1961, *123*, 521.
26 R. E. Watson and A. J. Freeman, *Phys. Rev.*, 1961, *124*, 1117.

Chapter 3

Formation and trapping of radicals

Certain radicals, such as nitric oxide, nitrogen dioxide, the ozonide ion and chlorine dioxide, are intrinsically stable even at elevated temperatures. Their preparation is well annotated and is not discussed here, attention being devoted instead to the preparation of less stable species in a state suitable for study by electron spin resonance methods.

We begin with a very brief section on preparation *in the gas phase*, which leads on to a consideration of matrix isolation techniques. As has already been stressed, a major development in the study of free radicals has been the recent discovery that even the most reactive species can be immobilised by "trapping" in a rigid medium. The properties of the trapped radicals can then be studied at leisure if the medium is not allowed to melt. Since the majority of radicals to be discussed in this book have been studied *in the solid state*, either by isolation in an inert matrix or by irradiation of a solid, these preparative methods are treated in some detail. The chapter concludes with a section on formation of radicals *in solution*.

3.1 RADICALS IN THE GAS PHASE

Radicals can readily be prepared in the gas phase by thermal, photochemical, shock-tube or electric discharge techniques[1]. A recent example was given by Radford[2] who reported a method for preparing the radicals HS, HSe and HTe in fairly high stationary concentrations simply by flowing hydrogen through an electric discharge and down a tube coated with the appropriate element.

In general, electron spin resonance methods are unsuitable for direct study of radicals in the gas phase because interaction with rotational levels leads to blurring of the spectral lines. This can be avoided, not by isolation in empty space but by isolation in a chemically inert solid, such as a rare gas. (We note, in passing, that recent developments in the chemistry of the rare gases may make the reader somewhat sceptical of the words "chemically inert" in this context. Indeed, a marked interaction is found between hydrogen and xenon atoms under certain conditions, which may be thought of in terms of molecular binding rather than simply as an "environmental effect"—this is discussed in more detail in Chapter 5.)

3.2 MATRIX ISOLATION METHODS

(a) Formation prior to trapping

One of the methods mentioned above for producing radicals in the gas phase is applied to a stream of the parent gas that is present as a dilute solution in an inert gas, the whole being deposited on a suitably placed cold finger, usually at 4.2 °K. Various geometries have been devised, one useful alternative being to stream the inert matrix down a separate tube on to the cold finger. The techniques involved have been described in detail in the book by Bass and Broida[1]. A wide range of radicals has been formed and studied by this means, and references to its use will be found in later Chapters.

(b) Formation by photolysis in situ

In this variation photosensitive molecules are isolated in a matrix and are then exposed to suitable ultraviolet radiation. Commonly, one or both primary fragments are trapped as such, although both may not be detected. For example, photolysis of methyl iodide with 2537 Å light gave methyl radicals which were characterised by an isotropic spectrum of four narrow lines[3]. Presumably iodine atoms were also trapped, but they were not detected (see Chapter 5).

Alternatively, secondary radicals can be produced if there are reactive species present in the matrix. Photolysis of hydrogen iodide, for example, gives hydrogen atoms which add readily to such unsaturated molecules as carbon monoxide, acetylene or hydrogen cyanide[4-6].

$$
\begin{aligned}
&H + CO && \to HCO \\
&H + CH \equiv CH && \to H_2C = CH \\
&H + HCN && \to H_2C = N
\end{aligned} \qquad (3.1)
$$

The interesting spin resonance spectra which characterise the products are discussed in detail in subsequent Chapters.

(c) Formation by reaction in situ

If two species which normally react vigorously are allowed to come together either just prior to impinging upon the cold finger or just after deposition, then the ensuing reaction, because of the rapidly falling temperature experienced, may be induced to stop at some intermediate stage. The initial products, then trapped in the inert matrix, can be studied by electron spin resonance methods if they are paramagnetic.

Thomas[7] has devised a rotating cryostat which facilitates this process by allowing alternating deposits of the reactants and matrix to be built on top of each other so producing a "Swiss roll" or "club sandwich" within which reaction proceeds only to a limited extent; once again reactive fragments are trapped as the temperature falls. Particular reference will be made to this procedure in Chapter 4 on trapped electrons.

3.3 IRRADIATION OF SOLIDS

The matrix isolation method suffers from the severe drawback that only envelope spectra can be obtained because the radicals are completely disoriented. One of the advantages of radiation damage is that single crystals of the substrate can be used and quite frequently nature is kind, and the radicals formed and trapped in this way remain locked in the crystal in discrete orientations. The method suffers, on the other hand, from the fact that far less is known about the likely identities of the resulting fragments, and frequently one has to use the spin resonance spectrum to aid in identification before using it as a structural probe.

Here we shall discuss the effects of high energy radiation and ultraviolet light on both pure solids and solid solutions.

(a) Pure materials

(i) Radiolysis

At first sight one might conclude that exposure of a relatively complex solid to high energy radiation would result in deep-seated, indiscriminate breakdown to give a wide variety of products. In practice, however, despite the fact that each quantum of radiation is much more energetic than is required for simple bond homolysis, selective homolyses are often the major outcome and so only one or two species are formed and trapped.

It is generally accepted that the primary process resulting from the inter-action of such high energy quanta and a molecule is the ejection of an inner electron. This "secondary" electron will exist initially as a "conduction" electron, but will be non-selectively trapped at defect or impurity sites if they are present. In the absence of such sites the electron may return to the parent cation and the resulting excited molecule will frequently have sufficient ener-gy to suffer homolytic bond fission.

It remains surprising that such homolyses are frequently highly selective. Another curious factor is that the fragments detected are often not those expected if the weakest bond had undergone rupture. Of various possible explanations, we consider that one important feature is the mobility of the fragments.

Consider the homolysis

$$AB \rightarrow A\cdot + B\cdot \qquad (3.2)$$

and the possible fate of $B\cdot$. There are at least three discrete events. A *"cage" back-reaction* with $A\cdot$ may occur to give either AB or other diamagnetic pro-ducts. Secondly, one may get *"pair-wise" trapping*, whereby $B\cdot$ escapes from $A\cdot$ but loses its mobility when only a few Ångstroms away from its partner. This form of trapping can be detected since it causes important modifications of the spin resonance spectra. Thirdly, $B\cdot$ may be so small that it can *migrate through the lattice*. The possibilities for its ultimate fate are again manifold —thus it may become trapped, or encounters with other $B\cdot$ radicals may give B_2 or other diamagnetic products, or attack on AB could give, say, $A\cdot + B_2$.

Yet another process is for $B\cdot$ to react with the medium, not by a homolytic displacement to give a new radical, but by heterolysis to give a modified species $B'\cdot$. Of particular importance here is proton transfer. Reference to this behaviour is given in Chapter 4 where it is suggested that after electron ejection, radicals R_2CHOH^+ react with the medium to give the detected spe-cies $R_2\dot{C}OH$:

$$R_2CHOH^+ + R_2CHOH \rightarrow R_2\dot{C}OH + R_2CHOH_2^+ \qquad (3.3)$$

Of the various sources of high energy available for radiolysis, one of the most convenient is a γ-ray emitter such as ^{60}Co. This radiation is highly penetrat-ing, passes relatively unattenuated through both Dewar flasks and coolants, and produces damage centres which are evenly distributed throughout the solid substrate. Thus, provided pair-wise trapping is avoided, the paramag-netic species are conveniently prepared in homogeneous solution throughout the crystal. As we have already stressed, this is a necessary condition if subtle features of the spectrum are to be detected. γ-Radiolytic methods have the added advantage that they by-pass the difficult task of growing magnetically dilute crystals.

(ii) Photolysis

Many of the principles outlined in (*i*) and summarised in Fig. 3.1. are also relevant to photolyses in the solid state. Points of difference are as follows:

(1) Initial electron-ejection (photo-ionisation) is far less common.

(2) Pair-wise trapping is likely to be more frequent since the excess kinetic energy possessed by the fragments is less.

(3) Homolysis is confined to those bonds which are sufficiently weak to be broken by the particular light used and which can, of course, be varied at

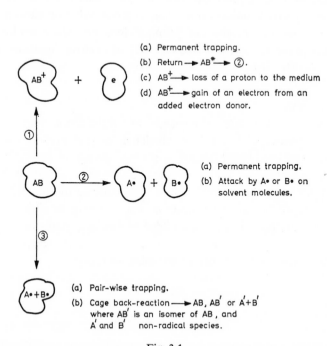

Represents the surrounding medium

(a) Permanent trapping.
(b) Return ⟶ AB* ⟶ ②.
(c) AB⁺ ⟶ loss of a proton to the medium
(d) AB⁺ ⟶ gain of an electron from an added electron donor.

(a) Permanent trapping.
(b) Attack by A• or B• on solvent molecules.

(a) Pair-wise trapping.
(b) Cage back-reaction ⟶ AB, AB′ or A′+B′ where AB′ is an isomer of AB, and A′ and B′ non-radical species.

Fig. 3.1.

References p. 42

will. For example, photolyses of peroxides by low-energy ultraviolet light is only expected to cause fission of the oxygen–oxygen bond.

(4) Damage is often confined to the surface of the solid. This is because the onset of absorption is commonly very sharp, so that light in the absorption tail, which penetrates the crystal satisfactorily, has insufficient energy to cause bond-fission, while light in the peak is often completely absorbed at the surface, where the damage is concentrated. Only when absorption coefficients within photo-active bands are low is it likely that an even distribution of fragments throughout the crystal will be produced.

(5) Photolysis may be arrested rapidly because one or more of the products may absorb the actinic light far more effectively than the parent material, thus acting as an efficient "inner filter". This material may also be photo-active, in which case the overall chemical reaction will be complex and new radicals may result.

(b) Solid solutions

Dilute solutions may be more effective than pure materials when the task is to produce a specified radical rather than to probe radiation damage *per se*. We shall first consider the effect of "doping" ionic crystals, when the object is frequently to incorporate a source or a sink of electrons, and then pass to the study of frozen solutions.

(i) Ionic crystals

It has long been a practice of physicists to aid the formation of electron-excess or electron-deficient centres in alkali halides (such as F- and V-centres by incorporating ions which can act as electron sources or sinks. On radiolysis, secondary electrons are trapped at the sink thus increasing the yield of deficit-centres; or the residual "holes" may migrate through the crystal, becoming trapped by electron-transfer on encountering an added electron-source. Typically, Ag^+ or Pb^{2+} are added to facilitate the formation of V-centres, because they readily form Ag° or Pb^+. Sometimes the net result at elevated temperatures is a disproportionation such as:

$$2\,Ag^+ \rightarrow Ag^{2+} + Ag^\circ \tag{3.4}$$

or $\qquad\qquad 2\,NO_2^- \rightarrow NO_2 + NO_2^{2-} \tag{3.5}$

Alternatively, if a photo-active ion is incorporated into a transparent host-crystal, then photolysis may give the required fragment in a specific orientation, so permitting an accurate study of anisotropic parameters.

(ii) Glasses

If interest centres around the mechanism of a particular photolysis in fluid solution then it is also generally profitable to study the reaction at low temperatures. This is often made simpler if the medium vitrifies on cooling for the actinic light can then penetrate the solid. If polycrystalline material is formed it is generally too opaque to permit photolysis.

The study of such glassy solutions is profitable because the reaction will probably stop at the first stage, whereas in fluid solution photolysis resulting in homolysis is frequently a multistage or chain process.

One exploitation of glassy solutions involves photolysis (with low-energy ultraviolet light) of dilute solutions of hydrogen peroxide in a reactive glassy solvent, such as an alcohol[8]. At present, we are not aware of any extension of this particular approach into the field of inorganic radicals.

3.4 TRANSIENT RADICALS IN SOLUTION

The three methods that have been used successfully are photolysis and radiolysis *in situ*, and continuous flow with mixing in or very close to the cavity.

(a) Photolysis and radiolysis

Photolysis is now readily accomplished since it is possible to construct a resonant cavity of high performance which has a grating on one side allowing access of light to the sample tube. *In situ* radiolysis is a far more difficult task at present, but has been undertaken with great success by Fessenden and Schuler[9], who streamed high-energy electrons through a small hole in one of the pole-pieces of the electromagnet and directly into the cooled sample.

These two methods so far have been confined to the formation and study of organic radicals. This is partly because solution spectra of organic radicals are generally more informative both with respect to identification and to providing useful structural information than are those of inorganic radicals.

(b) Flow techniques

When a reaction proceeds through radical intermediates, it is sometimes possible to attain sufficiently high concentrations to permit detection by the use of a flow system. In a typical experiment concentrated solutions of the reagents are streamed through concentric tubes and mixed turbulently either within the cell or immediately before passing through it. In this way a stationary concentration of radicals is achieved, and detection need not be too hurried. Observation times can be varied either by moving the mixing chamber relative to the cell or by altering the rate of flow. Primary and secondary radicals can be detected, and by adding a third component, the initial products of induced reactions can be detected.

For example, Norman and his co-workers[10,11] obtained well resolved spectra from a variety of organic radicals $(R \cdot)$ formed by the induced oxidation:

$$Ti^{3+} + H_2O_2 \rightarrow TiOH^{3+} + \cdot OH \qquad (3.6)$$

$$\cdot OH + RH \quad \rightarrow H_2O \quad + R \cdot \qquad (3.7)$$

A single line, obtained in the absence of organic substrate, was assigned to hydroxyl radicals formed according to (3.6). This assignment, which is by no means certain, is discussed in § 6.2a(i).

This technique appears to have considerable potential as a method of probing mechanism but it suffers from the experimental drawback that large quantities of solvents and reagents are required.

References

1 A. M. BASS AND H. P. BROIDA, *Formation and Trapping of Free Radicals*, Academic Press, 1960.
2 H. E. RADFORD, *J. Chem. Phys.*, 1964, *40*, 2732.
3 T. COLE, H. O. PRITCHARD, N. R. DAVIDSON AND H. M. McCONNELL, *Mol. Phys.*, 1958, *1*, 40.
4 F. J. ADRIAN, E. L. COCHRAN AND V. A. BOWERS, *J. Chem. Phys.*, 1962, *36*, 1661.
5 E. L. COCHRAN, F. J. ADRIAN AND V. A. BOWERS, *J. Chem. Phys.*, 1962, *36*, 1938.
6 F. J. ADRIAN, E. L. COCHRAN AND V. A. BOWERS, *Advan. Chem.*, 1962, *36*, 50.
7 A. THOMAS, *Trans. Faraday Soc.*, 1961, *57*, 1679; J. E. BENNETT AND A. THOMAS, *Proc. Roy. Soc. (London)*, 1964 *A280*, 123.
8 M. C. R. SYMONS, *Advan. Phys. Org. Chem.*, 1963, *1*, 283.
9 R. W. FESSENDEN AND R. H. SCHULER, *J. Chem. Phys.*, 1960, *33*, 935; 1963, *38*, 773.
10 R. O. C. NORMAN, *Nature*, 1962, *196*, 891.
11 W. T. DIXON AND R. O. C. NORMAN, *Proc. Chem. Soc.*, 1963, 97; *J. Chem. Soc.*, 1963, 3119.

Chapter 4

Trapped and solvated electrons

As we are concerned with properties of unpaired electrons it seems natural to begin with a discussion of trapped electrons. This is an unfamiliar situation to many chemists and our purpose is to present a simple rationale of a complex subject which is covered by a huge literature.

We start with a brief reference to F-centres in alkali halide and related crystals since these are both relatively well understood and well characterised by their electron spin resonance spectra. Thence we proceed to a discussion of electrons in liquids especially alkali metal ammonia solutions; here our measure of understanding is far less and the data relatively meagre. Finally we return to the solid state but this time to consider electrons in non-ionic solids, many of these being simply rigid solvents such as water or alcohols.

4.1 F-CENTRES

When an alkali halide crystal is heated in the presence of alkali metal vapour and then rapidly quenched it becomes coloured, the colour being due to a single narrow and intense absorption band, the F-band. These colour centres are associated with broad electron spin resonance absorption bands in the free spin region, which consist of a series of overlapping hyperfine lines due to interaction with the nuclei of both cations and anions.

(a) Information from hyperfine coupling

In most instances it has been necessary to use double resonance techniques to measure details of the hyperfine interactions[1], but these show clearly that in all cases the electron is primarily associated with six equivalent cations and, to a far smaller extent with twelve equivalent anions and a second set of eight equivalent cations.

The results strikingly confirm de Boer's model of the F-centre[2] which consists simply of an electron trapped in an anion vacancy.

F-centres, together with electron-deficit centres (V-centres) such as Cl_2^- (§ 6.2d(ii)) are also generally formed when alkali halide crystals are exposed to high energy radiation. Many aggregated centres, characterised in particular by their optical properties, can be formed when conditions are varied[3]. Of these we mention the F'-centre, which appears to consist of two (paired) electrons trapped in the same anion vacancy[3a] and the M-centre which consists of two coupled F-centres[3b]. These centres, which are far more difficult to study because they are diamagnetic, are formed when F-centres are bleached. In some instances, however, it has been possible to detect excited states of these centres by electron spin resonance[3c, 14].

As expected, the hyperfine structure of F-centres, especially as measured by the electron nuclear double resonance (ENDOR) method, provides data which not only established their overall structure, but also provide very detailed information about electron distributions against which mathematical approximations to F-centres can be gauged.

(i) Trends in hyperfine coupling constants

If one adopts the simplified concepts outlined in § 2.4a and uses the atomic parameters of Table 2.1 one can obtain a crude but informative map of the electron distribution in the centre. Typical results are given in Table 4.1 and these trends will now be considered. It is assumed that any interaction with ions more distant than those listed is small and therefore that the residual electron density is either largely located within the vacancy itself or is in the atomic $p(\sigma)$-levels of the cations. We stress that this is not meant to imply that the wave-function is cut off abruptly, but simply that we use the approximation that the electron is forced into the appropriate atomic level of the surrounding ions when it is in their vicinity. Any attempt to employ the anisotropic part of the hyperfine interaction to the cations is frought with difficulty since a high electron density within the vacancy will contribute directly, in addition to the occupancy of the outer $p(\sigma)$-levels and a possible polarisation of the inner $p(\sigma)$-levels. Thus all these contributions are gathered together as the residual density within the vacancy. Use of atomic parameters is clearly a very rough approximation for the ionic crystals, but trends are probably reflected correctly.

Two aspects are marked:

(1) The total spin-density on the first shell of six cations is very large com-

pared with that on any of the remaining ions. Indeed, it appears that a good approximation would be that the electron is confined to the vacancy and the outer s- and p-levels of these cations.

(2) After this initial and very abrupt decay, the electron interacts with many ions to a minor extent, the rate of decrease of spin-density with radius being slight.

Close examination shows that on going to larger cations for a fixed anion, the total s-character on the six nearest cations increases, whilst on going to larger anions (F^- to Cl^-) for a fixed cation, the s-character on the cations falls. In this approximation these trends can be understood in terms of a competition for the electron between the vacancy and the six cations. The latter trend then reflects an increasing stability of the electron within the cavity as the cavity size increases. Thus the need to use the outer levels of the cations decreases.

The former trend is not accommodated by this simple model because the

TABLE 4.1

OBSERVED HYPERFINE SPLITTINGS AND CALCULATED ELECTRON DENSITY
ON THE FIRST SHELL OF CATIONS SURROUNDING THE F-CENTRE

No.	Substance	Ion	Observed hyperfine splitting (gauss)	Temp. (°K)	S(%)*	Ref.
1	LiF	^{7}Li	13.95	1.3	58.3	a
2	LiCl	^{7}Li	6.82	1.3	28.6	a
3	NaF	^{23}Na	37.7	1.3	71.4	a
4	NaCl	^{23}Na	22.0	1.3	41.7	a
5	KF	^{39}K	12.3	90	89.2	b
6	KCl	^{39}K	7.36	1.3	53.4	a
7	KBr	^{39}K	6.71	300	48.9	b
8	KI	^{39}K	5.35	20	39.0	b
9	RbCl	^{85}Rb	35.1	90	58.2	c
10	RbBr	^{85}Rb	31–36	90	52.0	c
11	NaH	^{23}Na	26.5	77	50	d
12	NaCN	^{23}Na	19.	300	36.5	e

* Apparent s-character.

References
(a) W. C. HOLTON AND H. BLUM, Phys. Rev., 1962, 125, 89.
(b) H. SEIDEL, Z. Physik, 1961, 165, 218.
(c) H. C. WOLF AND H. SEIDEL, Z. Physik, 1963, 173, 455.
(d) W. T. DOYLE AND W. L. WILLIAMS, Phys. Rev. Letters, 1961, 6, 537.
(e) T. A. CLAXTON, D. J. GREENSLADE, K. D. J. ROOT AND M. C. R. SYMONS, Trans. Faraday Soc., 1966, 62, 2050.

References p. 77–79

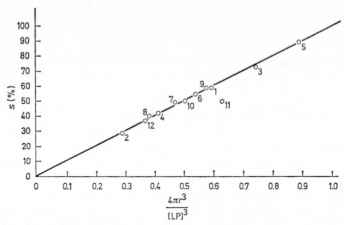

Fig. 4.1. Correlation of the apparent spin-density on the cations in the first shell of F-centres. The apparent spin-density (s) is plotted against $4\pi r^3/(LP)^3$ where r is the gas-phase radius of the metal atom and LP is the lattice parameter (J. C. SLATER, *J. Chem. Phys.*, 1964, 41, 3199). The numbers against each point on the plot refer to the crystals listed in Table 4.1.

vacancy remains approximately constant in size. It could be that the effective exclusion by the core electrons is less for the larger cations, or cation–cation overlap may make an appreciable contribution.

These results can all be well accommodated on a single straight line when the apparent s-character is plotted against the function $4\pi r^3/(LP)^3$ (r is the radius of the metal atom and LP is the lattice parameter) which can be thought of as a measure of the volume available to the electron in the crystal (Fig. 4.1.). Whatever may be the real significance of this plot, it certainly has an empirical value. This aspect is well illustrated by the way in which recent results for a paramagnetic centre in γ-irradiated sodium cyanide can be accommodated. In the absence of any other information, this agreement strongly supports the concept that this is an F-centre formed in a cyanide vacancy.

(ii) Theoretical interpretations

A wide variety of different approximations have been invoked in order to account for various properties of the F-centre, such as the energies of the F-bands, their oscillator strengths, luminescence, and electrical conductivity. Many of these are not directly suitable for discussions of hyperfine and g-tensors and so will not be outlined here. The reader is referred to the review by Gourary and Adrian[4] for detailed consideration of their worth.

An early theory proposed to accommodate the hyperfine coupling for F-electrons was by Kip, Kittel, Levy and Portis[5a], who supposed that the electron was in a molecular orbital constructed from the outer s- and $p(\sigma)$-orbitals of the six nearest neighbour cations. They used the simple approach outlined in (i) above except that after summing the electron over the six s-levels the difference was assigned entirely to the six $p(\sigma)$-levels. Thus their wave-function had the form

$$\phi_F = \frac{1}{\sqrt{6}} \sum_{\alpha=1}^{6} \left[\xi^{1/2} \psi_{\alpha s} + (1 - \xi)^{1/2} \psi_{\alpha p(\sigma)} \right] \qquad (4.1)$$

where α designates the cation and the $p(\sigma)$-orbital lies along the axis joining the centre of the vacancy to the ion α. For potassium chloride they found $\xi = 0.6$; that is, each ion contributes 60% s- and 40% p-orbital to the total wave-function. Nevertheless it has been suggested[4, 6] that if overlap integrals between the adjacent potassium ions are taken into account in estimating the normalisation factor, ξ has to be taken as unity to give the best agreement with experiments. This approach suffers from the fact that it does not recognise any tendency for the electron to dwell within the vacancy itself. It would be desirable to start with a smooth wave function (ϕ_F) derived from the potential of the ions surrounding the vacancy, and then to allow for the presence of the ions by making ϕ_F orthogonal to their core-orbitals. (This can be done using the Schmidt process, as outlined in § 5.1 for trapped atoms.) Thus the major hyperfine contributions arise from those orbitals of the surrounding ions which are mixed with ϕ_F by the orthogonalisation process.

A more successful approach to the problem has been developed by Gourary and Adrian[4] starting from the Hartree–Fock approximation. Their method assumes an averaged potential, but with the added simplification that the ions be treated as point charges.

(iii) Point–ion–lattice approximation

In this model, the ions of the lattice are replaced by charges located at the lattice points. The trapping potential is then a summation of the spherically symmetric contributions from the ions surrounding the vacancy. Gourary and Adrian used a variational technique to obtain the wave-function for the F-electron in this potential on the assumption that the ground state was an s-level, and the relevant excited state a p-level.

The justification for adopting this particular approximation is based on the experimental fact that the energy of the F-band maximum depends solely upon the lattice parameter, and not at all upon the properties of the individual ions. This, it is claimed, justifies the neglect of electronic polarisation, exchange, and overlap effects since these properties are functions of the separate ions. Lattice distortion was also neglected in the initial calculations of the F-band energy but a study of the errors introduced by these omissions showed that they were indeed small, thus establishing that the simple model is internally consistent. Indeed, further justification for these omissions is that the electron is strongly confined within the vacancy, since the potential used will be satisfactory in this region of space.

Fair results were obtained by this method, both for the F-band energies of a range of crystals, and for the hyperfine coupling constants. The results are consistently large and it was suggested that this may well reflect the neglect of the finite size of the surrounding ions. Exclusion forces from the ions would tend to increase the confinement of the electron within the vacancy and thus to reduce the hyperfine coupling constants. This situation has been explored in detail by Blumberg and Das[7].

(iv) Molecular orbital approximations

A more elaborate treatment than that of Kip *et al.*[5a] has been given by Inui and Uemura[8] and Kojima[9]. In addition to using the *s*- and *p*-orbitals of the six nearest cations they also included a term which takes into account the tendency for the electron to remain in the cavity, the potential being a smooth function of the distance from the cavity centre. The overall wavefunction was then made orthogonal to the orbitals of the surrounding ions. Very good agreement with experiment was obtained for the F-centre in lithium fluoride[9] which is the only centre so far treated by this more rigorous approach.

(b) Information from the g-tensor

The *g*-tensor is far less informative than the hyperfine tensor for F-centres. A small negative shift is always observed (Table 4.2) which increases with the atomic number of both cations and anions. Hence it would seem probable that the spin on these ions is the major factor involved, and that the most important interaction is *via* the vacant outer levels since the net shift is negative.

Kahn and Kittel[5b] were able to show that the orbital motion arising from mixing of *p*-levels on the six nearest neighbour cations was sufficient to ac-

TABLE 4.2

E.S.R. CHARACTERISTICS OF F-CENTRES IN ALKALI HALIDE CRYSTALS

Crystal	g-Value	Ref.
LiF	2.0029	a
	2.0023	b
LiCl	1.997	c
NaF	2.0023	a
NaCl	2.0011	a
NaBr	1.994	c
KCl	1.995	a
KBr	1.980	d
KI	1.971	e
CsCl	1.984	f

References
(a) N. W. LORD, Phys. Rev. ,1957, 105, 756.
(b) Y. W. KIM, R. KAPLAN AND P. J. BRAY, Phys. Rev. Letters, 1961, 6, 4.
(c) W. C. HOLTON AND H. BLUM, Phys. Rev., 1962, 125, 89.
(d) A. F. KIP, C. KITTEL, R. A. LEVY AND A. M. PORTIS, Phys. Rev., 1953, 91, 1066.
(e) G. A. NOBLE, Bull. Am. Phys. Soc., 1958, 3, 178.
(f) F. HUGHES AND J. G. ALLARD, Phys. Rev., 1962, 125, 173.

count for the magnitude of the g-shift for potassium chloride. Similarly Gourary and Adrian[4] found that their model gave a reasonable result for various crystals. For potassium chloride, for example, they estimate $\Delta g(K^+) = -0.0036$ and $\Delta g(Cl^-) = -0.0017$. The total value of -0.0053 should be compared with the experimental result of -0.007. Blumberg and Das used a somewhat different approach and found $\Delta g = -0.0047$.

Whilst their results are clearly satisfactory, the shifts themselves are so small that one can hardly say that the calculations do more than lend support to the theories tested.

(c) Other electron-excess centres

No paramagnetic resonance has been found for the ground states of any electron-excess centre besides the F-centre. Mention should be made, however, of an interesting modification to the F-centre which is achieved by using a mixture of two different cations. The F-band still approximately follows Ivey's rule that $\lambda_{max}(m\mu) \propto$ (lattice parameter)$^{1.84}$ but splits into two bands labelled A_1 and A_2 which reflect the new symmetry of the cavity. It is interesting that for KCl containing low concentrations of LiCl there is a large reduction in both the isotropic and anisotropic hyperfine coupling constants to ^{7}Li together with a smaller increase in the coupling to ^{39}K relative to the values for F-centres in pure LiCl and KCl respectively[10]. This was interpreted in terms of a shift of the lithium ion away from the centre of the cavity and hence into a less dense region of the F-electrons wave-function.

(i) The F′-centre

This centre is of interest here as it forms the basis of one theory for electron-pairing in metal ammonia solutions[11,12b]. Little is known about these centres, except that they are diamagnetic and relatively unstable. They are characterised by a broad band on the low energy tail of the F-band.

(ii) The F_2- or M-centre

Once again, these centres are of special interest since they form the basis of a second model for the diamagnetic species formed in metal ammonia solutions[12]. After many years of controversy, it now seems certain that the F_2 model of van Doorn and Haven[13] is correct. This consists of two F-centres associated along a [110] direction, the two electrons being paired in the ground state. The M-band is also on the low energy side of the F-band, the separation between the two falling steadily as the lattice parameter increases.

The major evidence in favour of this model comes from a study of the electron spin resonance spectrum of the lowest triplet level of the centre, which seems to have a remarkably long life-time at 90 °K. Seidel[14] found fine-structure in the electron spin resonance spectrum from which he estimated $D = \pm 161$ gauss and $E = \pm 54$ gauss. This value for D is close to that predicted for purely dipolar interaction between electron spins 4.44 Å $(\sqrt{2}a)$ apart.

Further, by using ENDOR, he found that an isotropic hyperfine coupling, assigned to the bridging potassium ions, had a magnitude of twice that for the remaining cations, which were themselves closely similar to the six equivalent cations of the F-centre. The angular dependence of these interactions clearly established that the F_2 model for the M-centre is indeed correct.

(d) Other ionic crystals

Centres having magnetic and optical properties as predicted for electrons in anion vacancies have also been detected in a variety of other crystals, such as irradiated NaH, NaN_3 and alkaline earth oxides, sulphides and selenides.

Results for alkaline earth salts are given in Table 4.3. As has been stressed by Wertz and co-workers[15] the trend to large values of $|\Delta g|$ on going from MgO to BaO is in reasonably good accord with the theories developed for F-centres in alkali halide crystals, discussed in the previous section.

This trend is retained on replacing oxide by sulphide or selenide. But for the series MgO, MgS and MgSe the g-value goes from 2.0023 to 2.0062 and back to 2.0035. The high electron donating power of these ions is probably responsible for the positive component.

TABLE 4.3

g-VALUES FOR F-CENTRES IN ALKALINE-EARTH SALTS[15]

	Oxide	Sulphide	Selenide
Mg	2.0023	2.0062	2.0035
Ca	2.0001	2.0033	2.0030
Sr	1.9846	2.0036	2.0032
Ba	1.936	1.9641	1.9670

In the next two sections we refer to the possibility that centres very similar to F-centres may be important in certain solvents and non-ionic solids. Since these centres are far less satisfactorily defined by their physical properties the quite detailed mathematical approximations used to describe F-centres are less suitable, and a good deal of the discussion is concerned with the qualitative identification of the entities under consideration rather than detailed attempts to describe them mathematically.

4.2 METAL SOLUTIONS

Although the fact that alkali metals are soluble in liquid ammonia was discovered over one hundred years ago by Weyl[16] it is only quite recently that wide interest in these solutions has been shown. The previous lack of interest is surprising in view of the apparent simplicity of these systems and the fundamental yet puzzling nature of the phenomena involved.

For years it seemed that an adequate description of the dilute blue solutions was simply that the metal ionised to give solvated cations and solvated electrons, the whole system having salt-like properties, with the solvated electrons having an unusually high mobility. Little consideration was given to the physical nature of solvated electrons or the structure of the non-conducting "ion-pairs".

Very recently it has been realised that solvated electrons probably play an important role in the reactions of water and aqueous solutions exposed to high-energy radiation. Their presence has been invoked in order to explain chemical and especially, kinetic phenomena. With the advent of pulsed radiolysis with high-energy electrons attempts have also been made to detect these transient species spectroscopically: in the absence of electron scavengers, a broad intense absorption band appears in the visible region with a maximum at about 14,300 cm^{-1} and it is generally accepted that this is due to aquated electrons[17].

For many years it has been known that localised blue colours appear when potassium is freshly exposed under water or alcohols, but a claim that bulk solutions could be prepared, having a band in the 11,000 cm^{-1} region[18] has never been substantiated, despite repeated attempts by various groups to repeat the experiments. Although the bulk of evidence does favour the concept that the species detected during pulsed radiolysis is the aquated electron, direct comparison with metal ammonia solutions does not directly confirm this as the band in water has a peak at approximately twice the frequency of the band in ammonia. (We recall this aspect of the problem in § 4.2d(ii).)

These studies have increased interest in the fundamental nature of metal ammonia solutions. Certainly the basic concept that metals such as sodium simply ionize to give solvated electrons sounds far-fetched but it is just this that makes the problem both fascinating and baffling.

In the following sections we present first a brief glossary of the species that are currently postulated. This is followed by a resume of the important properties of these solutions, and then attention is turned to information provided by electron spin resonance studies. We will also outline the application of nuclear magnetic resonance to the problem, for in this instance the latter technique is often the more informative. Finally, some details of theoretical work are outlined.

(a) Equilibria and species

The present situation is summarised in the following scheme:

(1) Possible one-electron species

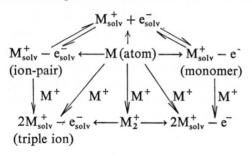

$$(4.2)$$

Basic equilibria:

$$M^+_{solv} + e^-_{solv} \rightleftharpoons M^+_{solv} - e^-_{solv} \rightleftharpoons M^+_{solv} - e^- \qquad (4.3)$$

i.e. conducting species $\rightleftharpoons$ non-conducting species

(2) Possible two-electron species

$$(4.4)$$

Basic equilibria:

$$2e^-_{solv} \rightleftharpoons e^{2-}_{2\,solv}; \quad 2e^-_{solv} + 2M^+_{solv} \rightleftharpoons 2M^+_{solv} - 2e^- \qquad (4.5)$$

i.e. paramagnetic species $\rightleftharpoons$ diamagnetic species

The symbol M^+_{solv}–e^- represents the centrosymmetric monomer or expanded metal atom, whilst M^+_{solv}–e^-_{solv} represents the ion-pair unit. Other symbols follow this pattern, the three anions M^-_{solv}, M^+_{solv}–$2e^-_{solv}$ and M^+_{solv}–$2e^-$ representing the various possibilities of two electrons paired in the outer *s*-level of the metal, the resulting ion being solvated in the manner normal for an *anion*, two solvated electrons closely associated with one solvated cation and two electrons centrosymmetrically bound to the metal ion solvated as a *cation*[19].

(b) Information from electron spin resonance

As a method for "counting spins" this technique is less satisfactory than is often supposed, especially when, as for metal solutions, the absorption line is very narrow. Measurements at radio frequencies are far easier to reproduce than at the more usual microwave frequencies, but the sensitivity is reduced. Hutchison and Pastor[20] working with potassium–ammonia solutions of concentration greater than about 10^{-2} M were able to detect a real difference between their measurements and static susceptibility studies[11,21] which they attributed to a diamagnetic contribution from the electron paired species. They showed that this susceptibility of $26 \cdot 10^{-6}$ could be interpreted in terms of the two electrons moving in orbits of root mean square radius of about 3 Å.

It has recently been found that a plot of the number of spins against concentration of sodium–ammonia solutions at room temperature is quite linear in the range 10^{-5} to 10^{-2} M but as the temperature is lowered the onset of curvature moves steadily to lower concentrations[22]. These results show that spin-pairing occurs in the 10^{-2}–0.5 M region, there being only about 3.5% unpaired electrons at the higher concentration at -33 °C.

(i) Solutions in ammonia

Since there is very efficient motional narrowing a single line is detected despite the fact, as obtained from nuclear magnetic resonance studies, that there is considerable coupling between the unpaired electron and the nuclei, which is apparently independent of concentration. The experimental line-width is then a result of almost complete motional narrowing, but still arises from hyperfine interactions, and the time of interaction between the electron and any one magnetic nucleus must be less than 10^{-7} sec. In support of this is the viscosity dependence found by Hutchison and O'Reilly[23]. If interactions with protons were important one would expect a large change in width on going from NH_3 to ND_3. In fact there is practically no change[23,24], the small increase being assigned to a longer correlation time in ND_3. On the other hand replacement of ^{14}N by ^{15}N decreased the value by a factor of about $\frac{5}{6}$, which is close to that expected if nitrogen hyperfine coupling is the cause of the residual broadening[24]. In very dilute solutions the width is independent of the alkali metal used although for rubidium and caesium solutions differences are found[25,40]. Hence one can conclude that the orbital of the unpaired electron in the blue species in dilute solutions interacts strongly with nitrogen nuclei but only weakly with protons and alkali metal nuclei. These results are in good agreement with those from nuclear magnetic resonance studies described in the next section.

The g-value for dilute metal–ammonia solutions is about 2.0008, at 25 °C, and is almost independent of the metal[25]. There is a slight shift to lower values on cooling, but addition of various salts has a marked effect upon both the g-values and the line-widths[25, 26]. Some results are displayed graphically in Fig. 4.2.

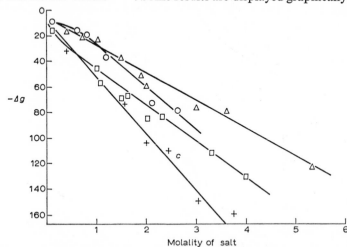

Fig. 4.2a (Ref. 26).   The variation in g-factor $[\Delta g=10^4 (g_{soln} - 2.0012)]$ at room temperature for dilute solutions of the alkali metals containing added alkali iodides. ○ Sodium solutions containing sodium iodide. △ Potassium solutions containing potassium iodide. + Rubidium solutions containing rubidium iodide; Point "c" sodium solution containing rubidium iodide. □ Caesium solutions containing caesium iodide.

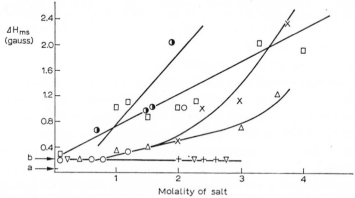

Fig. 4.2b.   The widths at room temperature of the electron resonance signals from dilute solutions of the alkali metals containing added alkali halides. ○ Na + NaI, ◑ 0.2 M Na + NaI; △ K + KI; ▽ K + KBr; × Rb + RbI; + Rb + RbBr; □ Cs + CsI. (a) Data of ref. 20 for sodium and potassium solutions; (b) limit of resolution for the spectrometer.

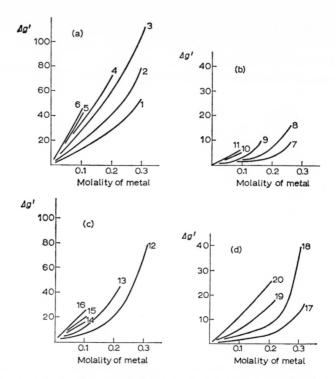

Fig. 4.2c.   The g-factor of metal solutions at room temperature as a function of metal and salt concentrations. (a) Rb + RbI, molality of salt: 1, 0.2; 2, 0.4; 3, 0.8; 4, 1.2; 5, 1.9; 6, 2.6. (b) Rb + RbBr, molality of salt: 7, 0.1; 8, 0.2; 9, 0.5; 10, 0.9; 11, 1.6. (c) Cs + CsI, molality of salt: 12, 0.2; 13, 0.5; 14, 1.0; 15, 2.0; 16, 3.0. (d) Na + NaI, molality of salt: 17, 0.2; 18, 0.5; 19, 1.0; 20, 2.0. $\Delta g' = \Delta g_0 - \Delta g_m$.

(ii) Solutions in ammonia with added salts

The original aim of studying the effect of added electrolytes upon the optical and e.s.r. spectra of metal ammonia solutions was to constrain the equilibrium $M^+_{solv} + e^-_{solv} \rightleftharpoons M^+_{solv} - e^-$ to favour the species $M^+_{solv} - e^-$. It was argued that, if before addition of salt the equilibrium was largely to the left, then there should be a marked change in both optical and electron spin resonance spectra as excess cations were added. Furthermore, had the non-conducting species, $M^+_{solv} - e^-$, a large spin-density on the cation it was expected that on addition of salt, hyperfine splitting from the cation nuclei would be manifest. In early work[27] no modification of the electron spin resonance spectrum was noticed, but a small shoulder in the 12,500 cm^{-1} region appeared on the high energy side of the main infrared band which was tentatively assigned to the species $M^+_{solv} - e^-$. More recent work[26] shows that both g-values and line-widths of the electron spin resonance spectra are modified as well as the optical spectra.

In summary, it seems that for a given cation, chlorides and amides have a negligible effect on the g-value, bromides give a small negative increment and iodides give a large negative shift (Fig. 4.2a.).

The effect of varying the cation is only noticeable for iodides, and no simple trend is apparent, Changes in line-widths were also observed which followed similar trends. Thus surprisingly, it is concluded that even when the concentration of cations is high, the electron does not choose to penetrate close to them, but, for iodide at least, that close contact with anions is relatively frequent. The subsidiary cation effect for the iodides may then result either because the relative concentration of ion-pairs, ion clusters and "free" solvated ions varies from cation to cation, or because the properties of iodide are a weak function of the nature of the nearby cation.

Perhaps this result is not so surprising. Certainly when the ions are well separated from the solvated electron cations will attract whilst anions will repel. If the electron were able to penetrate close to the ions and into the first solvent shell it would experience a strong repulsion force from the solvent molecules oriented about the cation, whereas that from solvent molecules around the anion would be attractive. Alternatively, we could say that the solvent is already polarised in the correct sense for close penetration in the case of solvated anions but in the wrong sense for the cations. This is then in accord with the results, since g-shifts and broadening will only result when the ions are in close contact with unpaired electrons.

The g-shift then arises from states in which the electron occupies a vacant orbital of the anion. These are only partly a property of the anion, being defined in part by the polarised shell of solvent molecules[28]. The resulting levels have been depicted as linear combinations of anion orbitals such as the 6s-level for iodide, and F-centre type expanded orbitals defined by the polarised solvent molecules. Since the lowest level will be an s-state, excited states must be invoked to explain the g-shift. This presumably involves the empty outer p-levels of the anions as Δg is negative.

The smaller shifts for bromides and chlorides is then at least partly a consequence of their smaller spin–orbit coupling constants, but since bromide causes relatively large negative g-shifts in F-centres this is probably not the only factor. It is significant that the energy of the first absorption band for solvated halide ions decreases markedly on going from chloride to iodide.

If this is due to a raising of the energy of the excited state, then this will be progressively less available for iodide, bromide and chloride ions.

Solutions of alkaline earth metals in ammonia have properties which are, in the dilute range, very similar to those of the alkali metals. Solutions of europium metal are of particular interest since it has been shown, by measurement of optical and electron spin resonance spectra, that dilute solutions consist essentially of Eu^{2+} ions and solvated electrons[25]. The important result is that, at high dilutions, the electron spin resonance lines from Eu^{2+} ions and the single line from the electrons are narrow and that, as the concentration is increased, they broaden without undergoing any other change. This result shows that interaction between the electrons and the cations is neither very intimate nor very extensive. In our view this result supports the loose "ion-pair" model for the non-conducting species in these solutions.

(iii) Solutions in amines

That these solutions are more complicated than those in ammonia is indicated by the variety of absorption bands detected for various systems[29-32]. In general, any of three absorption bands may be found, one in the infrared region at rather higher energy ($7,700 \text{ cm}^{-1}$) than that in ammonia ($5,600$ cm^{-1}), one in the visible region (generally between $15,800 \text{ cm}^{-1}$ and $13,300$ cm^{-1} and one between these two bands (at about $11,100 \text{ cm}^{-1}$) which in contrast with the others, is strongly dependent upon the cation.

In early work it was found that strong electron spin resonance absorption was only found for solutions having a band in the infrared region[30], and hence it was suggested that the species absorbing in the infrared was indeed a species comparable with that found in ammonia (*i.e.* in all probability, solvated electrons), but that the band in the $15,000 \text{ cm}^{-1}$ region was due to a diamagnetic species.

Very recently there has been an important advance inasmuch that two different groups have detected species exhibiting hyperfine structure from the nuclei of the metal. Vos and Dye[33] found that rubidium and caesium in methylamine gave rather poorly resolved hyperfine components superimposed upon a central line, and that the hyperfine splitting decreased markedly on cooling[33] (Fig. 4.3). For ^{133}Cs ($I = 7/2$) the electron density at the nucleus fell from about 7% to 1.6% of that for the free atom on cooling from $25 \degree C$ to $-95 \degree C$. For rubidium the spectra were more complicated because of the two isotopes ^{85}Rb ($I = 5/2$) and ^{87}Rb ($I = 3/2$), and estimates of the density are less sure. No hyperfine structure was detected for the lighter alkali metals.

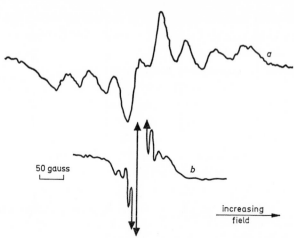

Fig. 4.3.   E.S.R. spectra of solutions of caesium in methylamine (a) at 25 °C and (b) at −95 °C (ref. 33).

The major conclusions to be drawn are that two different paramagnetic species coexist in these solutions only one being strongly associated with a single alkali metal nucleus. Furthermore, the unpaired electron in the latter must remain associated with a given nucleus for a relatively long period (greater than 10^{-7} sec) since resolved hyperfine structure was detected.

These conclusions are well supported by the results of Bar-Eli and Tuttle[34] for solutions of potassium in ethylamine. The four-line spectrum from ^{39}K in this instance was highly resolved, but these workers did not detect a central line due to a second species. Again, the hyperfine interaction was found to decrease markedly on cooling, such that the spin density at ^{39}K fell from about 16% to 5% of the free atom value on cooling from 48 °C to −36 °C. Recent work by Catterall[35] has shown that under certain conditions a very narrow central line with a slightly shifted g-value can be detected, and that this species is strongly favoured by dilution (Fig. 4.4).

At room temperature, these solutions have bands with maxima at about 14,800 cm^{-1} and 11,500 cm^{-1}, but no band is found in the infrared region[36]. The rate of decay of the former band accurately followed that of the electron resonance signal, whilst that of the latter band decayed at a first order rate of just twice this value. Hence, the 14,800 cm^{-1} band was assigned to paramagnetic monomers, the other to dimers. Dewald and Dye had previously assigned the latter band to a metal dimer (M_2)[32] but supposed that the 14,800 cm^{-1} band was due to a species $(M_2^+)e^-$. The electron spin resonance

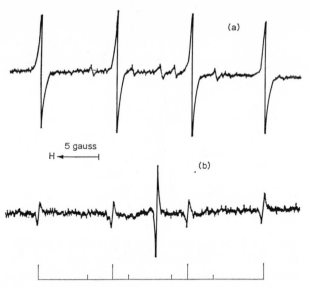

Fig. 4.4.   E.S.R. spectra (X-band) of solutions of potassium in ethylamine (a) *ca.* 10^{-5} *M* and (b) *ca.* 10^{-6} *M* (ref. 35).

results definitely eliminated the latter species, at least for solutions in ethylamine.

Solutions of lithium, rubidium and caesium in ethylamine all showed maxima in the infrared $(7,700 \text{ cm}^{-1})$ region and also had a single sharp electron spin resonance band close to $g = 2$. Therefore it seems reasonable to assign this band to the solvated electron.

Addition of methylamine or an excess of potassium ion (as a potassium salt) caused the ^{39}K hyperfine lines to broaden and ultimately to collapse to a single line[34] (Fig. 4.5). The latter change must be a result of the rapid electron transfer:

$$K_{solv}^+ + K_{solv}^+ - e^- \rightleftharpoons K_{solv}^+ - e^- + K_{solv}^+ \qquad (4.6)$$

The effect of methylamine is probably due to a loosening of the cation–electron unit, a process which is also manifest as a reduction in the ^{39}K hyperfine splitting.

One further observation of great interest was that solutions of lithium in ethylamine gave electron spin resonance spectra consisting of a single narrow line superimposed upon a seven- or possibly nine-line multiplet having a hyperfine splitting of 2.45 gauss[34]. It was suggested that this splitting arose

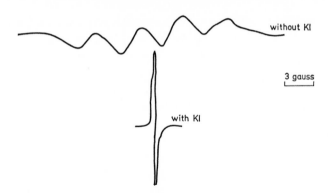

Fig. 4.5. Effect of adding KI in excess to a solution of K in 2:3 methylamine to ethylamine (ref. 34).

from an interaction between the electron and the four equivalent ^{14}N nuclei in the unit $(Li^+ (NH_3)_4)e^-$. If this assignment is correct it represents another major advance, since it means that the electron is confined so as to interact strongly with nearest neighbour solvent molecules only. Total spin-density on these nitrogen nuclei is very small, and is far less than that estimated for metal ammonia solutions. The original spectra do not show the outer lines at all clearly, but more recent results confirm their presence (Fig. 4.6).

The nature and properties of these species are discussed further in § 4.2d.

(iv) Solutions in ethers

Some alkali metals dissolve quite readily in various cyclic and poly-ethers to give rather unstable blue solutions, characterised by one or more bands having maxima in the 14,500 cm^{-1} region[37]. Results of electron spin resonance studies are inconclusive, but it seems to be unlikely that the major spe-

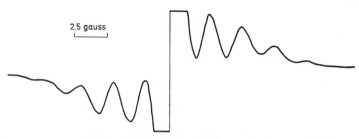

Fig. 4.6. E.S.R. spectrum of lithium in ethylamine at $-86\,°C$. (R. Catterall, unpublished result).

References p. 77–79

cies is paramagnetic. All that one can conclude at present is that the major species is probably a dimer and the electrons and cations must be closely associated because of the low conductivity of the solutions. It remains possible that the blue species *is* paramagnetic, but that one or other of the possible exchange processes were occurring at a rate just sufficient to broaden the hyperfine components under the conditions of measurement.

(v) Solutions in molten salts

Many metals are soluble in a variety of their molten salts. For alkali metals in alkali halide melts, the phenomenon is most likely to be closely related to the solid state situation: that is, for dilute solutions the metal probably dissolves as cations and electrons, the latter occupying anion vacancies to give units comparable with F-centres. Relatively little pertinent work has been carried out on such systems and other models, such as the interstitial atom model, are equally in accord with many of the properties so far measured.

Electron spin resonance studies of molten salt solutions are rendered difficult by the highly conducting nature of the solvent which greatly lowers the sensitivity (Q) of the cavity. Replacement of the normal cavity by a simple wave-guide system terminated by a copper block carrying the sample overcame this problem to a considerable extent, and spectra from various transition-metal ions in molten salts became detectable [38]. Even so, no resonance could be detected from solutions of lithium in molten lithium iodide, even when saturated solutions were used. This failure was explained in terms of the generalisation that the relaxation time (T_2) to be expected in molten salt solutions is small compared with that for aqueous solutions. This is thought to be due to the ionic nature of the medium and the high temperatures involved. If this is correct it is a pity, because these solutions provide an interesting link between F-centres in crystals and the other solutions discussed in this section.

We are not aware of any other media in which stable solutions of metals can be prepared. Clearly, one needs a solvent which solvates sufficiently well to overcome the lattice energy of the metal, but which cannot be reduced either by it or by solvated electrons. This rules out non-polar media since the solvation energy of alkali metal atoms or molecules must be small. It also eliminates unsaturated molecules (such as methyl cyanide or acetone) which can add an electron to the π-system or molecules having relatively acidic protons (such as water or alcohols) which more readily form hydrogen. It does require that the polar solvent interacts with the metal in such a way as to produce cations and anion-like species, or that solvent molecules can interact with the atom as if they were cations, with a resultant partial extrusion of the electron*.

(c) Information from nuclear magnetic resonance

Before turning to a more detailed consideration of the theories developed to describe these solutions, attention is given to the results obtained from nuclear magnetic resonance studies, since these have been particularly informative even though only solutions in ammonia have been studied so far.

(i) Knight shifts

It is fortunate that the rapidly modulated interactions between individual nuclei and electrons, which result in a single, relatively uninformative electron spin resonance absorption, are ideal for the observation of narrow nuclear spin resonance lines which, because of this coupling, will be strongly shifted from the normal resonant fields. This effect, known as the Knight shift, can be shown to arise from the Fermi contact interaction between the unpaired electrons and the nuclei concerned. The line detected appears at a weighted average field between the resonant fields for non-interacting nuclei, and those for the nuclei experiencing a direct interaction with the unpaired electrons.

The Knight shift, K, is defined as $(H_{ref} - H)/H_{ref}$ where H is the field at which resonance occurs for the metal solution and H_{ref} is the resonance field in the absence of unpaired electrons. For ^1H and ^{14}N resonances, pure liquid ammonia is used to give H_{ref} whilst for the alkali metal ions, suitable diamagnetic salts dissolved in liquid ammonia can be used.

This shift arises from isotropic hyperfine coupling because all dipolar effects average to zero: in principle K can therefore be related to the spin-density at the nuclei concerned. This, if it is large, can be described as a population of relevant s-levels by comparison with corresponding atomic parameters, as has been described in Chapter 2. If it is small, it may represent either a small population of s-levels, or simply a spin polarisation of paired molecular electrons.

The problem is far more difficult than that for ordinary radicals or even

---

* Very recently G. Fraenkel, S. H. Ellis and D. T. Dix (*J. Am. Chem. Soc.*, 1965, *87*, 1406) have prepared stable blue solutions of group I metals in hexamethylphosphoramide. A single line at $g = 2.0021$ was detected.

F-centres. For metal nuclei one needs to know the percentage of electrons interacting with these nuclei before one can deduce the s-character. This could be obtained using data from conductivity experiments if any certainty could be attached to the nature of the "ion-pairs" whose concentration is thereby estimated. In fact, all non-conducting species are counted, and these may include unknown amounts of monomer units, contact ion-pairs and various types of solvent separated ion-pairs, each of which may give rise to a different Knight shift. The experimental result is then the average of these. Unfortunately, spectrophotometry does not help in disentangling these different possibilities.

For ^{1}H and ^{14}N Knight shifts the problem is still more involved. It is necessary to know not only the relative amounts of the different paramagnetic species present, but also the number of equivalent ammonia molecules in each. The latter is unknown, so too is the number of different types of interacting molecules. This point is well illustrated by ENDOR results for halide ions interacting with F-centre electrons[1]. If these interactions were imagined to be rapidly fluctuating over all the halide ions of the crystal, then the mean hyperfine coupling is measured by K. This mean is far less informative but nevertheless, various attempts have been made to interpret it in depth.

Usually, following McConnnell and Holm[39], the Knight shift K(X) is used to estimate the total average unpaired electron density at nucleus X through the relation

$$|\psi_0(X)|^2 = K(X)\frac{3N_e}{8\pi\chi} \qquad (4.7)$$

where χ is the electron spin susceptibility and N_e is the number of unpaired electrons per unit volume. Electron spin resonance results give these parameters, thus enabling $|\psi_0(X)|^2$ to be calculated independently of any theory for the structure of the solutions. Also the nuclear spin-density P(X) at the unpaired electron is often quoted:

$$P(X) = |\psi_0(X)|^2(N_X/N_e) \qquad (4.8)$$

N_X being the number of nuclei X per unit volume.

(ii) Hyperfine coupling to cations

O'Reilly has recently measured Knight shifts K(M) for ^{7}Li, ^{23}Na, ^{87}Rb and ^{133}Cs in liquid ammonia at 300 °K [40]. His results are given in Fig. 4.7. as a function of R, the ratio of the number of moles of ammonia to that of

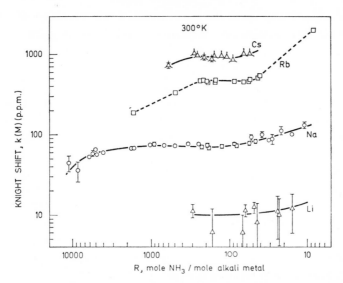

Fig. 4.7a. Knight shift of Li, Na, Rb and Cs – ammonia solutions *vs.* the mole ratio
of ammonia to alkali metal, 300 °K (ref. 40).

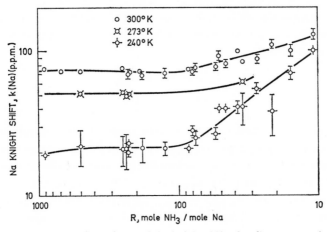

Fig. 4.7b. Temperature dependence of the knight shift of sodium–ammonia solutions.

metal. The most noteworthy results are that $K(Cs)$ is above one hundred
times greater than $K(Li)$ (there being a steady increase with atomic weight)
and that there is a real decrease in $K(Na)$ at concentrations of sodium below
about 0.02 M. $K(Na)$ was also found to decrease markedly on cooling.

TABLE 4.4

CALCULATED SPIN-DENSITIES AT MONOMER NUCLEI[47]
(Unit: $(10a_0)^{-3}$)

Monomer	Metal $|\psi(M)|^2$	Number of coordination shells [a]	Metal orthogonalised ψ $|\psi_0(M)|^2$
Li	1.6	1	0.56
		2	1.25
Na	7.5	1	1.9
		2	4.8
Rb	82	1	96
		2	226
Cs	143	1	165
		2	385

[a] Shell 1 consists of six solvent molecules directly coordinated to the cation. Shell 2 is the next layer of solvent molecules.

Values for the average electron density $|\psi_0(M)|^2$ at the metal nuclei estimated from these Knight shifts are compared with results for the corresponding gaseous atoms in Table 4.4. O'Reilly[40] has discussed these results in terms of the equilibria

$$M \rightleftharpoons M^+ + e^- \qquad (4.9)$$

$$M + e^- \rightleftharpoons M^- \qquad (4.10)$$

and he suggests that the latter is more satisfactory than the more usual reaction to give M_2 species. A pairing reaction within solvent cavities is not ruled out by the results. The resulting equilibrium constants K_1 and K_2 were about $2.04 \cdot 10^{-2}$ mole litre and 177 mole litre at 300 °K. These values are quite close to those estimated by Becker et al.[41] in terms of equations involving M and M_2 species, but still depend on a number of approximations.

(iii) Hyperfine coupling to ^{14}N

The Knight shift for ^{14}N falls rapidly as the metal concentration and temperature decrease, but it is independent of the nature of the alkali metal. Furthermore, P(N) was found to be almost independent of metal concentration in the dilute range at 300 °K[40].

(iv) Hyperfine coupling to ^1H

One advantage of the nuclear magnetic resonance method for estimating isotropic hyperfine coupling is that the sign of coupling can be derived from the direction of the shift. As expected, those for the alkali metal nuclei and ^{14}N were positive, but surprisingly, that for ^1H turned out to be negative. This result, which is reminiscent of the indirect coupling found for α-protons in π-systems (as, for example, in CH_3), suggests that direct coupling is either zero or small, in contrast to expectation for either the cavity model or the monomer unit. We stress, however, that this is an overall result. A situation could well be envisaged in which a small number of strongly interacting ammonia molecules give a positive coupling whilst a relatively large number of outer-shell ammonia molecules give a negative indirect coupling slightly overweighing the former.

Another factor which may well contribute is that as a result of the modification in hydrogen bonding there might be a substantial chemical shift superimposed upon the Knight shift for protons. While this would alter the magnitude of the interaction it is unlikely to alter the sign.

(d) Theories

Three approaches have been made: cavity and monomer models have been approximated in terms of a coulombic potential in a continuous dielectric[42] (the "expanded" or polaron model), electrons in cavities have been described in terms of a deep spherical well (the confined model)[43,44] and a point–dipole method similar to the point–ion–lattice method of Gourary and Adrian[4] has been applied to both monomer and cavity models[7,40,45]. Specific interactions with ammonia have been explained by Pitzer[46] in terms of the formation of NH_3^- ions, the electrons being housed in the $3s$-atomic orbital of nitrogen. In later theories, interactions with ^{14}N and ^1H have been estimated by using a wave-function for the bound electron orthogonalised to those of the surrounding ammonia molecules[47].

(i) The polaron model

In its various forms, this model has recently been considered in detail by Jortner, Rice and Wilson[42]. These authors start with a consideration of the Landau polaron theory[48] which was originally developed for F-centres in alkali halide crystals. The electron is bound by self-polarisation of the dielectric medium, no specific cavity being invoked. The binding energy estimated for such a system is small (about 0.1 eV) and the approach is clearly inappropriate for F-centres. For polar liquids the actual binding energy is thought to be between 1 and 2 eV. Self-polarisation in these cases can include partial orientation of dipolar solvent molecules which will both deepen the trap, and serve to localise the electron.

As with F-centres, one can now consider the interaction in terms of various approximations. The electronic adiabatic formalism is based on the assumption that the unpaired electron is very loosely bound relative to the core-electrons of the solvent. Hence the electrons of the solvent feel the charge of the unpaired electron as a point charge at any given instant, whereas the unpaired electron is in an averaged potential produced by the core-electrons.

This treatment, in effect, puts the binding energy from electronic polarisation of the medium equal to zero. Since the experimental binding energy of solvated electrons is quite large relative to the energy of the first electronic excitation of ammonia, this is not a very satisfactory approach. The alternative is to use the Hartree–Fock method as recommended for F-centres, in which any one electron experiences an averaged field of the other electrons. By this method contributions to the total binding from electronic polarisation will be accommodated.

(ii) The cavity model

An approach to the problem from the other extreme is the model in which an electron is confined within a deep spherical well of radius R. In seeking a physical meaning for R it would seem reasonable to think of an effective "lattice parameter" for the system, comparable in form to that for alkali halide crystals. Early calculations by Ogg[43] gave the energy (E) as the difference between the zero-point kinetic energy of the electron in this well and a single expression for the polarisation energy of the dielectric medium:

$$E = \frac{h^2}{8mR_0^2} - \frac{e^2}{2R_0}\left(1 - \frac{1}{D_s}\right) \qquad (4.11)$$

This gave the unlikely value of $R_0 = 10$ Å and $E = -0.38$ eV by minimising E with respect to R_0. These calculations were improved by Lipscomb[49] by including a term for the surface tension which measures the resistance of the medium to the creation of a cavity. This gave $E = +0.13$ which implies that the system would collapse, but the value for R_0, of 4.8 Å seems more reasonable for the "lattice parameter". Stairs[50] greatly improved these estimates, using the same basic model and obtained $E = -0.43$ eV and $R_0 = 3.2$ Å, in far better agreement with experiment.

Although this theory suffers from several shortcomings it accommodates the presence of the surrounding medium in a fairly satisfactory manner, and it is probably just this factor which is underestimated by most other formalisms. Since the simple spherical-well model reflects trends in F-band energies with the lattice parameters of the host crystals, it has been used to discuss results for the optical absorptions of electrons in various media[44]. When optical spectra are discussed, and if the electron is quite strongly confined within a cavity for both ground and excited states, then details of the polarisation of the surrounding medium are relatively unimportant because ground and excited states are equally affected. Thus $\Delta E(1s \to 2p)$ can be set equal to the difference in energy between the two spherical square-well states: $(\Delta E) = 1.04 h^2 / 8mR_0^2$. The way in which this simple equation accommodates data for F-centres is depicted in Fig. 4.8. Also included are the results for solvated electrons in water, alcohols and ammonia, as well as various glasses which are discussed in § 4.3. For these examples, the lattice parameter is set equal to the result estimated from Ivey's rule[51]. That those results are quite reasonable is shown in Table 4.5 where these lattice parameters are given together with an estimate of the cavity radius. These results accommodate satisfactorily the marked change in band energy on going from ammonia to water, a result which is remarkably reminiscent of the change found for the first electronic transition of iodide ions in these solvents. Results for electrons in various glasses also fit on to this correlating graph quite well.

Jortner et al.[42] have extended this simple model by supposing that the electron is in a cavity but is not bonded by short range interactions. Indeed, they suggest that the stabilisation stems entirely from long-range interactions, and that short-range effects are entirely repulsive. This is not too well substantiated, but is a necessary conclusion if the continuous dielectric approximation is to be used. Ultimately, they use a self-consistent field (Hartree–Fock) model, with various refinements, and obtain good agreement for various properties of metal–ammonia solutions. However, their results do not satisfactorily account for the new data for electrons in water even if the radius of the cavity is taken to zero[52].

(iii) The monomer model

The monomer unit can be treated similarly[42] and has also been treated by

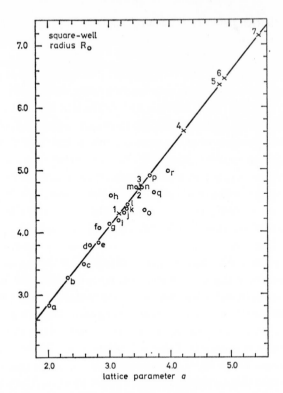

Fig. 4.8. Correlation of the calculated square-well radius R_0 with the experimental lattice parameter a at room temperature (R. Catterall, Ph. D. Thesis, Leicester University, 1964, p. 302).

Key
F-centres in:

(a) LiF;	(b) NaF;	(c) LiCl;	(d) KF;	(e) NaCl;
(f) RbF;	(g) NaBr;	(h) CsF;	(i) KCl;	(j) NaI;
(k) RbCl;	(l) KBr;	(m) RbBr;	(n) KI;	(o) CsCl;
(p) RbI;	(q) CsBr;	(r) CsI.		

Solvated electrons in:

(1) Alkali glasses (77 °K);   (2) EtOH;   (3) H_2O;
(4) dimethoxyethane;   (5) ethylenediamine;
(6) methylamine;   (7) NH_3.

a method similar to the point–ion–lattice method of Gourary and Adrian[4, 53]. Two different approaches were made by Blumberg and Das[53] both of which derive from a basic unit consisting of a sodium ion co-ordinated to six completely oriented ammonia molecules octahedrally located about the cation

TABLE 4.5

CAVITY RADII AND LATTICE PARAMETERS FOR SOLVATED ELECTRONS
AT ROOM TEMPERATURE IN VARIOUS MEDIA

Solvent	E_{max}[20] (K cal.)	R_0 (Å)	a (Å)	R_e (Å)
NH_3	17.77	7.13	5.48	4.08
$MeNH_2$	21.71	6.45	4.91	3.51
$(CH_2.NH_2)_2$	22.32	6.36	4.83	3.47
DME	28.59	5.62	4.23	2.83
H_2O	40.53	4.72	3.50	2.10
EtOH	41.08	4.69	3.48	2.08
Alkali glass	49.06	4.29	3.16	1.76

which is embedded in a dielectric and to which the unpaired electron is centro-symmetrically bonded.

In their first treatment, the potential was calculated by treating the cation as a point of positive charge, and the octahedron of ammonia molecules as point dipoles and quadrupoles, centred on the nitrogen nuclei. They postulated an effective radius for the monomer corresponding roughly to the distance between the centre and the next nearest solvent molecules, and assumed that only the optical dielectric constant should be used for the remaining solvent. When close to the cation, the electron was supposed to be entirely in the $3s$-atomic orbital.

Their second and more ambitious approach was similar except that the point multipoles were replaced by partial charges located at the nitrogen and hydrogen nuclei and in regions of space surrounding the bonding and lone-pair orbitals of the ammonia molecules. These regions, and the magnitudes of the charges, were estimated in terms of an s–p hybridised model with 25% ionic character attributed to the protons in order to simplify the calculation, and because the ground state of the electron is likely to be an s-state. The potential was then averaged on to centrosymmetric spheres. These two potentials, described as the multipole expansion and the distributed charge potential, were then used as a basis for estimating wave-functions for the unpaired electron. Finally, their functions were made orthogonal to the core-electrons of the six oriented ammonia molecules and values for spin-densities were calculated. These were compared with the experimental Knight-shift data of McConnell and Holm on the basis of the equilibria postulated by Becker et al.[41] and the assumption that only the monomer units contributed to the Knight shift.

Although this approach is full of approximations and arbitrary assumptions it is probably the most satisfactory one for treating nuclear spin resonance data, which, in turn, are perhaps the most searching of all the data so far gleaned from metal–ammonia solutions.

It is noteworthy that the result of orthogonalisation was to increase greatly the hyperfine coupling to ^{14}N, and to decrease the proton hyperfine coupling to a very small value. Blumberg and Das suggest that the negative shifts actually observed can then be understood as arising from configuration interaction[53].

O'Reilly has recently obtained a more complete set of Knight-shift data for all the alkali metals except potassium, which he considers are better interpreted in terms of equilibria involving M_{solv}^- as the diamagnetic species[40]. He has proposed that the major ^{14}N Knight shift comes from solvated electrons rather than monomer units, and has used the point multipole approximation of Blumberg and Das to calculate spin-densities at the metal nuclei (from monomers in small concentrations and ^{14}N (from cavity units in relatively large concentrations).

The solvated electron is supposed to be in a cavity defined by six ammonia molecules. These were then approximated as point dipoles on the periphery of the cavity for which a potential well was used which was based upon the experimental absorption spectrum and heat of solution. Spin-densities were calculated by orthogonalising the square-well wave-function and the molecular orbitals of the surrounding ammonia molecules.

The results of all these calculations are in fair accord with experiment, but so many approximations are involved that one can hardly accept the calculations as more than interesting exercises: much more experimental information is needed. One particularly vital question concerns the extent to which the electron, either in cavity or monomer units, is confined. Some experimental data relating to this question come from solid state studies outlined in the following section.

Another issue for metal-ammonia solutions which ought to be experimentally soluble is the question of the nature of the non-conducting species: is it a centro-symmetric monomer unit, a dipolar, ion-pair unit or is there an equilibrium mixture of both?

Certainly for solutions in amines, the monomer model seems to be fairly well established. The spin-density at the cation nucleus is strongly dependent upon temperature so that little importance can be attached to precise numerical results of calculations of such coupling constants. At present, the largest spin-density found for these units is for potassium in ethylamine for which a hyperfine coupling of about 16% of that for the free-atom was measured. It is just possible that ion-pair units could give a coupling as large as a result of slight transfer such as is found for certain anion radicals in media of poor ion-solvating power. Generally, hyperfine interaction with alkali metal cations is small in these solvents but for CO_2^- radicals in alkali metal formates, a coupling as large as 8.5% of the free-atom value was estimated for ^{39}K. It is therefore certainly possible for a non-centrosymmetric species to give rise to quite a large hyperfine splitting. Yet another factor requires consideration in this respect: there is no real justification for using the atomic value for the hyperfine splitting when one is considering relatively minor interaction with a cation. Use of atomic data seems to be a reasonable approximation for molecules or polyatomic ions, as is demonstrated in the subsequent chapters. It is also reasonable in the limit of large atomic character. For the present situation, however, where even in this approximation the atomic character is low, the real occupancy of the appropriate s-level may well be considerably smaller.

4.3 ELECTRONS IN GLASSES

It may have occurred to the reader that, since many of the problems posed above for solvated electrons arise because of the various rapid exchange processes which occur, one ought to study rigid solutions in order to minimise or even eliminate such exchanges. Abortive attempts to do this for metal-ammonia solutions are discussed in § 4.3a whilst experiments with other systems which appear to achieve the required result are outlined in subsequent sections.

(a) Rigid ammoniacal solutions

The simple device of freezing metal–ammonia solutions gives a grey opaque mass consisting of polycrystalline ammonia together with colloidal particles of metal. These solids have electron spin resonance spectra which are characteristic of the respective colloidal metals and have no bearing on the present problem.

An attempt to overcome this by adding high concentrations of sodium iodide was apparently successful in that blue glasses could be obtained on cooling to 77 °K[27] but further study[26] showed that the resulting broad electron spin resonance absorption was still due to colloidal metal. At present no system has been devised which, on freezing, gives a detectable signal, even though the fluid solutions absorb very strongly.

(b) Electrons in water

Two approaches to studying the interaction between the electrons and water molecules in the solid phase have been made. One apparently successful method involves irradiation of salt hydrates, and the other is essentially an adaptation of the matrix isolation method discussed in Chapter 3.

(i) Salt hydrates

In principle, the cavity theory could be tested if one could create an anion vacancy in a salt hydrate, such as $KF \cdot 4H_2O$, and then trap electrons in the vacancy. Unfortunately, anion vacancies are formed far less readily for hydrates than for anhydrous alkali halides, and to the present time the only crystals which appear to give the required products are alkali-hydroxide hydrates. These become blue after exposure to γ-rays [54-57], but are very readily bleached by visible light. The initial electron spin resonance spectrum is complex, but bleaching results in the loss of a single symmetrical band (Fig. 4.9.) having a g-value of about 2.001. From the proximity of the optical band to that found in irradiated water [17] at room temperature it can be inferred that the unpaired electrons are in comparable environments. The asymmetric

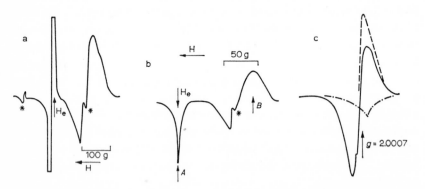

Fig. 4.9.   Electron resonance spectra of γ-irradiated sodium hydroxide glasses at 77 °K. (a) 10 M NaOD in D_2O. (b) 10 M NaOD in D_2O after exposure to visible light. (c) The difference spectrum in the free spin region attributed to the solvated electron. H_e, the field corresponding to a g-factor 2.0023. * Weak lines from trapped deuterium atoms. (ref. 57).

shape of this band is characteristic of spectra of trapped electrons[44], and the g-value is close to that for metal–ammonia solutions.

Furthermore, changing the cation has only a minor effect upon the electron spin resonance absorption and none on the optical absorption (in marked contrast to the behaviour of F-centres) but changing from H_2O to D_2O results in a decrease in the width of the electron spin resonance bands by a factor of about three[57].

These results are in good accord with expectation if the electron is indeed trapped at an anion vacancy, and we cannot discover any alternative explanation. The special role of hydroxide is then that, as the conjugate base of water, it has a good chance of being ejected provided it can also be protonated. A possible mechanism which has been outlined[57] would be electron loss by hydroxide, transfer of a proton from the resulting hydroxyl radical to a distant hydroxide ion *via* the water molecules leaving O^- in the OH^- site and finally trapping of the ejected electrons at the resulting hydroxide ion vacancies.

These results if correctly interpreted also suggest that the electron is strongly confined to the vacancy and the water molecules which define it. Qualitatively, one can argue that a continuum model which ignores the molecular nature of the environment or even a point–ion and point–multipole model must put a considerable spin-density on the nearest neighbour cations. It has been suggested[57] that this result tends to justify the use of a square-well approximation, and exposes the danger of neglecting the exclusion principle in the more complex calculations that have been undertaken.

The electron obviously will not be *totally* confined and one would expect to be able to measure its extension beyond the first shell of water molecules by a suitable probe. This has been attempted by incorporating iodide into the alkali-hydroxide glasses, since a small spin-density on iodide is known to cause a major shift in the g-value[26]. The results were interpreted in terms of two bands, one characteristic of electrons in standard vacancies, the other due to electrons in vacancies having one adjacent iodide ion. The latter band was indeed shifted to high fields ($g = 1.9993$) and was also considerably broader, thus confirming the ability of the electron to interact with iodide to a minor extent.

These results appear to provide a fairly exacting yardstick against which future theories should be matched.

(ii) Irradiated water deposits

High energy irradiation of water does not seem to yield trapped electrons in any guise even at liquid helium temperatures but Leach and his co-workers[58] have devised an ingenious experiment in which water vapour was exposed to low-energy electrons just before deposition on a cold finger at 77 °K. The resulting blue solids had electron spin resonance absorption spectra similar to those for irradiated hydroxide glasses except that the residual absorption was characteristic of hydroxyl radicals rather than O⁻ ions. These results are in good agreement with those described in § 4.3b above.

(iii) Metal–water deposits

A real step forward has been achieved by Bennett et al.[59] in their studies of the reaction between alkali metals and water. In this work a rotating cold finger was used such that in successive layers water and metal could be accumulated (see § 3.2). Again a blue deposit was obtained, though as yet no optical absorption data have been reported.

The electron spin resonance spectrum showed poorly resolved fine-structure which was attributed to interaction with four equivalent protons[59]. The hyperfine splitting of about 5.6 gauss was independent of the alkali metal but did not appear when D_2O was used. No evaluation of this hyperfine coupling has yet been attempted but in view of the results from proton magnetic resonance of metal–ammonia solutions the interaction is surprisingly large. The lines were very broad, however, and the splitting may well be largely dipolar in origin.

(c) Electrons in organic solvents

In view of these results it might be supposed that electrons would only be trapped provided well defined cavities were available. This is well borne out by the accumulation of results for irradiated organic solids in crystalline and glassy states. Crystalline solids are generally damaged with the formation and trapping of neutral fragments whereas the latter, which commonly decompose far more rapidly, tend to be highly coloured after exposure, and the radicals formed may be different from those obtained from the crystalline form. The colour is usually readily bleached with visible light and the electron spin resonance spectra are simultaneously modified. Sometimes the changes are complex, but under favourable circumstances the change can be traced to loss of a single line having a g-value of about 2.001[60].

Several factors support the contention that the coloured paramagnetic species are trapped electrons:

(1) In all cases the optical bands are characteristically broadened on the high-energy side [44b].

(2) For alcohols the band maxima bear the same relation to the transient absorption found in electron irradiated fluid alcohols [61] as the band for electrons in hydroxide glasses [57] bear to the aquated electron.

(3) The g-value for the electron spin resonance line is very close to that for dilute solution of alkali metals in ammonia.

Of some interest is the marked difference found for electrons trapped in glassy alcohols on the one hand and in glassy ethers on the other. The former are violet, with band maxima in the 19,500 cm^{-1} region, whilst the latter are blue, the maxima being at about 7,500 cm^{-1}. The electron spin resonance band for the former has a width (ΔH_{ms}) of about 14 gauss, narrowing to about 6 gauss when ROH is replaced by ROD whilst the band for the latter is only about 4 gauss in width.

These results have been rationalised in terms of trapping in cavities which are fortuitously present in glasses but not in crystals [60]. For alcohols which are known to be good anion-solvating media, it is supposed that the effect of the localised negative change is to twist some of the hydroxyl proton in towards the centre of the cavity thus stabilising the electron, causing a shift of the optical transition to high energies, and conferring width to the electron spin resonance band by hyperfine interaction. Such modification of the natural cavities cannot occur for the ethers, so that the optical absorption is at far lower energies, the range of trapping sites is far greater and the electron spin resonance band is narrow since there are no strongly interacting protons [60].

The case for trapped electrons in these solids is strong but much more information is required before more advanced theoretical studies are warranted.

References

1   G. FEHER, *Phys. Rev.*, 1957, *105*, 1122.
2   J. H. DE BOER, *Rec. Trav. Chim.*, 1937, *56*, 301.
3a A. R. REINBERG AND L. I. GROSSWEINER, *Phys. Rev.*, 1961, *122*, 1734.
3b C. J. DELBEEQ, *Z. Physik*, 1963, *171*, 560.
3c H. SEIDEL, M. SCHWOERER AND D. SCHMID, *Z. Physik*, 1965, *182*, 398.
3d J. N. MAYCOCK AND D. E. GRABENSTEIN, *Solid State Commun.*, 1964, *2*, 97.

4 B. S. GOURARY AND F. J. ADRIAN, *Solid State Phys.*, 1960, *10*, 127.
5a A. F. KIP, C. KITTEL, R. A. LEVY AND A. M. PORTIS, *Phys. Rev.*, 1953, *91*, 1066.
5b A. H. KAHN AND C. KITTEL, *Phys. Rev.*, 1953, *89*, 315.
6 W. C. HOLTON AND H. BLUM, *Phys. Rev.*, 1962, *125*, 89.
7 W. E. BLUMBERG AND T. P. DAS, *Phys. Rev.*, 1958, *110*, 647.
8 T. INUI AND Y. UEMURA, *Progr. Theoret. Phys. (Kyoto)*, 1950, *5*, 252.
9 T. KOJIMA, *J. Phys. Soc. Japan*, 1957, *12*, 908, 918.
10 R. L. MISHER, *Phys. Rev. Letters*, 1962, *8*, 362; *Proc. Collog. Ampère*, 1962, XI, 699.
11 S. FREED AND N. SUGARMAN, *J. Chem. Phys.*, 1943, *11*, 354.
12a M. GOLD, W. L. JOLLY AND K. S. PITZER, *J. Am. Chem. Soc.*, 1962, *84*, 2264.
12b R. CATTERALL AND M. C. R. SYMONS, *J. Chem. Soc.*, (A) 1965, 13.
13 C. Z. VAN DOORN AND Y. HAVEN, *Philips Res. Rept.*, 1956, *11*, 479; 1957, *12*, 309.
14 H. SEIDEL, *Phys. Letters*, 1963, *7*, 27.
15 J. E. WERTZ, J. W. ORTON AND P. AUZINS, *Discussions Faraday Soc.*, 1961, *31*, 140.
16 W. WEYL, *Pogg. Ann.* (now *Ann. Physik*), 1864, *121*, 601; *123*, 350; *Chem. News*, 1864, *10*, 85.
17 E. J. HART AND J. W. BOAG, *J. Am. Chem. Soc.*, 1962, *84*, 4090; J. W. BOAG AND E. J. HART, *Nature*, 1963, *197*, 45; J. P. KEENE, *Nature*, 1963, *197*, 47.
18 J. JORTNER AND G. STEIN, *Nature*, 1955, *175*, 893.
19 M. C. R. SYMONS, in G. LEPOUTRE AND M. J. SIENKO, *Metal-Ammonia Solutions*, Benjamin, New York, 1964, p. 1.
20 C. A. HUTCHISON, JR. AND R. C. PASTOR, *J. Chem. Phys.*, 1953, *21*, 1959.
21 E. HUSTER, *Ann. Physik*, 1938, [5] *33*, 477; 1948, [6] *4*, 183.
22 A. DEMORTIER AND R. CATTERALL, unpublished results.
23 C. A. HUTCHISON, JR. AND D. E. O'REILLY, *J. Chem. Phys.*, 1961, *34*, 1279.
24 V. L. POLLAK, *J. Chem. Phys.*, 1961, *34*, 864.
25 R. CATTERALL AND M. C. R. SYMONS, *J. Chem. Phys.*, 1965, *42*, 1466; *J. Chem. Soc.*, 1965, 3763.
26 R. CATTERALL AND M. C. R. SYMONS, *J. Chem. Soc.*, 1964, 4342.
27 H. C. CLARK, A. HORSFIELD AND M. C. R. SYMONS, *J. Chem. Soc.*, 1959, 2478.
28 M. SMITH AND M. C. R. SYMONS, *Trans. Faraday soc.*, 1958, *54*, 346.
29 H. BLADES AND J. W. HODGINS, *Can. J. Chem.*, 1955, *33*, 411.
30 G. W. A. FOWLES, W. R. MCGREGOR AND M. C. R. SYMONS, *J. Chem. Soc.*, 1957, 3329.
31 S. WINDWER AND B. R. SUNDHEIM, *J. Phys. Chem.*, 1962, *66*, 1254.
32 R. R. DEWALD AND J. L. DYE, *J. Phys. Chem.*, 1964, *68*, 121.
33 K. D. VOS AND J. L. DYE, *J. Chem. Phys.*, 1963, *38*, 2033.
34 K. BAR-ELI AND T. R. TUTTLE, *J. Chem. Phys.*, 1964, *40*, 2508.
35 R. CATTERALL AND M. C. R. SYMONS, *J. Chem. Soc.*, 1965, 6656.
36 M. OTTOLENGHI, K. BAR-ELI, H. LINSCHITY AND T. R. TUTTLE, *J. Chem. Phys.*, 1964, *40*, 3729.
37 J. L. DOWN, J. LEWIS, B. MOORE AND G. WILKINSON, *J. Chem. Soc.*, 1959, 3767; F. A. CAFFASSO AND B. R. SUNDHEIM, *J. Chem. Phys.*, 1959, *31*, 809; F. S. DAINTON, D. M. WILES AND A. N. WRIGHT, *J. Chem. Soc.*, 1960, 4283; E. S. PETROV, M. I. BELOUSOVA AND A. I. SHATENSHTEIN, *Zh. Obshch. Khim.*, 1964, *34*, 2465.
38 J. BROWN, *J. Phys. Chem.*, 1963, *67*, 2524.
39 H. M. MCCONNELL AND C. H. HOLM, *J. Chem. Phys.*, 1957, *26*, 1517.
40 D. E. O'REILLY, *J. Chem. Phys.*, 1964, *41*, 3729.
41 E. BECKER, R. H. LINDQUIST AND B. J. ALDER, *J. Chem. Phys.*, 1956, *25*, 971.
42 J. JORTNER, S. A. RICE AND E. G. WILSON, in G. LEPOUTRE AND M. J. SIENKO, *Metal-Ammonia Solutions*, Benjamin, New York, 1964, p. 222.

43 R. A. OGG, JR., *Phys. Rev.*, 1946, *69*, 668; *J. Chem. Phys.*, 1946, *14*, 114.
44a M. J. BLANDAMER, R. CATTERALL, L. SHIELDS AND M. C. R. SYMONS, *J. Chem. Soc.*, 1964, 4357.
44b M. J. BLANDAMER, L. SHIELDS AND M. C. R. SYMONS, *J. Chem. Soc.*, 1965, 3759.
45 T. P. DAS, *Advan. Chem. Phys.*, 1962, *4*, 303.
46 K. S. PITZER, *J. Chem. Phys.*, 1958, *29*, 453.
47 D. E. O'REILLY, *J. Chem. Phys.*, 1964, *41*, 3736.
48 L. LANDAU, *Physick Z. Soviet Union*, 1933, *3*, 664.
49 W. N. LIPSCOMB, *J. Chem. Phys.*, 1953, *21*, 52.
50 R. A. STAIRS, *J. Chem. Phys.*, 1957, *27*, 1431.
51 H. F. IVEY, *Phys. Rev.*, 1947, *72*, 341.
52 J. JORTNER, *Radiat. Res. Suppl.*, 1964, *4*, 24.
53 W. E. BLUMBERG AND T. P. DAS, *J. Chem. Phys.*, 1959, *30*, 251.
54 J. JORTNER AND B. SHARF, *J. Chem. Phys.*, 1962, *37*, 2506.
55 D. SCHULTE-FROHLINDE AND K. EIBEN, *Z. Naturforsch.*, 1962, *17a*, 445.
56 B. G. ERSHOV, A. K. PIKAEV, P. Ya. GLAZUROV AND V. I. SPITSYN, *Dokl. Akad. Nauk SSSR*, 1963, *149*, 363.
57 M. J. BLANDAMER, L. SHIELDS AND M. C. R. SYMONS, *Nature*, 1963, *199*, 902; *J. Chem. Soc.*, 1964, 4352.
58 R. MARX, S. LEACH AND M. HORANI, *J. Chim. Phys.*, 1963, *60*, 726.
59 J. E. BENNETT, B. MILE AND A. THOMAS, *Nature*, 1964, *201*, 919.
60 M. J. BLANDAMER, L. SHIELDS AND M. C. R. SYMONS, *J. Chem. Soc.*, 1965, 1127.
61 M. C. SAUER, JR., S. ARAI AND L. M. DORFMAN, *J. Chem. Phys.*, 1965, *42*, 708.

Chapter 5

Atoms and monatomic ions

From the trapped electron we take a further step in our progression towards a study of molecular radicals and turn to a consideration of the electron spin resonance spectra of atoms in a variety of host matrices. The importance of this Chapter lies not only in its function as a bridge between the concepts of an electron trapped by a surrounding potential well and an electron in a polynuclear potential but also inasmuch that environmental effects can be both monitored and, often, interpreted. This is so because in many instances free-atom parameters are available and perturbations due to the trapping matrix should be revealed in the deviation of the observed parameters between the trapped and the free species. The major part of this Chapter deals with matrix (medium) effects and little mention is made of that highly important aspect of interstitial atoms, namely their bearing on semiconductivity. Nor do we dwell on results for atoms in the gas phase, since no structural data result that have not already been deduced from optical studies. Suffice it to say that very precise parameters result, and the method is of importance from the viewpoints of monitoring reaction and identifying different atoms in low concentrations.

After considering results for hydrogen atoms in various solids in detail, we pass to a discussion of alkali metal atoms, silver atoms, atoms of Group V having ^{4}S ground states, O$^-$ ions and halogen atoms. Prior to these considerations, however, the theory of matrix effects is outlined (§ 5.1) in order to show the way in which electron spin resonance spectra for trapped atoms can be informative.

5.1 MATRIX EFFECTS

We shall give an account of the matrix effects on atoms in terms of the theory proposed by Adrian[1] and as developed by Jen *et al.*[2] so that results for highly polarisable interstitial atoms might be accommodated. The theory is based upon the sum of several opposing effects and may be summarised briefly as follows: two neighbouring particles will interact by the Van der Waal's mechanism; since this attraction depends on the interaction of instantaneous dipoles in the particles the wave-functions of the species will expand slightly so that the interaction energy is increased; this therefore leads to a reduction in the hyperfine splitting of the species. The second effect is that when the particles are very close their wave-functions overlap; to avoid a contravention of the Pauli principle the orbitals must be modified—in fact those of one particle effectively shrink away from those of the other, therefore the hyperfine interaction is increased. The mechanism which allows for this effect also mixes some of the other matrix wave-functions of particles with those of the trapped atom, hence a "superhyperfine" splitting due to nuclei of the matrix may be detected. Also the unpaired electron experiences a spin–orbit coupling characteristic of the matrix particle and a g-value shift may arise. This distribution of the electron also introduces short range repulsive (coulombic and exchange) effects which tend to increase the spin-density at the nucleus of the trapped atom.

Let us now, in § 5.1a and b consider a quantitative formulation of these effects.

The theory assumes that the effects of both long and short range forces are additive, as also are assumed to be the effects of each neighbouring matrix particle. Thus the system to be treated is the matrix particle (M)–impurity atom (A) pair. The procedure is to consider the sum of the M–A interaction energy and the hyperfine interaction (between the unpaired electron and the nucleus of the impurity atom) as a perturbation on the ground state wave-functions of the non-interacting particles.

(a) Long range interaction

The interaction is now a Van der Waal's effect and, as this is a manifestation of the intermolecular electronic correlation energy, the magnitude of the interaction should depend upon the polarisabilities, α_i, of the interacting particles. Adrian arrives at the result that the change in the hyperfine energy ΔA, is

$$\Delta A = - AE_v \left[\frac{2}{E_A} + \frac{1}{E_A + E_M} \right] \qquad (5.1)$$

where A is the unperturbed hyperfine interaction energy. E_v is the dispersion energy which may be calculated from the polarisabilities of the particles through the relations

$$E_v = CR^{-6} \tag{5.2}$$

and

$$C = \tfrac{3}{2}\alpha_M\alpha_A \left| \frac{E_A E_M}{E_A + E_M} \right| \tag{5.3}$$

In these expressions E_A and E_M are the mean values of the excitation energies for the impurity and matrix particles, and as both of these are negative and A is positive, it follows that ΔA is negative, in accord with the qualitative prediction.

(b) Short range interaction

The situation changes when the two particles are brought very close together, for then their wave-functions tend to overlap and so require modification in order that the Pauli principle be satisfied. The wave-functions are also distorted by the Coulomb and exchange components of the interaction. If the latter effects are ignored the situation may be described by a one-electron orbital which has been orthogonalised to the other one-electron orbitals of the system. Thus the proper orbital is

$$\psi = \sqrt{N}\,[\psi_A - \sum_M S_{AM}\psi_M] \tag{5.4}$$

where ψ_A is the unperturbed orbital of A which is occupied by the unpaired electron, the ψ_M are the orbitals of the surrounding matrix particles, S_{AM} is an overlap integral and $\sqrt{N}$ a normalising factor. This equation causes an increase, ΔA, in the hyperfine splitting, where

$$\Delta A = A \sum_M S_{AM}^2 \tag{5.5}$$

This model obviously leads to an increase in the spin-density at the nucleus of the impurity atom: physically the impurity atom orbitals shrink away from the matrix particles.

Jen et al.[2] allow for the perturbations caused by the Coulomb and exchange energies and obtain

$$\Delta A = A\left[\sum_M S_{AM}^2 + \frac{2}{|E_A|}\varepsilon^\circ \right] \tag{5.6}$$

where ε° is the matrix element of the perturbation in the ground state.

The shift in g-value may also be calculated on these models[1,2]. The theory supposes that during the orthogonalisation procedure the unpaired electron is distributed into the orbitals of the matrix particles and whilst there, experiences the spin-orbit coupling (λ_M) characteristic of an electron in the particular orbital of the matrix atom. Specifically Adrian obtained

$$\Delta g = \frac{4}{3E_A} S_{AM}^2 (2p\sigma) \lambda_M \langle \psi_M (2p\sigma) | L_z^2 | \psi_M (2p\sigma) \rangle \tag{5.7}$$

For an atom trapped isotropically by N matrix particles this becomes

$$\Delta g = \frac{8N}{9E_A} S_{AM}^2 (2p\sigma) \lambda_M \tag{5.8}$$

Since E_A is negative, according to this theory Δg is also negative. Jen et al.[2] obtained the similar expression

$$\Delta g = \frac{8N}{9E_A} S_{AM}^2 (2p\sigma) \left(1 + \frac{2}{|E_A|} \varepsilon^\circ \right) \tag{5.9}$$

Of course, it is necessary to estimate ε° in this equation. To do so it was assumed that this matrix element could be identified with the repulsive component of the Lennard–Jones 6–12 potential, and the Van der Waal's energy was identified with the attractive component. Using these identifications and eqn. (5.2) one deduces that

$$\varepsilon^\circ = C\sigma_{MA}^2 R^{-12} \tag{5.10}$$

σ_{MA} is the Lennard-Jones collision diameter which was determined from the sum of the gas phase collision radius of the matrix particles and the mean radius of the outermost occupied orbital of the matrix particle.

As we have anticipated, the general conclusions which may be drawn from these results are that the g-value shift will always be negative (and, incidentally, that the extra repulsive term in eqn. (5.9) has a negligible effect) and that the hyperfine interaction will decrease from the free-atom value as the atom approaches the matrix until the short range repulsive forces become dominant, from which point the hyperfine interaction will increase to a value possibly greater than that of the free atom. As a general rule[2]: for a given matrix those atoms which show an increase in their hyperfine interactions over the free-atom values will show a larger negative g-value shift than those atoms in which a negative hyperfine interaction shift is observed. Also, for a given atom the g-value is shifted to lower values as the atomic weight of the matrix particles increases. These theories were developed to account for the spectra of trapped hydrogen and alkali metal atoms, to which we shall shortly turn.

Before so doing we shall mention a further trapping mechanism proposed by Kazanskii and Pariiskii[3] to account for their results on hydrogen atoms trapped at a surface. Their model needs to explain both the lowered spin-density at the hydrogen nucleus compared with the free-atom value and a small anisotropy in the hyperfine interaction. It was held that these effects could be explained if the surface effect were imitated by a homogeneous electric field E. Perturbation theory led to

$$B_\perp = A - (47/60)\,A_0\lambda^2 \qquad (5.11)$$

$$B_\| = A + (47/30)\,A_0\lambda^2 \qquad (5.12)$$

$$A = A_0\,(1 - 15.5\,\lambda^2) \qquad (5.13)$$

where A_0 is the hyperfine interaction for the free atom and $\lambda = a_0^2 E/e$ is the perturbation expansion parameter (a_0 is the Bohr radius and e the electronic charge). This model predicts a lowered hyperfine interaction energy and an anisotropy of the correct order of magnitude.

Further information about trapping sites can be obtained if the interaction between the unpaired electron and magnetic nuclei in the matrix are moni-tored; ENDOR techniques are helpful in this respect and reference may be made to the particularly full study of hydrogen atoms trapped in calcium fluoride by Hall and Schumacher[4]. Another matrix effect, usually* only evident when the atom is not in an S state, is the possibility of a crystal field effect of the neighbouring matrix on the energy levels of the atom. This is manifest in a change of the magnetic properties of the impurity atom, and a study of this effect which also, by using ENDOR, revealed which matrix nuclei were involved, will be discussed in greater detail below.

5.2 HYDROGEN ATOMS

High-energy irradiation of crystals composed of molecules containing hy-drogen often results in the loss of hydrogen atoms, possibly because they can so readily escape the cage back-reaction which may hinder the escape of larger moieties. Normally the atoms will wander through the lattice until

---

* Zero field splitting in ^{4}S state atoms is discussed in § 5.4.

they can dimerise or, perhaps, cause secondary damage. Because of their mobility it is only infrequently that their electron spin resonance spectra can be observed and trapping the atoms in an inert gas matrix after passing an electric discharge through hydrogen gas has proved a useful technique.

When trapping is possible hydrogen atoms constitute a good system for the investigation of environmental effects for a number of reasons. Core-polarisation effects, which as has already been indicated stem from the cancellation of several large terms and therefore may be particularly sensitive to small perturbations, are non-existent in hydrogen atoms. Secondly, together with the structural simplicity of the atom, may be taken the fact that it is unequivocably orbitally non-degenerate; thus any distortion must be one impressed by the matrix. Thirdly, the gas phase parameters are known very accurately[5-7]. Fourthly, relative to the F-centre, which has been used to monitor environmental effects[8,9] (Chapter 4), the hydrogen atom interaction is somewhat simpler since the presence of the central force-field facilitates quantitative discussion. Finally, since the small size of the atom will hardly distort the crystal lattice, both interstitial and substitutional trapping sites are to be expected.

Hydrogen atoms have been detected in matrices of molecular hydrogen and rare gases[10], irradiated ice, hydrofluoric acid and methane at 4 °K[11], irradiated oxyacids[12], silica gel[13] and hydride-doped alkali halides[14] at 77° K and in calcium fluoride[4] and various phosphates[15,16] at both 77 °K and room temperature. Typical parameters are recorded in Table 5.1. Deuterium atoms have been detected in a number of these solids, a particular study being that of Sharnoff and Pound[17]. For gas phase experiments the reader is referred to Hildebrandt et al.[18] and Mazo[19].

One of the first observations of trapped hydrogen atoms was by Livingston et al.[12] who γ-irradiated various oxyacids ($HClO_4$, H_2SO_4 and H_3PO_4) at 77 °K. Of particular interest was the detection of satellite lines which were ascribed to a simultaneous neighbouring proton spin inversion. The separation was field dependent, being equal to the proton resonance frequency in the particular field employed. The intensity ratio of the satellites to the main line depended on the inverse sixth power of the distance from the hydrogen atom and the results were interpreted either in terms of a coupling with a range of protons distributed more or less randomly in the sample at distances generally greater than 1.74 Å or a single proton at this distance. Calculation showed that the satellite separation was strikingly insensitive to both the angular and radial distribution of the neighbouring protons.

TABLE 5.1

ELECTRON SPIN RESONANCE DATA FOR HYDROGEN
ATOMS TRAPPED IN VARIOUS MATRICES

Matrix	Temp. ($°K$)	Hyperfine splitting (Mc/s)	g-Value	Reference
Gas		1420.40	2.002256	5, 6, 7
H_2	4	1417.11	2.00230	10
Ne	4	1426.56	2.00207	10
Ar	4 (a)	1413.82	2.00220	10, 23
	(b)	1436.24	2.00161	
Kr	4 (a, b)	1411.79	2.00179	10, 23
	(b)	1427.06	1.99967	
Xe	4 (a)	1404.99	2.00170	10, 23
	(b)	1405.57	2.00057	
Silica gel	77	1411.5		3
	77	1420		13
$HClO_4$	77	1407.1	2.0022	12
H_2SO_4	77	1414.5	2.0024	12
H_3PO_4	77	1423.4	2.0024	12
KCl	77	1400.30		14
$Ca_3(PO_4)_2$	300	1410.3	2.0019	16
$Ca(H_2PO_4)_2H_2O$	77	1416	2.0018	16
NaH_2PO_4	77	1410	2.0020	16
Fused silica	77	1409.3	2.0019	16
CaF_2	300	1460.26	2.00247	4

(a) Deposition.
(b) Photolysis.

Decay experiments on these systems showed that the rate of loss of hydrogen atoms followed second order kinetics, thus suggesting dimerisation. The
data could, however, also be accommodated in terms of a reaction between
the hydrogen atoms and a species which had previously been formed in a
one-to-one correspondence with the hydrogen atoms. A kinetic study of the
decay of hydrogen atoms formed on γ-irradiation of ice at 4.2 °K has also
been reported [12, 20] and it was found that the dependence of the isothermal
rate upon the total concentration of hydrogen atoms was too great to correspond to a rate law of the form $d(H)dt = k(H)^n$. In fact the initially rapid
disappearance changed into an almost asymptotic approach to zero when
there was still a high atom concentration. A temperature dependence of the
activation energy for the decay (which varied from somewhat less than
1 Kcal·mole^{-1} near 30 °K to nearly 2.5 Kcal·mole^{-1} near 50 °K) suggested

that the atoms were trapped at a variety of sites. Alternatively the authors suggest that the reactions may be intra-spur rather than isotropic processes; inter-spur reactions should become important at the later stages of the decay after most of the closely coupled radical pairs have disappeared.

Delbecq et al.[14] investigated the effects of ultraviolet radiation on alkali halide crystals containing U-centres. Since a U-centre is a halide ion site occupied by a hydride ion, and since F-centres are produced on irradiation of U-centres, it was hoped that the other decomposition product, a hydrogen atom, would be trapped. This hope was realised and it was concluded that the hydrogen atoms so formed were located at interstitial positions in the lattice and gave rise, not only to an electron spin resonance spectrum with a splitting of 500 gauss, but also to an optical absorption (the U_2-band at 42,400 cm^{-1}. The results were confirmed by deuteration, when the electron spin resonance spectrum changed in the manner expected.

We mention also that Wall et al.[21] and Piette et al.[22] have reported trapped hydrogen atoms too (the former in γ-irradiated methane and hydrogen at 4.2 °K and the latter after the high-energy electron irradiation of hydrogen at the same temperature) and pass on to the work of Jen et al.[10] and Foner et al.[23].

These workers trapped hydrogen atoms in a variety of rare gas matrices either by using the apparatus that was described in Chapter 3 or by the photolysis of a photosensitive compound previously deposited in the matrix. The results which are reproduced in Table 5.2 show that at least two trapping sites are involved in argon, krypton and xenon whereas there is only one such site in neon. The multiplicity of trapping sites seems to depend upon the

TABLE 5.2

CALCULATION OF MATRIX EFFECTS FOR TRAPPED HYDROGEN ATOMS[23]

Matrix	Substitutional site		Octahedral site	
	$\Delta A/A(\%)$	$\Delta g \cdot 10^4$	$\Delta A/A(\%)$	$\Delta g \cdot 10^4$
Ar (a)	−0.46	−0.6	+1.15	− 6.5
(b)	−0.72	−0.3	+0.74	− 4.6
Kr (a)	−0.59	−4.7	+0.47	−26
(b)	−0.80	−1.1	+0.36	−21

(a) Experiment.
(b) Theory.

initial energy of the hydrogen atoms in the matrix, for this was only observed when the atoms were introduced photolytically and not by gas phase deposition of the atoms. The authors employed Adrian's theory[1], developed for just this purpose, and were able to ascribe the different trapping sites to either interstitial or octahedral sites (and possibly tetrahedral sites in the case of xenon) (Table 5.2). The most interesting aspect of these results is that additional structure was observed when xenon formed the trapping matrix. This was ascribed to a hyperfine interaction with the surrounding six (for an octahedral trapping site) xenon nuclei.

A study which impinges both on these results and those of Livingston *et al.*[12] is that of Rexroad and Gordy[11] who γ-irradiated a number of substances at 4.2 °K and searched for trapped hydrogen atoms. These were detected in water, hydrofluoric acid, hydrogen and methane, but not in hydrochloric acid, hydrogen disulphide, ammonia nor in sodium or lithium hydroxide. In water the high field line saturated much more readily than the low field line. It was proposed that another radical was present whose spectrum overlapped the low field component of the hydrogen atom spectrum; if this radical were assumed to have a shorter relaxation time than the hydrogen atom then the differential saturation phenomenon is explicable for the low field component can relax through the other radical. This contention was supported by the observation that the spectrum at a different field strength, when the resonances would probably not still overlap, exhibited no such differential relaxation. The authors proposed a mechanism to account for the production of hydrogen atoms in some compounds yet not in others[11]. They assumed that hydrogen atoms are formed in hydrofluoric acid and water on electron capture by the essentially ionic hydrogen; thus their production can occur in rigid solutions. It was supposed that electron capture in hydrochloric acid occurs by entry into the d-orbitals of chlorine to form what is really an HCl^- species. It should be remarked, however, that the species bearing the unpaired spins must at least virtually migrate, otherwise recombination will occur, and secondly that it is not necessarily a true deduction that if hydrogen atoms are not observed then they are not formed. With this point in mind it may be the depth of the trap for hydrogen atoms which determines whether or not the atom is observed since it has already been emphasised that the small size of the hydrogen atom renders it particularly susceptible to migration and possible reaction.

The concept of trapping at a basic anion was used by the present authors to explain the observation that hydrogen atoms were observed in γ-irradiated salts of phosphorus oxyacids and that some of the compounds, particularly those containing the highly basic orthophosphate ion (PO_4^{3-}), provided traps of such depth that the hydrogen atoms showed little sign of decay even at 100 °C[15,16]. The type of trap envisaged was one in which the hydrogen atom was stabilised by its tendency to form a hydrogen bond with the anion, the trap being envisaged as a "half-hydrogen bond". This trapping mechanism would also account for the fact that Livingston et al.[12] observed hydrogen atoms only in aqueous solutions of acids at 77 °K and not in pure water, since in ice there are few "vacant" H bond acceptor sites. An alternative pictorial explanation of the interaction[15] is that the proton forms a σ-bond to a basic oxygen and that the extra electron is then accommodated in the corresponding σ^*-level with an almost complete destruction of the bond. Since the σ-level would be concentrated strongly on oxygen, the σ^*-electron would be mainly on H and hence the centres might resemble hydrogen atoms to a considerable extent.

A similarly high stability of trapped hydrogen atoms was observed by Hall and Schumacher[4] in their experiments with hydrogen-doped calcium fluoride crystals. These authors attempted to explain their results (Table 5.1) in terms of Adrian's theory but as it was necessary to account for an increase in spin-density at the proton compared with the free-atom case they required the repulsive forces to overcome the attractive forces, but to a lesser extent than that predicted by the theory. A way of reducing the spin-density on the proton but which gives the correct repulsive terms from the fluoride environment (as measured by the superhyperfine splitting from the environmental fluorine nuclei) is to allow each hydrogen to "see" calcium ions through the six faces of a cube, this environment mixes $5g$-hydrogenic functions into the hydrogen ground state wave-function. Even so, Hall and Schumacher were unable to account for the positive g-value shift because Adrian's theory would always predict it to be negative (§ 5.1). The model was optimistically extended to a dynamic calculation in an attempt to account for the temperature variation of the magnetic parameters and the difference between hydrogen and deuterium which was also observed: it was thought that by considering the average values over the motion of the atoms in a potential well of a particularly simple kind the differences would be accounted for; the conclusions do not, however, convince even the authors themselves.

Kazanskii et al.[3,13] have studied the effect of γ-radiation on silica gel and observed hydrogen atoms which, they postulate, stem from scission of the surface O–H bonds followed by trapping at the surface by a mechanism which they imitated by an electric field, as was described earlier in this Chapter. The authors found[13] that the absorbed hydrogen atoms were highly reactive inasmuch that they reacted with oxygen and ethylene at −150 and −120 °C respectively. In the latter reaction ethyl radicals were produced and their electron spin resonance spectra observed.

5.3　METAL ATOMS

(a)　Alkali metals

Alkali metal atoms have been trapped in inert gas matrices[2] using an apparatus similar to that used for the isolation of hydrogen atoms, the main difference being that an oven was employed to generate the beam of alkali metal atoms. Lithium was trapped in a multiplicity of sites when the matrix was argon or krypton, yet in only one site in xenon. Likewise, sodium, potassium and rubidium were multiply trapped in argon: this was confirmed by following the electron spin resonance spectra as the sample was warmed. The deviations from the free-atom values are recorded in Table 5.3 which is taken from the paper by Jen et al.[2].

Only the results for lithium are well accommodated by the theory outlined in the earlier part of this Chapter. Since the alkali metal atoms are much more polarisable than hydrogen atoms the more complete theory as developed by Jen et al. was also employed but even so the spectra of sodium, potassium and rubidium are not well explained. The result of these calculations for lithium is illustrated in Fig. 5.1.

The authors remarked that it is not clear why there should be a discrete number of trapping sites, and this remains an interesting aspect of the problem.

(b)　Silver atoms

If alkali halide crystals, doped with a trace of the corresponding silver halide, are exposed to high-energy radiation, the silver ion can act both as a source and sink of electrons. The Ag^{2+} ions have a $4d^9$ configuration and are properly treated in the general field of transition metal chemistry. Electron capture, however, results in the formation of a species which can be formally represented as silver atoms, $Ag°$. Indeed, the electron spin resonance and optical spectra agree well with this model, as was shown by Delbecq et al.[24].

TABLE 5.3

ELECTRON SPIN RESONANCE DATA FOR ALKALI METALS IN VARIOUS MATRICES[2]

		^7Li	^{23}Na	^{39}K	^{85}Rb	^{133}Cs
Free atoms (Mc/s)	A	401.756	885.813	230.860	1011.912	2298.158
	g	2.00231	2.00231	2.00231	2.00241	2.00258
$\Delta A/A(\%)$	Ar	−1.6, 3.1	−0.9 ↔ 4.9	0.4 ↔ 11.8	2.6 ↔ 8.4	0.5
	Kr	−1.7, 2.2	−1.4 2.0	−1.2, 6.6	−0.56 ↔ 6.9	−0.9
	Xe	−1.2	−1.3	1.7	−1.6	—
$-100\Delta g$	Ar	0.05, 0.13	−0.5 ↔ 0.21	0.08 0.37	−0.85 ↔ 0.89	−0.25
	Kr	0.36, 0.57	0.45, 0.93	0.59, 1.74	0.65 ↔ 1.07	0.11
	Xe	1.09	0.98	1.66	2.02	—

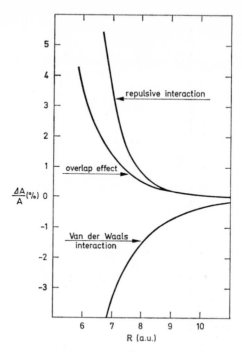

Fig. 5.1.   Calculated contributions to $\Delta A/A$ for a Li–Ar pair as a function of distance[2].

It has been suggested that the decrease in the hyperfine coupling constant from the free-atom [109]Ag value by about 8% (Table 5.4) arises from a real delocalisation on to the six surrounding halide ligands. The significance of this observation is that one can thereby probe the participation of metal *s*- and *p*-levels in σ-bonding to ligands. In a sense, we are suggesting that the problem is less one of an atom slightly perturbed by the surrounding medium as one of a loosely bonded molecule, $AgCl_6^{6-}$.

In support of this view are the superhyperfine coupling to the six chloride ligands and the modified optical spectrum. From the hyperfine interactions with [35]Cl and [37]Cl which are given in the Table, one can obtain an approxi-

TABLE 5.4

ELECTRON SPIN RESONANCE DATA FOR SILVER ATOMS
TRAPPED IN KCl[24]

$g = 2.000 \pm 0.003$
$A_{iso} = 649 \pm 2$ gauss $A_{iso}(Cl) = 13.3$ gauss

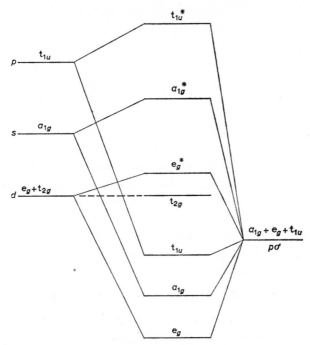

Fig. 5.2.   Bonding scheme for $AgCl_6^{6-}$.[40]

mate value of 0.1 for the total spin-density on chlorine, which agrees well with the more accurate value of 0.92 for that on silver. The low p/s ratio deduced from the chlorine hyperfine coupling, although of low accuracy, strongly suggests that the major effect is from σ-bonding rather than π-bonding.

The optical results accord well with this view. The first transition, which for the free atom is $\ldots5s^2 \to \ldots5s^1\,5p^1$ is shifted by about 6,500 cm^{-1} to low energies in the solid. This large shift would be expected for the $a_{1g}^* \to t_{1u}^*$ transition of the complex because the 5s-level will contribute to ligand bonding more than the 5p-level. The situation that is envisaged is illustrated in Fig. 5.2.

5.4 ATOMS OF GROUP V-ELEMENTS

The ground state of the atoms of Group V elements is ns^2np^3, ^4S; it is therefore expected that the hyperfine interaction will be small, for it can only

arise through mechanisms such as core-polarisation or configuration interaction. Consequently, as has already been explained in § 5.1, the observed
interaction is likely to be particularly sensitive to matrix perturbations. Furthermore, if the spherical symmetry of the atom's environment can be lowered,
for example, to an axial form, then a zero field splitting would be expected
and the electron spin resonance spectrum should display fine structure.

These expectations are well confirmed in the case of trapped nitrogen
atoms which have been observed in argon, hydrogen, nitrogen and methane
matrices at 4 °K[25] and in γ-irradiated potassium azide at 77 °K[26]. In each
of the non-polar matrices the hyperfine splitting was 10–30% greater than
the gas phase value of 3.7 gauss[27]. Irradiation of potassium azide at 77 °K[26]
led to the production of two nitrogen containing species one of which was
identified as trapped nitrogen atoms and the other as N_2^-; this latter we shall
return to in § 6.2b(ii). The nitrogen atoms were trapped in two magnetically
equivalent sites and for each site three easily saturated fine structure lines
were observed. The spectrum fits the spin Hamiltonian

$$\mathscr{H} = \beta\mathbf{H}\cdot\mathbf{g}\cdot\mathbf{S} + DS_z^2 + E(S_x^2 - S_y^2) + \mathbf{I}\cdot\mathbf{A}\cdot\mathbf{S} \qquad (5.14)$$

with an effective spin $S=\frac{3}{2}$, $g_{av}=2.001\pm0.001$, $D=0.0143\pm0.0001$ cm^{-1},
$E=-0.00199\pm0.00002$ cm^{-1} and $A=0.00051\pm0.00002$ cm^{-1} (5 gauss).
(Here D is a measure of the magnetic interaction between the unpaired electrons and E the deviation from axial symmetry of this interaction.)

Wall et al.[28] have observed the electron spin resonance spectrum of γ-irra-
diated solid $^{15}N_2$ and observed the expected doublet hyperfine spectrum and
fine structure in accord with the other results mentioned. It is interesting that
the molecule N_3 was apparently not formed under these conditions.

A theoretical treatment of matrix perturbations on the nitrogen atom has
been given, also by Adrian[29]. The calculations suppose that the effect of the
matrix is to mix the configuration $2s2p^4$ into the $2s^22p^3$ ground state; since
the ground state is ^4S the three $2p$-electrons must be parallel (α, say); the
excited $2s$-electron must therefore be β. It was therefore predicted that the
hyperfine splitting would increase as a result of this perturbation. This would
be true if the hyperfine structure of the unperturbed atoms arose by the same
mechanism. The effect was shown to increase with the polarisability, and
hence the size, of the matrix particles.

A poorly resolved doublet having a hyperfine separation of 23.8 gauss
which was detected after photolysis of phosphine in a rare gas matrix[30] has
been assigned to phosphorus atoms. That the doublet is due to ^{31}P rather

than ^{1}H was established by using PD_3 for which the same spectrum was observed. If the magnetic species were in fact phosphorus atoms, the matrix has again effected a small increase in the isotropic coupling, since phosphorus atoms in the gas phase have a hyperfine coupling constant of 20.0 gauss[31]. Furthermore, the lines narrowed and the hyperfine splitting increased as the sample was warmed, but no explanation was offered.

Phosphorus, antimony and arsenic have all been studied as donor impurities in silicon, particularly by double resonance techniques. For reports of these the reader is referred to the original papers, especially that of Feher[32].

5.5 OXYGEN ATOMS AND O⁻ IONS

Oxygen atoms are orbitally degenerate and the spin is therefore likely to be strongly coupled to the environment. This being so the resonance lines are likely to be broadened beyond detection. In fact attempts to observe trapped oxygen atoms in rare gas matrices have failed[10] presumably for just this reason.

A gas phase study of oxygen atoms which is of particular interest is that reported by McDonald[33] although the spectrum was first observed by Rawson and Beringer[34]. By using the saturation differences of the lines due to absorptions involving different numbers of quanta it was possible to observe all the transitions within the $^3P_2$ ground state, that is four 1-quantum transitions, three 2-quantum transitions, two 3-quantum transitions and one 4-quantum transition. The experimental arrangement was to pass the effluent gas stream from an electric discharge in oxygen through a quartz tube in the cavity of the spectrometer and gradually to decrease the microwave attenuation.

The species O⁻ has been postulated to explain a number of results including those for γ-irradiated hydroxide glasses[35] and γ-irradiated calcium fluorophosphate $(3Ca_3(PO_4)_2 \cdot CaF_2)$[36]. In both cases the spectrum was characteristic of a species with axial symmetry having a perpendicular g-value much larger than the parallel component which had about the free-spin value. The species in the hydroxide glasses has $g_{\parallel} = 2.002$ and $g_{\perp} = 2.07$, the values being relatively insensitive to the cation present. It is postulated that the O⁻ species are formed from solvated hydroxide ions, in which case it is not unreasonable to suppose that the g-tensor anisotropy is caused by a crystal field formed by the surrounding water molecules which may reflect the symmetry of the

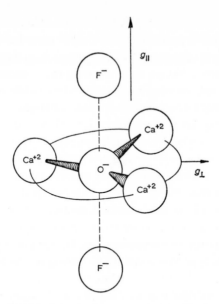

Fig. 5.3.   Model of the O^- ion centre in $3Ca_3(PO_4)_2.CaF_2$[36].

solvation of the hydroxide ion[35]. Alternatively the O^- ion could be considered as being so closely associated with one neighbouring water molecule that the unpaired electron occupied an essentially σ^*-orbital of a species which in some ways would resemble a hal_2^- species (§ 6.2d(ii)).

The g-values for the species in calcium fluorophosphate[36] were $g_\parallel = 2.0012$ and $g_\perp = 2.0516$ but the spectrum differs from that of the ion in the hydroxide glasses since there was also a small hyperfine splitting resulting in a $1:2:1$ triplet. ENDOR experiments showed that the triplet was due to two equivalent fluorines. These and other factors were interpreted in terms of O^- ions in fluoride vacancies, the structure of the species being that shown in Fig. 5.3. Other possible species, such as F_2^-, an electron in a fluoride vacancy, or a hole in a calcium ion vacancy were ruled out by a consideration of the presence, although very small in magnitude, of the ^{19}F hyperfine splitting ($A_\parallel^{(F)} = \pm 7$ gauss and $A_\perp^{(F)} = \pm 3$ gauss).

5.6 HALOGEN ATOMS

The electron spin resonance spectra of halogen atoms in the gas phase have been observed[37], but attempts to detect trapped halogen atoms in non-polar matrices have failed[10], probably for the same reason that trapped oxygen atoms have not been observed. Halogen atoms have been trapped in irradiated halide crystals, but as these centres, the V-centres, consist of the trapped atom strongly bonded to a neighbouring halide ion, the centres are more properly considered as (hal'–hal)⁻ molecular ions and are discussed in § 6.2d(ii).

(a) The ion F^{2-}

This ion, which is isoelectronic with the sodium atom, seems, at first sight, even less probable than the anion Ne⁻. Recent results by Šronbek et al.[38] for X-irradiated beryllium oxide powder, doped with fluoride, strongly suggest that this centre is stable under these conditions. Indeed, it is very hard to discover any alternative explanation for the isotropic doublet, centred on $g = 2$ and having a hyperfine coupling of 760 gauss which is detected under these conditions.

Subsidiary, but well defined splitting of the high and low field lines into an unsymmetrical pattern of ten components was assigned to weak interaction between the F^{2-}-centre and three neighbouring Be^{2+} ions[38]. Although it is difficult to understand why only three beryllium ions should interact it must be recalled that only powder spectra were obtained, and that the intensity distributions were far from those expected for three equivalent cations. The concept of an electron trapped at a fluoride ion seems compelling, despite this complication. The authors concluded that the $3s$-orbital on F contributes primarily to the orbital of the unpaired electron, and support this with some calculations based upon those for the $2s$-level, which show that a value of 760 gauss is quite reasonable.

The importance of this centre is that it links closely with models for the first excited state for halide ions which have been discussed in terms of a combination between the outer s-level of the anion and an F-centre type level on the surrounding cations, or solvent molecules[39]. A unit similar to this has been discussed in § 4.2b(ii) in connection with the effect of added salts on the properties of metal–ammonia solutions.

References

1 F. J. ADRIAN, J. Chem. Phys., 1960, 32, 972.
2 C. K. JEN, V. A. BOWERS, E. L. COCHRAN AND S. N. FONER, Phys. Rev., 1962, 126, 1749.

3 V. B. KAZANSKII AND G. B. PARIISKII, *Proc. 6th Intern. Conf. on Free Radicals, Cambridge, 1963.*

4 J. L. HALL AND R. T. SCHUMACHER, *Phys. Rev.*, 1962, *127*, 1892; 1963, *131*, 2839.

5 N. RAMSEY, *Nuclear Moments*, Wiley, 1953.

6 P. KUSCH, *Phys. Rev.*, 1955, *100*, 1188.

7 R. BERRINGER AND M. A. S. HEALD, *Phys. Rev.*, 1954, *95*, 1474.

8 M. C. R. SYMONS AND W. T. DOYLE, *Quart. Rev.*, 1960, *14*, 62.

9 B. S. GOURARY AND F. J. ADRIAN, *Phys. Rev.*, 1956, *105*, 1180.

10 C. K. JEN, S. N. FONER, E. L. COCHRAN AND V. A. BOWERS, *Phys. Rev.*, 1958, *112* 1169.

11 H. N. REXROAD AND W. GORDY, *Phys. Rev.*, 1962, *125*, 242.

12 R. LIVINGSTON, H. ZELDES AND E. H. TAYLOR, *Discussions Faraday Soc.*, 1955, *19*, 166; *Phys. Rev.*, 1954, *96*, 1702.

13 V. B. KAZANSKII, G. B. PARIISKII AND V. V. VOEVODSKII, *Discussions Faraday Soc.*, 1961, *31*, 203.

14 C. J. DELBECQ, B. SMALLER AND P. H. YUSTER, *Phys. Rev.*, 1956, *104*, 599.

15 P. W. ATKINS, N. KEEN, M. C. R. SYMONS AND H. W. WARDALE, *J. Chem. Soc.*, 1963, 5594.

16 S. OGAWA AND R. W. FESSENDEN, *J. Chem. Phys.*, 1964, *41*, 1516.

17 M. SHARNOFF AND R. V. POUND, *Phys. Rev.*, 1963, *132*, 1003.

18 A. F. HILDEBRANDT, F. B. BOOTH AND C. A. BOOTH, *J. Chem. Phys.*, 1959, *31*, 273.

19 R. M. MAZO, *J. Chem. Phys.*, 1961, *34*, 169.

20 J. M. FLOURNOY, L. H. BAUM AND S. SIEGEL, *J. Chem. Phys.*, 1962, *36*, 2229.

21 L. A. WALL, D. W. BROWN AND R. E. FLORIN, *J. Phys. Chem.*, 1959, *63*, 1762.

22 L. H. PIETTE, R. C. REMPEL, H. E. WEAVER AND J. M. FLOURNOY, *J. Chem. Phys.*, 1959, *30*, 123.

23 S. N. FONER, E. L. COCHRAN, V. A. BOWERS AND C. K. JEN, *J. Chem. Phys.*, 1960, *32*, 963.

24 C. J. DELBECQ, W. HAYES, M. C. M. O'BRIAN AND P. H. YUSTER, *Proc. Roy. Soc.*, 1963, *A271*, 243.

25 S. N. FONER, C. K. JEN, E. L. COCHRAN AND V. A. BOWERS, *J. Chem. Phys.*, 1958, *28*, 351.

26 D. W. WYLIE, A. J. SHUSKUS, C. G. YOUNG, O. R. GILLIAM AND P. W. LEVY, *Phys. Rev.*, 1962, *125*, 451.

27 T. P. DAS AND A. MUKHERJEE, *J. Chem. Phys.*, 1960, *33*, 1808.

28 L. A. WALL, D. W. BROWN AND R. E. FLORIN, *J. Chem. Phys.*, 1959, *30*, 602.

29 F. J. ADRIAN, *Phys. Rev.*, 1962, *127*, 837.

30 F. J. ADRIAN, E. L. COCHRAN AND V. A. BOWERS, *Advan. Chem.*, 1962, *36*, 50.

31 H. G. DEHMELT, *Phys. Rev.*, 1955, *99*, 527.

32 G. FEHER, *Phys. Rev.*, 1959, *114*, 1219.

33 C. C. MCDONALD, *J. Chem. Phys.*, 1963, *39*, 3159.

34 E. B. RAWSON AND R. BERINGER, *Phys. Rev.*, 1952, *88*, 677.

35 M. J. BLANDAMER, L. SHIELDS AND M. C. R. SYMONS, *Nature*, 1963, *199*, 902; *J. Chem. Soc.*, 1964, 4352.

36 B. SEGALL, G. W. LUDWIG, H. H. WOODBURY AND P. D. JOHNSON, *Phys. Rev.*, 1962, *128*, 76.

37 N. VANDERKOOI, JR. AND J. S. MACKENZIE, *Advan. Chem.*, 1962, *36*, 98.

38 Z. ŠRONBEK, L. NOVÁK AND K. ŽEĎÁNSKÝ, *Phys. Stat. Sol.*, 1964, *6*, 173.

39 T. R. GRIFFITHS AND M. C. R. SYMONS, *Trans. Faraday Soc.*, 1960, *56*, 1125.

40 M. C. R. SYMONS, *J. Chem. Soc.*, 1964, 1482.

Chapter 6

Diatomic radicals

In those sections headed STRUCTURAL ASPECTS a brief outline of structural principles is presented and the way in which these are probed by electron spin resonance data is outlined. This is a plan which we shall follow throughout the remaining chapters.

6.1 STRUCTURAL ASPECTS

In this section we consider both briefly and qualitatively what characteristics are expected for various species of diatomic radicals. In particular we treat AH and AB radicals in which the unpaired electron occupies either a σ- or a π-orbital.

(a) AB π-radicals

The presence of orbital degeneracy causes a number of problems in π-radicals. Both $^2\Pi_{\frac{1}{2}}$ and $^2\Pi_{\frac{3}{2}}$ states need to be considered for radicals in the gas phase; these states are further subdivided by coupling with rotational states. The problems associated with these gas phase spectra are so different from those that we are now dealing with, the few studies so far undertaken will not be elaborated upon here. Only the results will be reported where relevant: the problem of coupling with rotational levels does not normally arise for radicals in condensed phases, but has been invoked to explain line-widths in a few cases[1, 2].

Experimental experience has shown that for linear radicals in solids and liquids one either obtains no spectrum at all or one centred close to the free-spin g-value. The latter situation can only arise if there is a strong quenching of the orbital momentum by the crystal field of the medium: an unsymmetrical environment lifts the degeneracy of the π_x- and π_y-orbitals (Fig. 6.1) and to a first approximation the electron is confined to one of them (π_x, say). If this splitting is sufficiently large the g-tensor will have a value close to

2.0023 along x. When the external field is parallel to the molecular axis it will couple π_x and π_y and so produce a relatively large negative or positive increment in the g-value for one and three electron π-systems. The value of Δg_{yy} (where $\Delta g_{qq} = g_{qq} - 2.0023$) will be both relatively small and positive or negative, depending upon the relative proximities of the filled and empty σ-levels. These interactions are depicted in Fig. 6.1.

A more quantitative account of this discussion is presented in Appendix 3 where it is shown that the quenching of the orbital degeneracy causes the value of $g_{\parallel}(g_{zz})$ to fall from 4, for a π^3 radical, to the free-spin value, and the value of g_{xx} and g_{yy} to rise from zero to the free-spin value and a value close to it respectively as the energy difference between the π_x and π_y components of the original π-level is increased.

The hyperfine spectrum from an AB π-radical will in general show interactions characteristic of both nuclei: if the hyperfine tensor for an electron in a p_x-orbital is

$$\mathbf{B}^{(A)} = (2\beta_A, -\beta_A, -\beta_A) \tag{6.1}$$

for nucleus A and

$$\mathbf{B}^{(B)} = (2\beta_B, -\beta_B, -\beta_B) \tag{6.2}$$

then the observed spectrum will be described by the tensor

$$\mathbf{A} = \mathbf{A}_{iso}^{(A)} + \mathbf{A}_{iso}^{(B)} + \mathbf{B}^{(A)} + \mathbf{B}^{(B)} \tag{6.3}$$

which is axially symmetric about the x-axis. Small deviations from axial symmetry may be observed and these can often be attributed to either slight occupancy or polarisation of other orbitals as was described in Chapter 2. Thus if π_y is involved there will be an additional contribution

$$\mathbf{B}' = \pm(-\beta', 2\beta', -\beta') \tag{6.4}$$

Usually β' is much smaller than either $\beta^{(A)}$ or $\beta^{(B)}$.

Since the population of the s-orbitals on A and B must arise through an indirect mechanism and is normally small, one might expect the sum of the spin-density in the p_x-orbitals of A and B [$c^2(p_xA)$ and $c^2(p_xB)$] as calculated from $\beta^{(A)}$ and $\beta^{(B)}$ by the route outlined in Chapter 2 to be unity. Minor deviations will reflect the various approximations involved in the determination of spin distribution (for example, neglect of overlap); any major deviations may stem from such factors as librations about the z-axis or participation of d-orbitals, both of which will lead to an underestimate of the total spin-density.

The sign and magnitude of $\mathbf{A}_{iso}^{(A)}$ will be a function of the spin-density on

both A and B. For first row elements it is expected that there will be positive
and negative contributions respectively. A knowledge of A_{iso} for A and B,
derived for example from AB radicals in fluid solutions, will not therefore
be very informative alone. Nevertheless, this knowledge may be helpful in
the task of unravelling the information contained in complex envelope spectra obtained in solid-state studies.

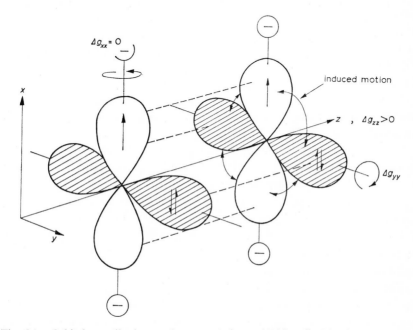

Fig. 6.1.   Orbital contribution to the g-tensor in an AB(π)-radical in the presence of
an asymmetric crystal field.

In addition to libration or restricted rotations of trapped AB π-radicals
one can imagine another form of fluctuation which could modify their electron spin resonance spectra. This is a fluctuating crystal field which inter-
changes the order of the π_x- and π_y-levels at a rate rapid compared with the
frequency of measurement. The electron could follow this fluctuation and an
apparent axial symmetry would be conferred upon the spin system. This pro-
cess would average g_{xx} and g_{yy}, giving $g_\perp$. In like manner A_{xx} and A_{yy} would
average to $A_\perp$. Thus the purely anisotropic part of the hyperfine tensor would
have the form $B_\parallel = -\beta$ and $B_\perp = +\beta/2$.

(b) AH π-radicals

The hyperfine tensor for A and the g-tensor will resemble those for the AB π-radicals discussed above. Coupling to the proton, however, will take the form found[3] for α-protons in organic π-radicals, R_2CH provided that the unpaired electron is confined to p_x by a suitable environmental interaction. The purely dipolar part is generally of the form $B_{xx}^{(H)} \sim 0$, $B_{yy}^{(H)} \sim -a$ and $B_{zz}^{(H)} \sim +a$, but the magnitudes of the coupling constants are very sensitive to changes in bond length and electronegativity of A (Appendix 4). A rotating fluctuation will average $B_{xx}^{(H)}$ and $B_{yy}^{(H)}$ leaving $B_{zz}^{(H)}$ unchanged; the anisotropic tensor would then have the form $B_\parallel^{(H)} \sim +a$ and $B_\perp^{(H)} \sim -a/2$.

(c) AB σ-radicals

We shall consider only radicals of structure $\ldots\sigma_3^1$, $^2\Sigma$ and $\ldots\sigma_3^2\sigma_4^1$, $^2\Sigma$ with appropriate occupation of the π-levels.

Radicals having an unpaired electron in σ_4 will have axial symmetry with $g_\parallel$ close to 2 and $g_\perp > 2$ as the extent of coupling to the occupied π^*-level is likely to be far greater than that with any outer unoccupied levels.

To a good first approximation the σ_4-orbital will be built from p_z-atomic orbitals on both A and B and so A_{iso} may be due to polarisation effects rather than direct mixing of s-levels, although in principle these can contribute to σ_4 (Fig. 6.2). The tensors for A and B will then be of the form $A_{xx} = A_{yy} = -\beta + A_{iso}$, $A_{zz} = +2\beta + A_{iso}$.

The situation is less clear for σ_3^1-radicals. Certainly $g_\parallel$ ought to be close to the free-spin value, but Δg can now be either positive or negative depending upon the relative proximities of the π- and π^*-levels. There will also be larger contributions from the s-levels of A and B, the amount decreasing with increasing relative electronegativity.

Once again these points are developed more quantitatively in Appendix 3 where it is shown that the values of Δg_{xx} and Δg_{yy} depend upon the mixing of σ_4- and π_1-orbitals if the radical is a homonuclear diatomic but upon the mixing of σ_4 with both π_1 and π_2 if the radical is a heteronuclear species. Thus when one turns from the species A_2 to the species AB one might expect a greater g-tensor anisotropy than would be predicted merely by a consideration of the change in the spin–orbit coupling parameters of the atoms A and B. Similarly, for σ_3^1 species, only in heteronuclear species will both π_1 and π_2 mix; in homonuclear species $\sigma_3(\sigma_g)$ will only mix with $\pi_2(\pi_g)$; consequently $g_\perp$ will be less than free spin for these species.

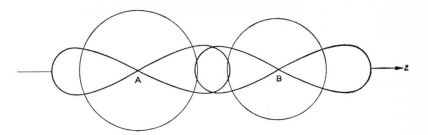

Fig. 6.2.　Bonding in AB(σ)-radicals.

(d) Order of levels

The order of orbital levels for AB is generally $\sigma_1\sigma_2\pi_1\sigma_3\pi_2\sigma_4$. This is not, however, a necessary situation for all linear molecules and in particular an inversion of the $\pi_1\sigma_3$ pair is conceivable.

(e) Contribution from A and B

This will be a function of electronegativity and charge-distribution. In general one expects a strong resistance to any major charge separation, but this will stem from slight polarisations of the total electronic system rather than complete localisation of one or two electrons. Because most of the species which we shall consider in both this and succeeding chapters are such that the unpaired electron occupies an antibonding orbital it follows that if we wish to discuss the effect of electronegativity on the distribution of the unpaired electron, the system of both antibonding and bonding orbitals must be considered. The electrons in the bonding orbitals are most tightly bound partly because they are concentrated in the region of lowest potential energy which is between the bonded nuclei but closer to the atom with the higher electronegativity. Consequently, the antibonding electrons are repelled from the favoured region towards the atom of lower electronegativity. It is a corollary that as the electronegativity of an atom increases the unpaired electron density on it decreases. An equivalent conclusion is arrived at if the problem is considered as that of a (relatively positive) hole in the system of bonding and antibonding orbitals: the hole is attracted to the atom of lower electronegativity.

6.2 RESULTS FOR DIATOMIC RADICALS

(a) AH π-radicals

In this section the hydroxyl radical will be considered in detail, and only minor reference will be made to a radical which has been tentatively formulated as $NH^{\pm}$ by Morton[4].

(i) *Hydroxyl*, OH

Hydroxyl radicals have been studied in the gas phase by Radford, who has given a detailed description and interpretation of the electric-dipole spectrum of the $^2\Pi_{\frac{3}{2}}$-radical[5]. This is essentially a rotational spectrum with Zeeman splitting. His most significant result for our purposes is that the isotropic proton hyperfine coupling was found to be about -27 gauss, in good accord with expectation for a π-radical.

Hydroxyl radicals in solid rare-gas matrices do not give any detectable spectra, but species thought to be hydroxyl have been studied in γ-irradiated ice[6-8] and in liquid water using a flow system involving the redox reaction[9]

$$Ti^{3+} + H_2O_2 \rightleftharpoons TiOH^{3+} + OH. \qquad (6.5)$$

The task of identifying this important radical in condensed media has proved more difficult than had been expected. It is complicated by the propensity of systems containing hydrogen peroxide to form the more stable radical HO_2 according to the equation

$$OH + H_2O_2 \rightleftharpoons HO_2 + H_2O \qquad (6.6)$$

Thus for example, an asymmetric single line obtained from the ultraviolet photolysis of dilute rigid solutions of hydrogen peroxide in water or alcohols[10-12] is almost certainly due to HO_2 rather than OH (see Chapter 7).

The species formed from titanous salts and hydrogen peroxide is characterised by a single narrow line having a g-value of 2.0119[9]. If this species is either $-OH$ or HO_2, then there must be a proton transfer process such as

$$H_2O + OH^* \rightleftharpoons HOH^* + OH \qquad (6.7)$$

which proceeds so fast that the mean life-time of a hydroxyl radical associated with a particular proton is short compared with the reciprocal of the isotropic hyperfine coupling frequency. All known attempts to reduce this rate sufficiently to broaden the absorption line by varying such parameters as temperature and pH have failed. Nevertheless, in view of the observed g-value, we are inclined to feel that this radical is also HO_2 formed by a secondary reaction, rather than OH. A possible alternative would be the complex $TiO\dot{O}^{4+}$.

It is highly probable that the major paramagnetic species detected in γ-irradiated ice is the hydroxyl radical, although identification is not certain because other radicals also appear to be present so that some reactions besides simple bond fission to give OH and ·H are possible. One of these species which is more stable (or less mobile) than that thought to be OH has properties similar to those assigned to HO_2 [10].

Results of a study of a single crystal of irradiated ice have been briefly reported [6] and are given in Table 6.1. There is some ambiguity about the g-tensor, but it seems probable that the results originally reported ought to be reversed and that $g_{\parallel}$ is in fact close to the free-spin value. Since the signs of the hyperfine coupling constants are unknown, there are four alternatives, but only the tensor given by McMillan *et al.* is included in Table 6.1.

TABLE 6.1

ELECTRON SPIN RESONANCE DATA FOR THE HYDROXYL RADICAL

Medium	g-Tensor			Hyperfine tensor (gauss)				Reference
	$g_{\perp}$	$g_{\parallel}$	g_{av}	B_{xx}	B_{yy}	B_{zz}	A_{iso}	
H_2O	2.0127	2.0077	2.011	$- 6$	$- 6$	12	41.3	6, 8
	2.008	2.050	2.022	-14	-14	29	-29	13
				-15.9	-15.9	31.7	-26.7	5
				-16.0	-16.0	31.9	-26.7	a
$Li_2SO_4·2H_2O$	2.002	2.040	2.015	± 7.3	± 2.3	∓ 9.6	∓ 13.6	14, 15

[a] Calculated assuming the gas phase value for A_{iso} and using the method of MCCONNELL AND STRATHDEE, *Mol. Phys.*, 1959, **2**, 129, with $A_{\parallel} = A_z$ and $A_{\perp} = \frac{1}{2}(A_x + A_y)$.

Many aspects of these results are surprising if the species bears any resemblance to the hydroxyl radical. Thus, the form of the hyperfine coupling requires that the π_x^* and π_y^* levels must be effectively equivalent[†]. The relatively large positive value (+41.3 gauss) for the isotropic hyperfine coupling is out of line with results for CH_3, NH_3^+ and NH_2 radicals which are all close to -25 gauss, and also with the value found by Radford (-27 gauss) for radi-

[†] The asterisk in π_x^* or the bar in $\bar{\pi}_x$ denotes antibonding character.

cals in the gas phase. Also, as has been stressed elsewhere[8], the value of $+12$ gauss for B_{zz} is too small, being less than half that calculated for the hydroxyl radical ($+31.9$ gauss) or that estimated from Radford's data ($+31.7$ gauss). Finally, the g-tensor is quite incompatible with expectation for the hydroxyl radical.

In view of all these difficulties, and to follow up a tentative suggestion that hydrogen bonding from surrounding water molecules had modified the electronic structure in a major way[8], further studies of irradiated ice crystals and powders were undertaken. The most informative results were obtained from mixtures of H_2O and D_2O, such that the major product was "OD" and the minor product, "OH", was produced in an environment consisting largely of D_2O. This gave relatively narrow lines which could be monitored more readily than those for "OH" in an H_2O environment[13].

Our preliminary conclusions are given in Table 6.1. The major reason why these results differ so much from those given earlier is that a feature found at relatively high field strengths, both for powders and crystals, is now taken to be a property of hydroxyl radicals lying close to the parallel position, whereas others assumed that it was due to a chemically different species.

Nearly all the anomalies listed above are now removed. The isotropic and anisotropic parts of the proton hyperfine tensor are in good accord with those obtained from radicals in the gas phase. Also, the large value for $g_{\parallel}$ is as expected for a radical having a hole in the π^*-level, but for which the degeneracy of this level has been removed. This requirement, however, leads to the major residual difficulty of the new theory, namely that the proton hyperfine interaction has axial symmetry. We feel that this is incompatible with the g-tensor unless one postulates the presence of a perturbation which can quench the orbital motion but which is being modified at frequencies high compared with that corresponding to the expected difference in the x and y components of the proton coupling (about 14 gauss).

The perturbation involved is presumably part or all of the hydrogen bonding which held the parent water molecule in the lattice. It is not easy to see how this can vary in such a way as to cause a rapid fluctuation of the π-levels. The problem is a difficult one, because there are many magnetically non-equivalent sites for hydroxyl radicals and, in fact, for many orientations the spectra of single crystals closely resemble those of the powder. If it proves to be possible to unravel these complex spectra then the reason for the equilibration of π_x^* and π_y^* may become clear.

Finally, mention should be made of a radical found in various irradiated salt hydrates such as $Li_2SO_4 \cdot 2H_2O$[14]. Results, given in Table 6.1, have been interpreted in terms of trapped hydroxyl radicals having the unpaired electron confined to one π-level[15]. This radical clearly differs from that found in ice, but this is not in itself a sufficient reason for rejecting the proposal.

If one takes the large g-factor as lying along the axis of OH, then the lower set of signs must be used for the hyperfine tensor because $B_{zz}^{(H)}$ must be positive. Then again, the value $+9.6$ gauss for $B_{zz}^{(H)}$ is remarkably small for such a system.

Nevertheless, the fact remains that an apparently similar species is formed in several other salt hydrates, and it is not impossible that a radical such as hydroxyl has properties so dependent upon its interaction with different environments that no one set of data either for the g-tensor or the proton hyperfine interaction tensor is sufficient for identification.

We conclude that the search for hydroxyl radicals in condensed media is far from complete and that further systematic study, including the use of ^{17}O-enriched samples, is required.

(ii) The radical ion $NH^{\pm}$

A radical trapped in γ-irradiated $(NH_4)_2HPO_4$ crystals, characterised by hyperfine lines arising from one nitrogen nucleus and one hydrogen nucleus, has been tentatively described as $NH^{\pm}$. It is probably linked by hydrogen bonds to one or more phosphate ions[4]. Data are given in Table 6.2 whence it may be deduced that the electron is about 60% localised on nitrogen in a $2p$ orbital and that the $2s$ contribution is negligible. The proton hyperfine coupling tensor is that expected for a π-system with the electron confined to π_x. The isotropic coupling is -23.3 gauss if the anisotropic coupling along the N–H bond is taken to be $+12$ gauss. The g-tensor then gives 2.0026 along x, that is along the density axis of the p-orbital, but the other two principal

TABLE 6.2

ELECTRON SPIN RESONANCE DATA[4] FOR THE RADICAL ION $NH^{\pm}$

Medium	g-Tensor				Hyperfine tensor (gauss)			
	g_{yy}	g^a	g^a	g_{av}	B_{xx}	B_{yy}	B_{zz}	A_{iso}
$(NH_4)_2HPO_4$	2.0026	2.0089	2.0048	2.0054	12.1	0.7	-12.7	$-23.4(^1H)$
					-7.9	20.1	-12.2	$15.9(^{14}N)$

^{a} These are approx. g_{zz} and g_{zx}.

values of 2.0089 and 2.0048 are along axes on either side of the molecular x-axis, and at about 45° to it.

Taken in isolation, the formulation NH^+ is unsatisfactory: (1) because at least one of the g-values ought to be considerably less than 2, (2) because only about 60% of the electron is on the nitrogen atom and (3) because, as with the results for OH, the anisotropic proton hyperfine coupling constants have about half the expected magnitude for the system. Furthermore, it is not easy to see why this ion should form strong hydrogen bonds.

The formulation NH^- is in some ways more satisfactory for the g-values would be expected to be equal or greater than the free-spin value as is indeed found; the stronger hydrogen bonds would be expected also. This ion could be formed from the cation NH_3^+ by loss of two protons, but although NH_3^+ is known to be an important product of irradiation of ammonium salts, it is not easy to understand why *two* protons should then be lost.

It is noteworthy that the data for NH_3^+ in irradiated NH_4ClO_4 are quite comparable with those for the $NH^\pm$ species under consideration[16]. Thus for NH_3^+ $g_{av} = 2.0034$, $A_{iso}^{(H)} = -23.3$ gauss and $A_{iso}^{(N)} = 19.5$ gauss; these are not at all dissimilar to the data for $NH^\pm$ given in Table 6.2. It is at least conceivable that the species is NH_3^+ so distorted by hydrogen bonding to phosphate that only one proton appears to interact. Another alternative, more satisfactory from the physical aspect but less readily understood chemically would be that the species is the π-radical X–N–H. Here X might be a phosphate oxygen, and there would be a lone-pair on nitrogen in addition to the unpaired π-electron. Such a formulation adequately accommodates all the results recorded.

(b) AB π^1*-radicals*

(i) Nitric oxide, NO

Despite the fact that nitric oxide is one of the very few stable inorganic radicals, little can be said about its spin resonance spectrum. It has been studied extensively in the gas phase but has never been unambiguously detected in any condensed phase[17]. That it does not give rise to a detectable absorption in solid rare-gas matrices is not surprising as the environmental interaction is not expected to quench the orbital motion sufficiently; nevertheless, one might have expected that an ionic crystalline environment would lift the π-orbital degeneracy sufficiently. Despite various proposals[18,19] we do not consider that its detection has been established[20], since the various spectra assigned to NO seem to be more satisfactorily interpreted in terms of other species.

It is worth recalling that nitric oxide readily acts as a ligand to low valency transition metal ions, and that if the resulting complex is paramagnetic the nitrogen of NO often contributes strongly to the resulting spectra. Analysis of the anisotropic spectra for various complexes of this type has revealed, however, that the unpaired electron is generally largely confined to the d-system of the metal ion, and that the ligand in no sense resembles a distorted NO molecule[21].

(ii) The radical ion N_2^-

This radical has been identified[22, 8] as one of the products of ultraviolet irradiation of potassium azide crystals. The spin resonance data, which clearly prove the presence of two equivalent nitrogen nuclei are summarised in Table 6.3. The only alternative seems to be the molecule N_3 which might have a coupling to the central nitrogen too small to detect because the unpaired electron is expected to be in a non-bonding π_g-level on the outer atoms. The g-tensor is not however in accord with this model which is therefore rejected in favour of the anion N_2^-.

Since the g-tensor is not axially symmetric the degeneracy of the π-levels must be lifted by an asymmetric crystal field; a reasonable assignment for N_2^- is that 2.0027 is g_{xx}, 1.983 is g_{zz} (along the axis of the molecule) and so g_{yy} is 2.0008. The hyperfine tensor (Table 6.3) is then as expected provided that A_{iso} is positive. (This is reasonable, but since spin-density on $N^{(a)}$ is likely to give rise to a negative isotropic coupling on $N^{(b)}$ but a positive contribution on $N^{(a)}$ the ultimate sign will depend upon the relative magnitude of these terms together with that for inner shell polarisation.)

TABLE 6.3

ELECTRON SPIN RESONANCE AND STRUCTURAL DATA[22,8]
FOR THE RADICAL ION N_2^-

Medium	g-Tensor				Hyperfine tensor (gauss)			
	g_{xx}	g_{yy}	g_{zz}	g_{av}	B_{xx}	B_{yy}	B_{zz}	A_{iso}
KN_3 (i)	2.0027	2.0008	1.9832	1.9956	10.6	−5.2	−5.4	1.4
(ii)					5.3	−2.6	−2.7	6.7
(i) $c_s^2 = 0.002$ $c_{p_x}^2 = 0.37$ $c_{p_z}^2 = 0.01$								
(ii) $c_s^2 = 0.012$ $c_{p_x}^2 = 0.185$								

Summation over the two nitrogens accounts for about 75% of the electron, but the error in the experimental results was of the order of 20%.

It should be stressed that because the signs of the experimental coupling constants are unknown, alternative tensors can be calculated ((i) and (ii) in Table 6.3 for N_2^-). The above argument is based on (i) because (ii) accounts for only 37% of the electron[8].

(iii) The radical ion $PF^{\pm}$

Here we consider a species formed in irradiated hexafluorophosphates[23] and identified as either PF^+ or PF^- by Morton[23]. There is no evidence that the species is not one containing two dissimilar phosphorus or fluorine atoms. Unfortunately the radical appears to be tumbling rapidly in the crystal lattices at room temperature, whilst the envelope spectrum obtained at low temperatures is greatly overlapped by that assigned to PF_4 and hence is quite uninterpretable (see Fig. 9.8.).

The results for the tumbling radical, given in Table 6.4 on the assumption that Morton's identification is correct, serve to show that the atomic s-orbital contribution from P and F are both small and hence that the radical is either $(\pi^*)^1$ or $(\pi^*)^3$; that is, either PF^+ or PF^-. The only possible clue to the resolution of this choice is that the average g-value is 1.9988. Our expectations would be that PF^+ would have $g_{\parallel} < 2.0023$ and that PF^- would have $g_{\parallel} > 2.0023$, the other values being considerably closer to the free-spin value. Thus on balance we favour the formulation PF^+, but unfortunately nothing further can be said about its structure at this stage.

TABLE 6.4

ELECTRON SPIN RESONANCE DATA[23] FOR THE RADICAL ION $PF^{\pm}$

Medium	g_{av}	Hyperfine tensor (gauss)	
		A_{iso}(P or F)	A_{iso}(P or F)
NH_4PF_6	1.9988	697	168

(c) AB $(\pi^*)^3$-radicals

(i) The superoxide ion O_2^-

The superoxide ion was studied unambiguously as its sodium and potassium salts some years ago[24]. The g-tensor had apparently axial symmetry, but as only powders were studied small differences between g_{xx} and g_{yy} could not be detected.

The relatively large value for $g_{\parallel}$ is as expected for a hole in the π^*-level, and the small negative shift for $g_{\perp}$ was interpreted as arising from incomplete quenching of the orbital motion[24]. Känzig and Cohen[25] have postulated that O_2^- is formed in alkali halide crystals heated in an oxygen atmosphere. Their result for doped KCl is also given in Table 6.5. If their identification is correct their data show clearly how unsafe it is to rely solely upon the magnitudes of a g-tensor for identification purposes.

TABLE 6.5

ELECTRON SPIN RESONANCE DATA FOR THE SUPEROXIDE ION,
O_2^- AND THE RADICAL ION O_2^+

Radical	Medium	g-Tensor				Reference
		g_{xx}	g_{yy}	g_{zz}	g_{av}	
O_2^-	NaO_2	2.00	2.00	2.175	2.058	24
	KCl	1.9512	1.9551	2.4359	2.1140	25
O_2^+ (?)	KCl	2.010	2.042	2.003	2.018	18

(ii) Chlorine monoxide[†], ClO

Photolysis of chlorine dioxide in various organic media at 77 °K is known from optical studies to give chlorine monoxide[26] but the electron resonance results are obscured by the fact that organic radicals formed simultaneously have spectra which overlap with that of ClO.

Photolysis of rigid solutions of the dioxide in sulphuric acid gives only one radical, and the growth of its spin resonance spectrum parallels the decay of that due to ClO_2[27]. It has been postulated that the oxygen atoms liberated from the dioxide simply add to an oxygen of the sulphuric acid so that no second paramagnetic species is formed[27].

There can be little doubt therefore that the spectrum shown in Fig. 6.3. is correctly assigned to the monoxide[27]. Interpretation of this envelope spectrum is neither easy nor unambiguous, but the data given in Table 6.6 have

† By chlorine monoxide we shall denote the species ClO although the material Cl_2O is also known by this name. It would be be better, we feel, if the latter were henceforth known as chlorine suboxide: indeed this raises the whole question of a system of nomenclature for all of these recently prepared radicals.

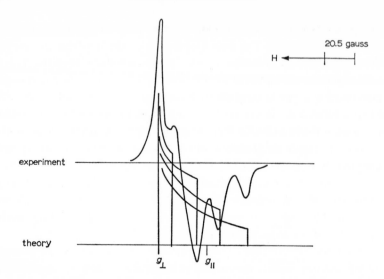

Fig. 6.3.   Electron spin resonance spectrum of ClO in rigid sulphuric acid.

been proposed as being in reasonable accord with both the spectrum and expectation.

If this interpretation is correct, the radical has axial symmetry but the orbital component is largely quenched. This quenching is probably due to strong hydrogen bonding to the sulphuric acid, and the required x–y fluctuation could then easily arise as an oscillation between weak and strong H-bonds. (A similar situation may well account for the axial symmetry of OH.) The only reasonable alternative is that ClO has an asymmetric environment and that the unpaired electron is confined to (say) π_x^*. The resulting parameters are far less similar to those expected and will not be considered further here.

TABLE 6.6

ELECTRON SPIN RESONANCE AND STRUCTURAL DATA
FOR CHLORINE MONOXIDE, ClO

Radical	Medium	g-Tensor			Hyperfine tensor (gauss)			Reference
		$g_\perp$	$g_\parallel$	g_{av}	$B_\perp$	$B_\parallel$	A_{iso}	
ClO	H_3PO_4	1.9909	2.0098	1.9972	5.7	−11.4	−5.7	27
Cl…ClO₃(?)	KClO₃				$\begin{cases} -22.4 \\ -\ 2.6 \end{cases}$	$\begin{cases} 44.8 \\ 5.2 \end{cases}$	$\begin{cases} 41.0 \\ 5.0 \end{cases}$	28

ClO: $c_s^2 = 0.004$ $c_p^2 = 0.27$

If the results of Table 6.6 are correct for ClO then the g-tensor is characteristic of a $(\pi^*)^3$-radical. The anisotropic part of the hyperfine tensor for ^{35}Cl is also as expected provided that A_{iso} is assumed to be negative. This is reasonable because the unpaired electron is about 73% on oxygen and might well contribute a negative term through polarisation of the σ-electrons.

This strong localisation on oxygen is not an immediately obvious result. If one considers the radical FO, then the reasoning given in § 6.1e leads to the conclusion that the outer electrons will be somewhat more on oxygen and the more deeply bound electrons strongly associated with the more electronegative fluorine. A similar argument explains our results for ClO, but it should be stressed that molecular libration and the participation of chlorine d-orbitals would serve to increase the real spin-density on chlorine whilst leaving unaltered the experimental data.

A radical trapped in irradiated potassium chlorate containing one strongly interacting and one weakly interacting chlorine atom has been identified as ClO by Hasty and co-workers[28]. The results, also given in Table 6.6, are so different from those discussed above that it does not seem possible that both species are ClO. Since a second weakly interacting chlorine was also detected the species is clearly not a simple diatomic radical: a variety of dimeric radicals are conceivable that would have the required properties.

(d) AB σ-radicals

(i) The cyanide radical, CN
Cochran and Adrian exposed hydrogen cyanide in an argon matrix at 4.2 °K to far-ultraviolet light and obtained a three-line spectrum which they assigned to the radical CN[29].

Unfortunately, very little structural information can be obtained because the only interpretable spectra were those obtained on warming to about 37 °K when an asymmetric triplet of lines appeared. This was assigned to rotating CN and an isotropic hyperfine coupling to ^{14}N of 4.6 gauss was measured. As the temperature was lowered the outer lines became progressively broader until they were hardly discernible at 4.2 °K, whereas the central line remained quite narrow. No anisotropic parameters could be derived from these spectra, and it seems probable that the broadening of the outer lines arose from some dynamic factor rather than mere anisotropy in the interaction tensors.

The isotropic coupling is surprisingly small; for if the radical is CN, as expected, some real admixture (hybridisation) of the $2s$ nitrogen level ought to occur (Fig. 6.2.). In the absence of further information it seems unsafe to conclude more than this. This is a pity, because CN is the only diatomic radical so far detected by spin resonance that has less than eleven valence electrons. Such radicals are of interest because the results would probe the order of the σ- and π-levels discussed in § 6.1d.

(ii) The radical ions F_2^-, Cl_2^- *and* FCl^-.

These radicals are of particular interest because they constituted the first clearly defined examples of "electron deficit" centres (V-centres) in alkali halide crystals[30]. Loss of an electron from a halide ion leaves an atom which is stabilised by displacement from its site towards a neighbouring anion which also moves to leave the hal_2^- ion symmetrically placed with respect to the crystal lattice (Fig. 6.4.).

The electron spin resonance results, besides establishing this geometry, also demonstrate that the unpaired electron is in a σ^*-orbital built from halogen p_z-orbitals. The isotropic coupling is in all instances too small to assign to direct participation of s-orbitals in the molecular orbital. The spin populations calculated for F_2^- and Cl_2^- from these results (Table 6.7) are very close to 50%, and hence it has been argued that the σ^*-bond for Cl_2^- has little if any d-character. This conclusion is of some importance since it is often supposed that d-levels contribute importantly to such bonds.

The radical FCl^- is of particular interest because there is now the opportunity for an unsymmetrical distribution of the σ-electron. Although there is a wealth of data relating to the distribution of π-electrons, there is very little direct information about the distribution of σ-electrons.

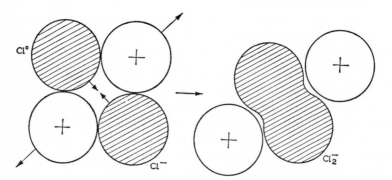

Fig. 6.4.   Formation of an hal_2^- radical-ion.

TABLE 6.7

ELECTRON SPIN RESONANCE DATA FOR THE DIHALOGEN RADICAL IONS

Radical	Medium	g-Tensor				$B_{xx} = B_{yy}$	B_{zz}	A_{iso}	References
		g_{xx}	g_{yy}	g_{zz}	g_{av}				
F_2^-	LiF (i)	2.0227	2.0234	2.0031	2.0164	−276	552	335	30, 8
	(ii)					−315.3	630.6	256.3	30, 8
Cl_2^-	KCl (i)	2.043	2.045	2.001	2.030	−25.8	51.7	43.6	30, 8
	(ii)					−37.6	75.3	20	
I_2^-	KCl				(1.992)	−97	193	207)	34
FCl^-	KCl–KF	2.030	2.030	2.0023	2.0215	−242	483	323 (Fi)	31
						−295	591	215 (Fii)	
						−35	70	56 (Cli)	
						−49	98	28 (Clii)	

(i) F_2^- : $c_s^2 = 0.02$ $c_{p_z}^2 = 0.51$ (ii) FCl^-: (F) $c_{p_z}^2 = 0.55$

(i) Cl_2^- : $c_s^2 = 0.026$ $c_{p_z}^2 = 0.51$ (Cl) $c_{p_z}^2 = 0.98$

(i) FCl^-: (F) $c_{p_z}^2 = 0.44$

          (Cl) $c_{p_z}^2 = 0.7$

$c_{p_z}^2 / c_s^2 = 22 \pm 2$ for all radicals in this Table.

References p. 117–118

This radical was obtained by γ-irradiation of a mixed KCl–KF crystal at 77 °K and was identified without ambiguity by its electron spin resonance spectrum[31]. The results given in Table 6.7 are, as is so frequently the case, somewhat ambiguous with respect to the relative signs of the parallel and perpendicular hyperfine coupling constants. Alternatives are tabulated, set (i) being preferred on the basis that it gives the most satisfactory sum of spin-densities[8, 31]. Using this set, one can compare the results with those for F_2^- and Cl_2^-. Qualitatively the expected drift of the hole towards chlorine is demonstrated. The trend is relatively small, however, and can be compared with the results discussed in (iii) below, for XeF and KrF radicals.

(iii) The radicals XeF *and* KrF

In addition to the spate of diamagnetic xenon compounds isoelectronic with corresponding compounds of iodine, the interesting paramagnetic fluoride XeF has been identified by Morton and Falconer[32] in γ-irradiated XeF_4. The results given in Table 6.8 show that this is a σ-radical but in contrast to the dihalide anions, the total p-character summed over F and Xe is considerably less than unity. This reduction may well indicate that the $5d$-level on xenon contributes to the bond. It would require only a slight admixture to give the required total.

TABLE 6.8

ELECTRON SPIN RESONANCE DATA FOR THE RADICALS XeF AND KrF

Radical	Medium	g-Tensor			Hyperfine tensor (gauss)			Ref.
		$g_\parallel$	$g_\perp$	g_{av}	$B_\parallel$	$B_\perp$	A_{iso}	
XeF	XeF_4	1.9740	2.1264	2.0756	505	-252	440 (^{19}F)	32
					274	-137	575 (^{129}Xe)	
KrF	KrF_4	2.000	2.068	2.045	660	-330	600 (^{19}F)	33

XeF: $c_{p_z}^2(F) = 0.47$ $c_{p_z}^2(Xe) = 0.36$ KrF: $c_{p_z}^2(F) = 0.61$
     c_s^2 (F) $= 0.03$ c_s^2 (Xe) $= 0.05$ c_s^2 (F) $= 0.04$

If one takes the value of 47% on fluorine as a measure of the electron distribution, then the electron is surprisingly uniformally distributed despite the extreme differences in the nature of the two atoms. This is in marked contrast to the results for ClO and may indicate that the π-levels have a greater tendency to polarise than the σ-levels. The $5s$-character for xenon is quite high, the p/s ratio being only 7.2. This strongly suggests that there is a real contribution to the σ^*-bond for this orbital, as might be expected from a consideration of the differences in electronegativity.

Results for KrF are comparable[33], the most interesting new feature being the greater spin-density on fluorine. This can be deduced by comparing the hyperfine data for fluorine in F_2^- (giving a measure of the result to be expected, for $c^2(p\sigma)=0.5$) with XeF and KrF. This comparison (Table 6.8) suggests that the electron affinity of Xe is comparable with that of fluorine in F_2^-, whilst that of Kr is considerably greater. Taken together, these results give the order $Kr > F > Xe > Cl$ for relative electronegativities.

References

1 P. W. ATKINS, A. HORSFIELD AND M. C. R. SYMONS, *J. Chem. Soc.*, 1964, 5220.
2 P. W. ATKINS AND D. KIVELSON, *J. Chem. Phys.*, 1966, *44*, 169.
3 M. C. R. SYMONS, *Advan. Phys. Org. Chem.*, 1963, *1*, 284.
4 J. R. MORTON, *J. Phys. Chem. Solids*, 1963, *24*, 209.
5 H. E. RADFORD, *Phys. Rev.*, 1961, *122*, 114.
6 J. A. MCMILLAN, M. S. MATHESON AND B. SMALLER, *J. Chem. Phys.*, 1960, *33*, 609.
7 S. SIEGEL, L. H. BAUM, S. SKOLNIK AND J. M. FLOURNOY, *J. Chem. Phys.*, 1960, *32*, 1249.
8 M. C. R. SYMONS, *J. Chem. Soc.*, 1963, 570.
9 W. T. DIXON AND R. O. C. NORMAN, *Proc. Chem. Soc.*, 1963, 97; *J. Chem. Soc.*, 1963, 3119.
10 R. C. SMITH AND S. J. WYARD, *Nature*, 1960, *186*, 226.
11 R. LIVINGSTONE, J. GHORMLEY AND H. ZELDES, *J. Chem. Phys.*, 1956, *24*, 483.
12 J. F. GIBSON, M. C. R. SYMONS AND M. G. TOWNSEND, *J. Chem. Soc.*, 1959, 269.
13 J. A. BRIVATI, M. C. R. SYMONS, D. J. A. TINLING, H. W. WARDALE AND D. O. WILLIAMS, *Chem. Commun.*, 1965, 402.
14 P. E. WIGEN AND J. A. COWEN, *J. Phys. Chem. Solids*, 1960, *17*, 26.
15 D. W. OVENALL, *J. Phys. Chem. Solids*, 1961, *21*, 309.
16 T. COLE, *J. Chem. Phys.*, 1961, *35*, 1169.
17 R. BERINGER AND J. G. CASTLE, *Phys. Rev.*, 1950, *78*, 581.
18 C. JACCARD, *Phys. Rev.*, 1961, *124*, 60.
19 J. CUNNINGHAM, *5th Intern. Symp. on Free Radicals, Uppsala, 1961*.
20 P. W. ATKINS AND M. C. R. SYMONS, *J. Chem. Soc.*, 1962, 4794.
21 I. BERNAL AND E. F. HOCKINGS, *Proc. Chem. Soc.*, 1962, 361; I. BERNAL AND S. E. HARRISON, *J. Chem. Phys.*, 1961, *34*, 102.
22 R. B. HORST, J. H. ANDERSON AND D. F. MULLIGAN, *J. Phys. Chem. Solids*, 1962, *23*, 157.
23 J. R. MORTON, *Can. J. Phys.*, 1963, *41*, 706.
24 J. E. BENNETT, D. J. E. INGRAM, M. C. R. SYMONS, P. GEORGE AND J. S. GRIFFITH, *Phil. Mag.*, 1955, *46*, 443.
25 W. KÄNZIG AND M. H. COHEN, *Phys. Rev. Letters*, 1959, *3*, 509.
26 I. NORMAN AND G. PORTER, *Proc. Roy. Soc.*, 1955, *230A*, 399.

27 P. W. ATKINS, J. A. BRIVATI, N. KEEN, M. C. R. SYMONS AND P. A. TREVALION, *J. Chem. Soc.*, 1962, 4785.
28 T. E. HASTY, W. B. ARD, JR. AND W. G. MOULTON, *Phys. Rev.*, 1959, *116*, 1459.
29 E. L. COCHRAN AND F. J. ADRIAN, 5*th Intern. Symp. on Free Radicals, Uppsala*, 1961.
30 T. G. CASTNER AND W. KANZIG, *J. Phys. Chem. Solids*, 1957, *3*, 178.
31 J. W. WILKINS AND J. R. GABRIEL, *Phys. Rev.*, 1963, *132*, 1950.
32 J. A. MORTON AND W. E. FALCONER, *Proc. Chem. Soc.*, 1963, 95.
33 W. E. FALCONER, J. R. MORTON AND A. G. STRENG, *J. Chem. Phys.*, 1964, *41*, 902.
34 E. BOESMAN AND D. SCHOEMACHER, *J. Chem. Phys.*, 1962, *37*, 671.

Chapter 7

Triatomic radicals

We shall be concerned in this Chapter with the species AB_2. We shall include the species XAB, where X may be a polyatomic moiety (such as SO_3^-) wherever it seems appropriate because they are basically similar in structure.

7.1 STRUCTURAL ASPECTS

(a) Linear molecules

The bonding scheme is essentially similar to that discussed in Chapter 6 for diatomic species. Let us consider ten atomic orbitals from which the same number of molecular orbitals can be constructed; for a linear triatomic species BAB each one can be classified as σ or π and g or u. For simplicity we shall ignore the possibility of sp^n-hybridisation on the outer atoms and will, therefore, treat the ns-electrons on the B atoms as lone-pairs.

The molecular orbitals which can be constructed are illustrated in Fig. 7.1a. σ_g, σ_u and π_u are bonding orbitals, the last being doubly degenerate. The level π_g is doubly degenerate, and as it is confined to the outer atoms it may be considered to be non-bonding. $\bar{\pi}_u$, $\bar{\sigma}_g$ and $\bar{\sigma}_u$ are the antibonding orbitals corresponding to the π_u, σ_g and σ_u bonding orbitals respectively.

Species with less than seventeen valence electrons can accommodate all the electrons in the bonding and non-bonding orbitals; there is therefore no need for the radical to bend to relieve any antibonding character and so such species are linear. To consider the situation when there are more than sixteen valence electrons we shall use the scheme presented by Walsh[1].

(b) Bent AB_2 molecules

Using the LCAO approach for linear molecules and considering the effects of bending on the energies of the orbitals, Walsh was able to derive a consistent scheme by making the following assumptions.

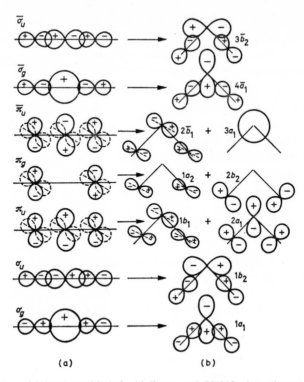

Fig. 7.1. Molecular orbitals in (a) linear and (b) 90° triatomic molecules.

(1) In a 90° AB_2 molecule the s-atomic orbital $(3a_1)$ on A does not contribute to the molecular orbitals and so accommodates the lone-pair on A.

(2) If, on a change of bond angle, a molecular orbital changes from being built from a p-orbital on A to an s-orbital on A, the orbital becomes more tightly bound and more confined to A.

(3) If there is no change in the valence of A when the bond angle varies, the following effects determine the binding energies:

(a) if the molecular orbital is antibonding between the ligand atoms a linear state is favoured,

(b) if the molecular orbital is bonding between the ligand atoms a bent state is favoured.

It is to be noted that this scheme entirely neglects both hybridisation in the ligand atoms and the inclusion of d-orbitals (which may be important when

A is a heavy atom). This latter point has been mentioned by Walsh[2]. A more subtle point is that the degrees of freedom that a distorting molecule is allowed may be more numerous than those permitted in the present scheme. Thus there is abundant but not unequivocal evidence that in some dioxides (NO_2, ClO_2) the excited states are distorted to C_s from C_{2v} symmetry[3–5] (one bond may be longer than the other). This is because the antibonding character of the $2b_1$-orbital cannot be reduced by a distortion which retains C_{2v} symmetry. Furthermore, the possibility of a Jahn–Teller distortion occurring when the occupied level is orbitally degenerate cannot be over-looked.

Nevertheless, the scheme is appealing because of its simplicity. The correlation diagram for the bending of an AB_2 molecule is shown in Fig. 7.2. which was constructed by considering the orbitals illustrated in Fig. 7.1a. in conjunction with the rules outlined above[1]. Fig. 7.1b. illustrates the molecular orbitals in the 90° molecule.

As we remarked in § 7.1a. the species with sixteen or less valence electrons can accommodate all the electrons in the bonding orbitals, therefore no

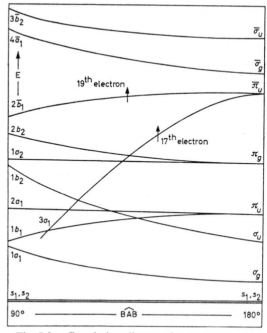

Fig. 7.2.   Correlation diagram for AB_2 molecules[1].

strain need be relieved and the molecule is linear: this is illustrated in the correlation diagram Fig. 7.2.

When the next electron is introduced to form a seventeen electron species it will enter the $\bar{\pi}_u$ antibonding orbital. As shown on the correlation diagram, if the molecule were now to bend the "$\bar{\pi}_u$" orbital would become increasingly built from the s-orbital on A until, in the 90° molecule, it would occupy an s-lone-pair orbital on A. The lowering in energy brought about by the inclusion of the s-orbital favours a bent molecule.

An eighteen electron species (e.g. nitrite ion) is a $(3a_1)^2$-species and would therefore be even more bent than the seventeen electron $(3a_1)^1$-species. Yet a further electron (the nineteenth) would enter the $2b_1$-orbital which, because its energy is only slightly dependent on bond angle (by rule 3b), will have little further effect on the bond angle. Consequently eighteen and nineteen valence electron species should have similar bond angles, a conclusion well borne out experimentally.

(c) Electronegativity and bond angle

It is reasonable to ask what is meant by the "binding energy" used as the ordinate in Walsh's diagrams. This problem has been considered by several authors[6-8]. Coulson and Neilson[8] conclude that because the diagrams are applicable to many problems, something of physical significance is being plotted as the "binding energy". That which is plotted does not, however, seem to be the ionisation potential, the core energy E_i, the hydrogen-like one-electron energy, or the additive-partitioned energy e_i, where

$$e_i = E_i + \sum_j (J_{ij} - \tfrac{1}{2}K_{ij}) \qquad (7.1)$$

J_{ij} and K_{ij} being the Coulomb and exchange energies.

It may be remarked that the diagrams include implicitly the Sidgwick–Powell approach to stereochemistry; that inter-electronic terms are of prime importance is shown in Coulson and Neilson's paper. This point may be developed somewhat in order to show the dependence of bond angle on the relative electronegativity of the atoms A and B.

We shall first recall the discussion of § 6.1e in which the distribution of the unpaired electron was discussed in relation to the electronegativities of A and B. Since it is the distribution of the unpaired electron in seventeen and nineteen electron molecules which determines the bond angle it would seem reasonable that this could be related to electronegativity differences.

Whether or not a molecule bends depends largely on the repulsion between the electrons in the $3a_1$-orbital and those in the AB bonds. As the electron population on A increases, in Sidgwick–Powell language the electronic repulsion term is increased and the molecule becomes more bent. In terms of Walsh's scheme, as the population on A increases it is energetically expedient for the antibonding character to be reduced, which it is if the orbital becomes non-bonding, that is, an s lone-pair on A; consequently the molecule bends. Thus both schemes lead to the situation that the bond angle increases with increasing electronegativity of A.

There are, of course, complicating factors. If the electronegativity of the ligands B is sufficiently large, changes in the electronegativity of A will cause negligible perturbations on the molecular geometry which the ligand electronegativity has defined. A schematic illustration of this point is given in Fig. 7.3. in which the variation of bond angle (ϕ) with the electronegativity of A (χ_A) is shown for the cases when the electronegativity of B (χ_B) is either high or low.

A further complication lies in the possibility of d-orbitals being involved in the bonding. This situation is rather too complex for fruitful *a priori* discussion, but will be recalled in particular cases subsequently.

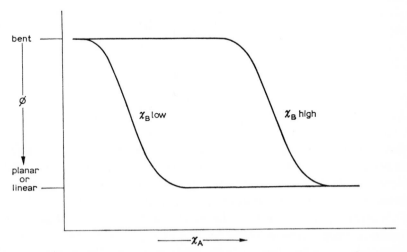

Fig. 7.3.   Bond angles in AB_n species in which the relative electronegativities of A and B differ.

References p. 160–161

(d) Expected electron spin resonance spectra

(i) Seventeen electron radicals

According to the above theory the unpaired electron in seventeen valence electron species will occupy an orbital $(3a_1)$ which is delocalised and built from both s and p-orbitals on the central atom because the seventeenth electron will cause the molecule to bend, but not to the full extent of $90°$. We therefore expect the hyperfine spectra to display a considerable isotropic splitting and a superimposed anisotropy that should have a maximum value when the radical is aligned such that the field lies along its C_2-axis. Although this scheme would predict an axial hyperfine tensor, owing to polarisation of orthogonal orbitals, small deviations from this symmetry are to be expected. For example, if there is a polarisation of a b_1-orbital the hyperfine tensor will be of the form

$$\mathbf{A} = \mathbf{B} + \mathbf{A}_{iso} = \mathbf{A}_{iso} + (-\beta, -\beta, 2\beta) + (2\beta', -\beta', -\beta') \qquad (7.2)$$

where β' is small compared with β. The directions refer to (x, y, z) where z is the C_2 axis and x is perpendicular to the molecular plane.

The qualitative features of the g-tensor were outlined in § 2.2. A more quantitative approach is given in Appendix 3 in which it is shown that, to a reasonable approximation, the principal values of the g-tensor are given by

$$g_{xx} = \frac{f_1(c_i c_i', \lambda_A, \lambda_B)}{\varepsilon(A_1) - \varepsilon(B_2)} + 2.0023 \qquad (7.3)$$

$$g_{yy} = \frac{f_2(c_i c_i', \lambda_A, \lambda_B)}{\varepsilon(A_1) - \varepsilon(B_1)} + 2.0023 \qquad (7.4)$$

$$g_{zz} = \frac{f_3(c_i c_i', \lambda_A, \lambda_B)}{\varepsilon(A_1) - \varepsilon(A_2)} + 2.0023 \qquad (7.5)$$

where the $f_k(c_i c_i', \lambda_A, \lambda_B)$ are functions of the spin–orbit coupling constants on the atoms A and B (λ_A and λ_B) and the products of coefficients of the orbitals on the atoms. Explicit equations are given in Appendix 3 but those shown here are sufficient for us to conclude that, since the order of orbitals is $...(1a_2)^2(2b_2)^2(3a_1)^1(2b_1)^0$ in the vicinity of $3a_1$, the signs of Δg_{xx}, Δg_{yy} and Δg_{zz} are positive, negative and positive respectively as they are determined by the sign of the denominator in the above equations. The orbitals $3a_1$ and $2b_1$ are but little separated in energy and so one might expect Δg_{yy} to be large and negative. Since the orbital $1a_2$ is strictly confined to the ligand atoms, in the absence of d-orbitals on A, there will be no contribution from the spin–orbit coupling on A to Δg_{zz}. The latter is therefore expected to be small and positive. It should be remembered, however, that an A_2 state can also arise from the configuration $(1a_2)^2(2b_2)^1(3a_1)^1(2b_1)^1$ and the mixing of this state with the ground state may affect the sign and magnitude of Δg_{zz}.

To summarise: the direction of the maximum value of the hyperfine tensor should coincide with a g-value close to 2.0023. At right angles to this a smaller hyperfine splitting will be observed centred on a low g-value. This corresponds to the y-direction (B–B direction). Perpendicular to these will be a hyperfine splitting of a similar magnitude but based on a g-value which is greater than that of the free spin.

(ii) Nineteen electron radicals

The electronic structure of nineteen electron triatomic radicals on Walsh's scheme, would be expected to be...$(1a_2)^2(2b_2)^2(3a_1)^2(2b_1)^1$, $^2B_1$.

The hyperfine tensor is now less clearly predictable, for although an isotropic splitting would not be expected from an electron in a b_1-orbital (which cannot be formed from an sp^n-hybrid on A) one does expect a certain amount of polarisation from the unpaired p-electron density on both the A and B atoms and a concomitant but small isotropic component (§ 2.3e) in the spectrum.

Superimposed upon this isotropic splitting (which normally corresponds to about 1% of an electron in an ns-orbital on A) will be an anisotropic spectrum with the maximum value observed when the field is perpendicular to the molecular plane (along the x-axis). Although the anisotropic tensor would be axially symmetric on a simple picture, polarisation might cause deviations from this simplicity.

The g-tensor is characteristic and differs markedly from that for seventeen electron species. A simple application of the methods outlined in Appendix 3 shows that, if d-orbitals are neglected, Δg_{xx} is zero. This is because the p-orbitals which constitute the $2b_1$-molecular orbital have zero component of angular momentum about the x-axis and so cannot couple with the applied field. If d-orbitals are admitted then it can be shown that

$$\Delta g_{xx} = \frac{2d_i d_i' \lambda_A}{\varepsilon(B_1) - \varepsilon(A_2)} \tag{7.6}$$

where the d_i are the coefficients of the d-orbitals involved.

References p. 160–161

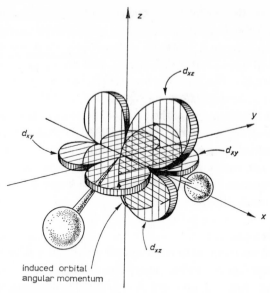

Fig. 7.4.   Contribution of d-orbitals to the value of Δg_{xx} in $^2B_1$ AB_2 radicals.

The reason for the shift in g_{xx} is that the $d_{xz}(b_1)$ orbital is composed of complex orbitals which do not have zero components of angular momentum about the x-axis, consequently the applied field can mix it with the $d_{xy}(a_2)$ orbital which is analogously constructed (Fig. 7.4.). This point will be mentioned later where it will be used to estimate the possible extent of d-orbital involvement in SeO_2^- (§ 7.2b(v)).

The value of Δg_{yy} depends on the same mixing as that responsible for the shift of g_{yy} in seventeen electron species. The major difference is that the expression for the g-shift is now

$$\Delta g_{yy} = \frac{f_2(c_i c_i', \lambda_A, \lambda_B)}{\varepsilon(B_1) - \varepsilon(A_1)} \tag{7.7}$$

because B_1 is the ground state. This expression differs only in sign from the earlier analogue; consequently Δg_{yy} is expected to be large and positive.

Δg_{zz} arises from the mixing of a B_2 state with the ground B_1 state (see Appendix 2). The configuration $\ldots(1a_2)^2(2b_2)^1(3a_1)^2(2b_1)^2$, $^2B_2$ is generally close-lying and its admixture will produce a positive shift.

To summarise, the largest hyperfine splitting from A will correspond to a nearly free-spin g-value and will be observed when the applied field lies along the x-axis. Perpendicular to this will be observed a smaller hyperfine splitting based on a high g-value (y-direction) and a similar hyperfine splitting based upon a g-value between g_{xx} and g_{yy} (z-direction). Only a relatively small s-contribution is expected, and the p/s ratio should be greater than about 10.

(iii) Twenty-one electron radicals

The electron configuration of twenty-one electron radicals is expected to be $...(3a_1)^2(2b_1)^2(4a_1)^1(3b_2)^0$, $^2A_1$ (see Fig. 7.2). Consequently the theoretical discussion is similar to that of seventeen electron species. The only point which ought perhaps to be made is that the level $4a_1$ lies beneath $3b_2$ yet above $2b_1$ whereas in the seventeen electron species the corresponding $3a_1$ orbital lay beneath $2b_1$ and above $2b_2$. This merely results in a predicted negative shift in g_{xx} and positive shift in g_{yy} which is contrary to those predicted for seventeen electron radicals, but is still distinct from the predictions for nineteen electron species. A structural implication is that the radical should be nearly linear because the effect of occupying the $4a_1$-orbital is, as illustrated in Fig. 7.2, to counter the bending influence of the lower orbitals. It should also be stressed that participation of higher atomic orbitals is now more important.

7.2 RESULTS FOR TRIATOMIC RADICALS

Results for electron spin resonance studies of radicals known to be triatomic, thought to be triatomic, or simply related to the general class of radicals under consideration will be discussed. We begin with one of the best known of all inorganic radicals, nitrogen dioxide.

(a) Seventeen electron radicals

(i) Nitrogen dioxide, NO$_2$

An outline of the interesting history associated with electron spin resonance studies of this radical was given in Chapter 1. Together with chlorine dioxide it shares the distinction of providing a link between the known and the unknown in the study of radiation damage of inorganic solids. We briefly consider the results obtained from the dioxide in the gas and liquid phases, and then pass to results for molecules isolated in rare-gas matrices at low temperatures. These are then linked with results for the dioxide formed in various crystals by high-energy radiation. Now that an unambiguous set of results is established the overall picture is clear; the pitfalls were many, however, and their description seems worthwhile since several important principles are thereby illustrated and an awareness of these may help future studies of such systems.

Castle and Beringer[9] observed a triplet for the dioxide in the gas phase with a hyperfine splitting of 47.1 gauss. Bird and co-workers[10] claimed to have measured a splitting of about 107 gauss for the dioxide in carbon tetrachloride, but attempts to repeat this have failed[11], and it seems that, for a wide range of solvents and temperatures, only a single broad line is obtained which is of almost Lorentzian shape and which has a g-value of about 2.00 and a width* of about 150 gauss.

It seems probable that a major contributing factor to this excessive width is rapid dimerisation to the diamagnetic N_2O_4. We were unable, however, to resolve the expected hyperfine components even when the concentration had been reduced to the limit of detection. Other possible factors contributing to the line-width are discussed in § 7.2b(i).

Failure to resolve hyperfine structure in the spectra from fluid solutions was capped by failure to detect any resonance at all from rapidly frozen solutions of the dioxide, again presumably because of the speed at which dimerisation proceeds. The discovery that a well resolved triplet can be obtained when the dioxide is isolated in certain molecular sieves[12] was therefore most encouraging. There was a marked line-width variation which clearly arose from the anisotropic part of the hyperfine and g-tensors, so that rotation in the sieve must be hindered in the manner found for viscous solutions. The greatly improved resolution relative to that for radicals in the gas or fluid phases was comparable with that for the radical NF_2 [13]. In both cases this was probably due to suppression of dimerisation, caused by the inability of the dimers to fit into the sieve cavities.

The difficulties discussed above were overcome by isolating the dioxide in an argon matrix at 4 °K[14], but the spectra remained incorrectly interpreted for some time because the relatively large isotropic hyperfine coupling gave rise to such a clear-cut triplet component that the shoulders were ignored. Farmer et al.[15] extended these studies to different rare gases and suggested that extra features reflected a range of trapping sites as is ob-

* By "width" we shall always imply the separation between points of maximum slope of the absorption line.

TABLE 7.1

ELECTRON SPIN RESONANCE DATA FOR NITROGEN DIOXIDE IN VARIOUS MATRICES

Matrix	g-Tensor				Hyperfine interaction (gauss)				Reference
	g_{xx}	g_{yy}	g_{zz}	g_{av}	B_{xx}	B_{yy}	B_{zz}	A_{iso}	
Ice (77 °K)	2.0066	1.9920	2.0022	2.0003	−6.28	−7.24	13.33	56.88	11
La$_2$Mg$_3$(NO$_3$)$_{12}$·24H$_2$O	2.005	1.994	2.004	2.001	0.36	−7.14	6.78	60.7	18
NaNO$_2$				2.000				67.5	17
Ar	2.0037	1.990	2.0037	1.9991	3.6	−7.2	3.6	54.2	14
				2.0005				54.6	15
CCl$_4$				2.008				107.6	10
Gas								47.1	9
Pb(NO$_3$)$_2$	2.004	1.995	1.995	1.9994	−4.7	2.3	2.3	54.7	72
NaNO$_2$	2.0057	1.9910	2.0015	1.9994	−5.27	−7.95	13.22	54.71[a]	16
	1.9983	1.9983	2.0015	1.9994	−6.61	−6.61	13.22	54.71[b]	52
	2.0036	1.9910	2.0036	1.9994	3.97	−7.95	3.97	54.71[c]	52
	2.0057	1.9962	1.9962		−5.27	2.63	2.63		52
					−6.8	−3.4	10.2	39.8	19
					−9	−1	9.5	43	20

[a], [b], [c] Refer to NO$_2$ undergoing rotation restricted to the xy, xz and yz planes respectively.

served for hydrogen atoms. In fact, these features were undoubtedly just the shoulders expected for axially symmetric molecules having their magnetic axes parallel to the applied field, the strong features being due to perpendicular orientations.

Recognition of this was not enough since the dioxide does not have axial symmetry, and the spectra of radicals thought to be the dioxide formed in irradiated sodium nitrite[16] were indeed not axially symmetric. The link with species formed in various crystals by high-energy radiation was clear, however, and led to the recognition that the apparent axial symmetry arose from the rotation about the axis of least moment of inertia of the molecule (the y-axis)[11]. This, if sufficiently rapid, would average the x and z components such that $g_\perp = \frac{1}{2}(g_{xx} + g_{zz})$ and $g_\parallel = g_{yy}$. The results for radicals in rare-gas matrices and in irradiated crystals are then in good agreement (Table 7.1) and there is no longer any need to postulate alternative trapping sites.

This conclusion was confirmed by trapping the dioxide in ice. Frozen aqueous solutions of dinitrogen tetroxide were exposed to 3650 Å ultra-

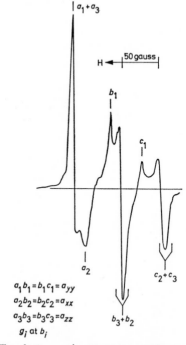

Fig. 7.5.   The electron spin resonance spectrum of NO_2 in ice.

violet light at 77 °K and the resulting electron spin resonance spectra[11] showed greater complexity than that for the dioxide in argon. Analysis of the spectrum, according to the method outlined in Appendix 5 and indicated in Fig. 7.5. gave results quite comparable with those obtained from single crystals.

In 1955, Ard[17] reported the detection of an isotropic triplet in γ-irradiated sodium nitrate crystals at 20 °K which he ascribed to rotating nitrogen dioxide. The hyperfine splitting of 67.5 gauss which he observed is surprisingly high (see Table 7.1) however, and is close to the maximum value of about 69 gauss. Subsequently Bleaney et al.[18] reported a triplet in irradiated lanthanum magnesium nitrates which they assigned to nitrogen dioxide. Their results, given in Table 7.1 are in fair agreement with those of Zeldes and Livingstone[16] for a radical in γ-irradiated sodium nitrite. The latter were encouraged in their identification in that the addition of silver ions greatly increased the yield of radicals. This suggested that the radical is formed by electron loss, the net reaction being

$$NO_2^- + Ag^+ \xrightarrow{h\nu} NO_2 + Ag^\circ \tag{7.8}$$

Their results agree extremely well with those from powder spectra discussed above, and there can be little doubt that this identification is correct. More recent reports of the spectra of NO_2 include those of Tateno and Gesi[19] and Atherton et al.[20].

One might remark that this conclusion receives confirmation from theoretical considerations. Certainly if one uses the atomic parameters calculated for ^{14}N (Table 2.1) then agreement is excellent (Table 7.2). In fact the bond angle, as estimated for the p/s ratio derived therefrom, is equal to

TABLE 7.2

MOLECULAR PARAMETERS FOR NITROGEN DIOXIDE, NO_2

Matrix	$c_s{}^2$	$c_{p_z}{}^2$	$c_{p_x}{}^2$	$c_o{}^2$	λ^2	$O\widehat{X}O$	Reference
Ice	0.103	0.398	0.15	0.50	3.864	132°	11
NaNO₂	0.099	0.44	0.052	0.49	4.182	133	16
Ar	0.099	0.42			4.24	133	14
Pb(NO₃)₂	0.099	0.28			2.83	126	72
Ar	0.099						15
CCl₄	0.196						10
Calculated	0.168	0.222		0.610	1.32		73

the experimental angle for the dioxide in the gas phase (134°) within experimental error. In this instance, however, since in the several experiments the *identity* of the radical is not in question, we prefer to say that these results strikingly confirm the simple ideas that atomic parameters are useful for such molecules, that the calculated parameters are not gravely in error, and that the Mulliken–Walsh approach to the structure of such molecules is valid and quite adequate to explain these new and searching results.

In subsequent discussions it is just this agreement with theory that is used, initially, to help in the identification of the radical. Had we been in doubt concerning the present identification of, for example, the radical detected in irradiated sodium nitrite, and had nitrogen dioxide been unobtainable, the following reasoning could have been used.

(a) The radical contains only one strongly interacting nitrogen atom. This suggests the species NO_2^{2-}, NO_2, $NO^{2-}NO$ or N as chemically reasonable products.

(b) The large $2s$-character on nitrogen together with the small $2p/2s$ ratio of 4.2 is satisfied only by NO_2 since NO_2^{2-}, NO^{2-}, NO and N should all have their unpaired electron in π- or p-levels.

Identification arguments of this type are used extensively in the subsequent sections.

(ii) The radical ion CO_2^-

Exposure of sodium formate to high-energy radiation results in the formation of a radical, the electron spin resonance spectrum of which consists of a well-defined quartet of lines with a nearly isotropic hyperfine coupling[11, 21–23]. This structure could only be assigned to an interaction with ^{23}Na nuclei, and corresponds to about 2.6% transfer of spin from the parent radical which was identified as CO_2^- because of its great similarity to NO_2. This can be seen by reference to Table 7.3 from which several pertinent correlations emerge. These are:

(a) the increase in spin-density on the central atom on going from ^{14}N to ^{13}C,

(b) the corresponding marked decrease in the $2p/2s$ ratio,

(c) the increase in interaction with alkali metal cations on going from Li^+ to K^+.

These will be considered in turn.

The change in spin-density distribution on going from NO_2 to CO_2^- is at first sight surprising but is in good accord with the prognostications of

TABLE 7.3

ELECTRON SPIN RESONANCE AND STRUCTURAL DATA FOR THE RADICAL CO_2^-

Medium	g-Tensor			M^{+-}	^{13}C—Hyperfine tensor (gauss)				Reference
	g_{xx}	g_{yy}	g_{zz}	A_{iso}	B_{xx}	B_{yy}	B_{zz}	A_{iso}	
NaHCO₂	2.0032	1.9975	2.0014	8.2	−11.43	−16.43	27.86	167.2	23
Mg(HCO₂)₂·2H₂O			2.0017						11
KHCO₂			2.0048	7.0					11
LiHCO₂·H₂O			1.9998	<4					11
Calcite	2.00320	1.99727	2.00161		−13.24	−16.17	29.42	147.86	24

NaHCO₂ $c_s^2 = 0.15$ $c_{p_z}^2 = 0.50$ $c_{p_z}^2 = 0.08$ $c_o^2 = 0.36$ $\lambda^2 = 3.33$ $\widehat{OCO} = 128°$

§ 6.1e. Thus both bonding and antibonding electrons have to be considered, and as the oxygen atoms will take a greater share of the bonding electrons in CO_2^- they must take a smaller share of the antibonding electron in this radical. The decrease in the $2p/2s$ ratio follows from this: a greater localisation on the central atom corresponding to a greater tendency for the molecule to bend and so to increase the $2s$-character of the unpaired electron.

Both these trends have an interesting bearing on the reactivity of NO_2 and CO_2^-. Thus dimerisation will be energetically favoured for CO_2^- because it involves less localisation of the bonding electrons and less change in bond angle (See discussion § 8.2c(i) and Fig. 8.4.). Again, reaction with a hydrogen atom results in addition to carbon to give formate, but to oxygen to give nitrous acid.

A strong specific interaction with one cation is most unusual for radicals trapped in ionic crystals, although it is frequently found for radical-anions in solvents of low dielectric constant, such as ethers. For sodium formate there are two different sodium ions which could be responsible for the hyperfine interaction, both lying on the C_2-axis of the radical, one being strongly associated with the negatively charged oxygen atoms, the other being linked to the oxygen atoms of an adjacent ion, but exposed to the unpaired electron by the loss of formate hydrogen. It is not clear which cation is responsible for the observed hyperfine splitting.

The marked increase in atom-character on going from Li^+ ($<2.6\%$) to Na^+ (2.6%) to K^+ (8.5%) is reminiscent of the trend discussed in Chapter 4 for cations in F-centres. This trend runs contrary to that expected if the electronegativity of the cation dominated, but is in accord with the effect of co-ordination, in this instance from the oxygen atoms of neighbouring formate ions. Such co-ordination, which opposes charge-transfer by partially filling the outer s-level, will fall from Li^+ to K^+ and hence the hyperfine coupling will increase.

The trends in g-value for various salts (Table 7.3) conform to this postulate. There is a marked increment on going from Li^+ to K^+ which can be understood in terms of a decrease in the energy gap between the $1a_2$- and $4a_1$-levels which govern Δg_{zz}. This decrease is thought to occur because the movement of an electron from the $1a_2$-level, which is non-bonding on oxygen, will be opposed by co-ordinated cations, but this opposition will fall on going from Li^+ to K^+. Similar reasoning suggests that the $4a_1$-level will alter in such a way as to reinforce this trend.

The radical CO_2^- has also been observed in irradiated calcite[24].

(iii) The formyl radical, HCO

The formyl radical is a well-established species in the gas phase, being formed, for example, by flash-photolysis of acetaldehyde[25]. The ultraviolet spectrum was interpreted in terms of a bent radical with a bond angle of 120°, and a $^2A'$ ground state. Early electron spin resonance studies of irradiated organic systems often revealed a radical having an asymmetric doublet spectrum with an unusually large hyperfine splitting of about 130 gauss. This was firmly identified as the formyl radical simultaneously by Brivati *et al.*[26] and by Adrian *et al.*[27]. The latter workers obtained spectra which were far better resolved and also studied the radical DCO; from the combined results they were able to obtain additional information. Their data, given in Table 7.4 will be used in the present discussion.

The two major items which establish the identity of the radical which has this large hyperfine splitting, are its preparation by the addition of hydrogen atoms to carbon monoxide[27] and the results of experiments with deuterated methanol[27] and formic acid[28] which demonstrated that the strongly interacting proton is directly attached to carbon. Also of considerable importance is the conclusion, drawn in § 2.5b, that those radicals of the form AH_n which have considerable *s*-character in the orbital of the unpaired electron on A should exhibit a large positive isotropic hyperfine coupling to the α-protons; this is indeed found for the formyl radical[26, 27].

Interpretation of the envelope spectra for HCO and DCO was particularly complicated because the principal directions of the hyperfine and *g*-tensor are not coincident as is usually approximately true. The task was unravelled by Adrian *et al.* who first obtained the principal values for the *g*-tensor directly and accurately from the centre line of the DCO triplet (Table 7.4) and then used these values to interpret the spectrum of HCO. To get satisfactory agreement it was necessary to include a term B_{yz} in the hyperfine tensor given in relation to the principal axis system of the *g*-tensor. This showed that the *x*-axis is normal to the radical plane and that this direction is common to both tensors. This study illustrates well one of the pitfalls associated with the interpretation of powder spectra: had the principal values of the *g*-tensor not been known, then the usual procedure for analysing the HCO spectra would have given an incorrect result.

Adrian *et al.* discussed the *g*-tensor in terms of a $^2A_0'$ ground state, the unpaired electron being in the $4a'$ -level and largely localised on carbon. When the magnetic field is applied perpendicular to the radical plane along *x* a positive *g*-shift is expected due to the mixing of excited states which involve

TABLE 7.4

ELECTRON SPIN RESONANCE DATA FOR THE FORMYL RADICAL

Radical	g-Tensor				Hyperfine tensor (gauss)				Reference
	g_{xx}	g_{yy}	g_{zz}	g_{av}	B_{xx}	B_{yy}	B_{zz}	A_{iso}	
HCO	2.0031	2.0031	1.9961	2.0007	−4	−4	8	136	26
DCO	2.0041	2.0027	1.9960	2.0009	−4.2	−0.8	5	137	27
					−0.86	0.11	−0.9	21.2	27

The latter two sets of results for the hyperfine tensor refer to the g-tensor axis system; there is an off-diagonal term $B_{yz} = 5.8$ gauss.

promotion of σ-electrons. They concluded that for the field along the C–O bond direction (z) there will be strong coupling between the A_0' and A_0'' states, involving promotion of the unpaired electron into the $a_2(\pi^*)$-level. This should give a relatively large reduction in g and hence the low value of 1.996 was identified as g_{zz}. The remaining orthogonal direction is parallel to the density axis of the p-orbital of the unpaired electron so the g-shift in this direction should be small. This is in good agreement with the experimental value of 2.0027.

(iv) Some related radicals

By "related" we mean radicals having the basic structure BAX in which B and X can be polyatomic groups, the angle BAC is less than 180° and the unpaired electron is considerably localised on A in an sp^n-hybrid orbital (z being in the BAX plane and close to the bisector of the angle BAX). Such species are often described as σ-radicals to distinguish them from the π-radicals which are related to the nineteen electron AB_2 molecules discussed in § 7.2b.

All the known radicals in this class are organic and might therefore be considered outside the scope of this work, but the factors involved are of more general significance and so some discussion is warranted.

We first discuss results for the related radicals $H_2C=CH$ and $H_2C=N$. The former was prepared by addition of hydrogen atoms to acetylene in a rare-gas matrix [29] and the latter by a similar treatment of hydrogen cyanide. Spectra assigned to $H_2C=CH$ were difficult to interpret because the lines were broad [29], but by photolysis of hydrogen iodide in the presence of excess deuteroacetylene to give $HDC=CD$ a major splitting of about 68 gauss was observed which was ascribed to one of the β-protons. Two further proton splittings of about 34 and 16 gauss were recognised, and assigned to the other β- and to the α-proton respectively.

Adrian and Cochran [30] have given a theoretical interpretation of this spectrum which indicates that the strongly coupled proton is *trans* to the orbital of the unpaired electron, and that the bond angle (ϕ) is about 140° (Fig. 7.6.). It seems that addition of a hydrogen atom to acetylene causes a slight bending of the molecule; two electrons remain in the π-level, and the unpaired electron occupies an orbital which has some carbon $2s$-character. Unfortunately there are no data for radicals containing ^{13}C to support this assignment.

Results for $CH_2=CH$ in liquid ethane, although apparently anomalous,

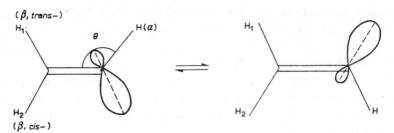

Fig. 7.6.   The structure and inversion of the radical $CH_2=CH$.

have been interpreted in a manner which strongly supports this assignment[31]. The problem was that only four lines were obtained; these could be assigned to only one strongly interacting proton (102.4 gauss) and one weakly interacting proton (13.4 gauss). The key to understanding this spectrum is that the large coupling constant is almost exactly equal to the sum of the coupling constants assigned to the β-protons in $CH_2=CH$ in the solid state (68 gauss + 34 gauss). Both groups of workers have postulated that in fluid solution the radical readily inverts, as indicated in Fig. 7.6. If such an inversion were very rapid then a 1:2:1 triplet would stem from the β-protons, which would appear equivalent with a hyperfine coupling constant of 51 gauss. As this inversion rate slows, the central line, which is an average of two lines having a separation of 68–34 = 34 gauss, would broaden since the spin-state giving rise to the central lines appears discrete to the electron during the time of observation if the inversion is sufficiently slow. At intermediate inversion

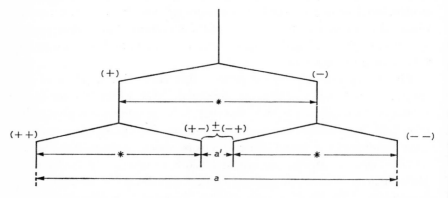

Fig. 7.7.   The modulation of the hyperfine spectrum of the radical $CH_2=CH$ (* denotes the interchanged splittings).

rates the two lines blur into a broad single resonance (Fig. 7.7.). The outer lines of the triplet, separated by 102 gauss would remain constant. These narrow lines are then further split by the α-proton, which retains its identity; hence four narrow lines are expected together with a broad central feature. This fits well with the observed spectrum and the results confirm the assignment given in Table 7.5.

The small hyperfine coupling of 16 gauss assigned to the α-proton is in marked contrast to the large positive coupling found for HCO and HPO_2^-. Had this proton been on the carbon–carbon axis, one would have expected an isotropic coupling constant in the region of -23 gauss, since the coupling would now arise through spin-polarisation. On bending this has to fall to zero before rapidly increasing (§ 2.5) and the relatively slight bending ($\phi \sim 140°$) suggested by Adrian and Cochran is in reasonable accord with a value of $+16$ gauss for the α-proton coupling.

It is interesting to compare these results with those[24] for the radical H_2CN, which is isoelectric with the anion $H_2C=C^-$. Here the unpaired electron is expected to be in the in-plane $2p(\pi)$-level of nitrogen which is, formally, a non-bonding level. However, the β-protons are ideally placed for hyperconjugation, and the short carbon nitrogen double bond forces the $p(\pi)$-orbital close to the CH σ-orbitals: this ensures considerable overlap. One therefore might expect a proton hyperfine coupling greater than the 20–30 gauss generally found for β-protons in neutral organic radicals[32]. In fact, the observed hyperfine coupling of 87.4 gauss was assigned to the protons, and the smaller coupling of about 30 gauss to the nitrogen. The latter result is not necessarily the isotropic nitrogen coupling constant for the outer lines were broad and poorly resolved.

The value of 87.4 gauss may be compared with the mean of 51 gauss

TABLE 7.5

ELECTRON SPIN RESONANCE DATA FOR THE RADICALS

$\dot{C}H_2\dot{N}$ AND $H_2C=\dot{C}H$

Radical	Medium	Hyperfine coupling constants (gauss)			Reference
		$A(H_\alpha)$	$A(H_{\beta 1})$	$A(H_{\beta 2})$	
$CH_2=\dot{C}H$	Liquid–ethane	13.4	51	51	31
	Solid rare-gas	16	68	34	29
$\dot{C}H_2\dot{N}$		–	87.4	87.4	29

found for the β-protons of $H_2C = CH$: the difference may in part be due to the greater tendency for nitrogen to attract the C–H σ-bonding electrons. The change to 68 and 34 gauss on bending has been considered in detail by Adrian and Cochran[30]. Qualitatively it can be understood in terms of a movement of the axis of the hybridised orbital in such a way that the electron approaches the *trans* proton but avoids the *cis* (Fig. 7.6.).

In their studies of acetylene in rare-gas matrices, Adrian *et al.* found that, in the absence of a source of hydrogen atoms, ultraviolet photolysis gave a simple spectrum consisting of two very narrow lines separated by 16.1 gauss[30]. This they assigned to the ethynyl radical, $HC \equiv C$, which is expected to have the unpaired electron in the original σ-orbital. The remaining proton is so far away that anisotropic coupling to it should be quite small, and the isotropic coupling must be an indirect process involving spin-polarisation of the bonding electrons. Again, ^{13}C hyperfine information would be of considerable interest. It was suggested that direct polarisation should be very small[30] and hence that the proton splitting is the result of indirect interactions. We stress, however, that the conjugate base C_2^- (isoelectronic with the cyanide radical) should have an even distribution of spin on both carbons, and a minor residual delocalisation of this sort in $HC \equiv C\cdot$ might well account for the splitting observed.

A group of radicals which have received considerable attention and which belong to this class are the *iminoxy radicals*, often written as $R_2C = NO$. Although these can be formed readily in fluid solution in both flow and even static systems[33], the most thoroughly studied radical in this class is that derived from dimethyl glyoxime by γ-irradiation[34, 35]. Miyagawa and Gordy[34] used a single crystal in their study, and derived the g-tensor and ^{14}N hyperfine coupling tensor given in Table 7.6. These workers assumed that the radical detected was formed by loss of an electron to give a positive ion, but a consideration of the derived parameters for nitrogen suggests that the formulation

$$\begin{array}{c} HON \diagdown \qquad \diagup Me \\ C - C \\ Me \diagup \qquad \diagdown N\dot{O} \end{array}$$

is more satisfactory[35]. The p/s ratio for this radical is 6.6, whereas that for NO_2 is 4.5. Thus it seems that the $C\hat{N}O$ bond angle has opened somewhat: the angle corresponding to this ratio being $140°$. Since, in a sense, this radical lies between NO_2 and $H_2C = CH$ it is reasonable to deduce that the $C\hat{C}H$

TABLE 7.6

ELECTRON SPIN RESONANCE DATA AND MOLECULAR PARAMETERS
FOR γ-IRRADIATED DIMETHYLGLYOXIME[28]

g-Tensor				^{14}N Hyperfine tensor (gauss)			
g_{xx}	g_{yy}	g_{zz}	g_{av}	B_{xx}	B_{yy}	B_{zz}	A_{iso}
2.0095	2.0063	2.0026	2.0061	-6.67	-6.67	13.33	31.67

$c_s{}^2(N) = 0.058$ $c_{p_z}{}^2(N) = 0.39$ $\lambda^2 = 6.6$ $\overset{\frown}{CNO} = 140°$

angle in the vinyl radical is 140°. In view of the large β-proton coupling, it is rather surprising that there was no detectable coupling to the protons of the methyl group.

It is noteworthy that Δg_{yy} for this radical is positive, whereas that for NO_2 was strongly negative. Also the ^{14}N isotropic hyperfine coupling constant of 31.67 gauss is very close to those observed for a wide range of organic radicals identified by several workers[32, 36] as iminoxy radicals, $R_2C=NO$. For example, Gilbert et al. oxidised a range of oximes, such as bibenzyl ketoxime, benzophenone oxime and fluorenone oxime with lead tetra-acetate in methylene chloride at 0 °C and obtained radicals of fair stability, with ^{14}N hyperfine splittings of 29.3, 30.6, and 30.8 gauss respectively[33] (Table 7.7).

Two interesting results were derived from the splittings from neighbouring protons. Thomas[37] suggested that a very large isotropic coupling to a single proton stemmed from radicals in which the latter was cis to the unpaired electron in RHC=NO radicals. This result seems to be at variance with

TABLE 7.7

ELECTRON SPIN RESONANCE DATA FOR OXIME RADICALS[33]

Oxime	Hyperfine splitting (gauss)	
	A	A
Dibenzyl ketoxime	29.3	1.25
Benzophenone oxime	30.6	1.25
Fluorenone oxime	30.8	2.7
α- and β- Benzil monoxime (1)	32.4	1.25
(2)	29.4	—
Camphor oxime	29.8	2.5
1-Methylnorcamphor oxime	30.6	2.5

Adrian and Cochran's suggestion, based on theory, that *trans*-protons should couple more strongly[30], and this seems to be reason to suspect the assignment[35]. The magnitude of the interaction is, of course, reduced, because the unpaired electron is considerably delocalised on to oxygen (probably to the extent of about 50%).

The second, more interesting observation is that there is a large coupling specifically to ortho-protons in aryl oximes of the type studied by Norman *et al.*[33]. For example, there is a splitting of 2.7 gauss from *one* ortho-proton in the radical derived from fluorenone oxime which is possibly associated with the incipient formation of a six-membered ring as indicated in the inset formula.

(b) Nineteen electron radicals

Here we discuss evidence pertaining to the identity of radicals AB_2 having nineteen electrons, and hence an expected configuration $\ldots (3a_1)^2 (2b_1)^1$, $^2B_1$. The identification of NO_2^{2-} and SeO_2^- rests upon both theory and comparison with results for the firmly established radical ClO_2 and the fairly well established species O_3^- and SO_2^-. Finally, as in § 7.2a, we briefly discuss results for related "π-radicals", BAX. In order to set the stage we start with chlorine dioxide.

(i) Chlorine dioxide, ClO_2

The electron spin resonance spectrum of chlorine dioxide in fluid solution was reported many years ago by Bennett and Ingram[38]. The spectrum from a dilute fluid solution in ethyl alcohol consisted of a single very broad line at room temperature, which separated into four components on cooling[38]. Spectra of solutions in sulphuric acid were better resolved, even at room temperature, but all attempts to obtain further resolution by modifying the environment have failed.

In marked contrast, the spectrum in rigid sulphuric acid at 77 °K[39] although complex, is far better resolved (Fig. 7.8) and features due to both

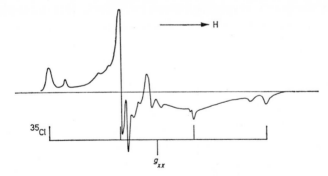

Fig. 7.8. Electron spin resonance spectrum of ClO_2 in sulphuric acid at 77 °K (diagrammatic).

^{35}Cl and ^{37}Cl are separated. One principal value of the g- and hyperfine tensors can be obtained readily from this spectrum (Table 7.8) which, together with the isotropic data derived from fluid solutions, is enough to identify a radical formed in γ-irradiated potassium perchlorate[40] as the dioxide with little or no ambiguity. Since the data from irradiated potassium perchlorate are the most complete, they have been used[39] for a discussion of structure. Our derived parameters differ from those of Cole[40], and the treatment used is in marked contrast with that given earlier by Bennett and Ingram[38] who concluded that the unpaired electron was largely in a chlorine $3d$-level.

In treating the data summarised in Table 7.8 our first step, just as for NO_2 and CO_2^-, was to resolve the anisotropic hyperfine tensor into two axially symmetric components, this gave

$$(57.6, -30.8, -26.8) = (58.92, -29.46, -29.46) + (-1.33, -1.33, 2.67)$$
$$\text{gauss} \quad (7.9)$$

the large component being identified with A_{xx} and used to derive a value for $c_{p_x}^2(Cl)$ of 0.69. This result is in very good accord with expectation[39] and gives, by difference, a value of c_0^2 for the density on oxygen of 0.31. Here we have ignored the isotropic hyperfine coupling to chlorine because this gives the negligible value of 0.01 for $c_s^2(Cl)$. Also the second component of the separated anisotropic tensor gives 0.03 for $c_{p_z}^2(Cl)$. Both these results can be accommodated by postulating that the unpaired electron in the p-orbital on chlorine polarises the electrons in the a_1-molecular orbital, thus conferring slight s- and p-character on the hyperfine tensor. For the known bond angle of 118.5° a value of 0.03 for $c_{p_z}^2$ would require a value for c_s^2 of about

TABLE 7.8

ELECTRON SPIN RESONANCE AND STRUCTURAL DATA FOR CHLORINE DIOXIDE

Medium	Temp. (°K)	g-Tensor				Hyperfine tensor (gauss)				Reference
		g_{xx}	g_{yy}	g_{zz}	g_{av}	B_{xx}	B_{yy}	B_{zz}	A_{iso}	
$KClO_4$	300	2.0036	2.0183	2.0088	2.0102	57.6	−30.8	−26.8	15.4	40, 39
H_2SO_4	300				2.0093				16.5	39
H_2SO_4	77	2.0015								39
$KClO_4$	300	2.0015								39

$c_s^2 = 0.01$
$c_{p_z}^2 = 0.03$ } (in $KClO_4$)
$c_{p_x}^2 = 0.69$

0.017. The discrepancy is small, and the effect of unequal spin-polarisabilities of the p- and s-orbitals has been neglected, but we feel that this is probably the main source of isotropic coupling, and that other interactions by way of the chlorine oxygen σ-bonds are relatively small.

The g-tensor for chlorine dioxide is also as expected: g_{xx} is close to the free-spin value, as is generally found for an electron in a b_1-orbital composed of p_x-atomic orbitals. This conclusion can be compared with that drawn for the SeO_2^- radical (§ 7.2b (v)) where a negative Δg_{xx} is associated with a small admixture of the selenium d_{xz}-level into the b_1-orbital[41]. This comparison strengthens our tentative conclusion that for chlorine dioxide participation of the $3d(\text{Cl})$-orbital is small. Also, in agreement with the theory outlined in § 7.1d(ii), Δg_{yy} has a relatively large positive value and g_{zz} lies between g_{yy} and g_{xx}.

Apart from this structural information the spectrum of ClO_2 has features which are potentially important probes of environmental effects: these are the peculiar line-width dependence upon solvent viscosity and the markedly greater line-widths compared to those of the isoelectronic radical SO_2^- [42]. In aqueous solution the ClO_2 lines are about a magnitude wider than those of SO_2^- yet the anisotropies of the interaction tensors are not expected to differ greatly. Furthermore, a solution of ClO_2 in carbon tetrachloride gave a spectrum consisting of a very broad absorption with only a hint of an inflection. Addition of methanol to this latter solution, or cooling, increased the resolution of the electron spin resonance spectrum yet had the opposite effect upon the vibrational structure of the optical band at 33,000 cm^{-1}. This information implies that the line-width increases with decreasing inter-action with the solvent, a tendency opposite to that normally observed.

Three mechanisms could account for these observations. The first is exchange between the ClO_2 molecules: the molecules diffuse more rapidly in low viscosity solvents than in those with higher viscosity, consequently radical encounters become more frequent and exchange broadening more efficient. This mechanism is concentration dependent but no narrowing was observed at the limits of resolution.

The second possible mechanism could be that if the transverse relaxation time (T_2) of the nucleus were sufficiently short it would dominate the line-width, and in a particular range of solvent viscosity would show the observed dependence. It is still difficult to account for the difference between ClO_2 and SO_2^- on this model.

The third mechanism which could account for all the observations is that of relaxation caused by spin-rotation coupling. As a molecule rotates the electrons do not follow the motion rigidly but tend to slip past the nuclei. Such an imbalance of rotating charges produces a magnetic field which is experienced by the unpaired electron. In a gas, molecular collisions modulate both the orientation and the magnitude of the rotational angular momentum, and the resulting modulation of the rotational magnetic moment is felt by the electron which is then relaxed. In weakly interacting solvents incipient rotational motion is possible and it has been shown by Atkins and Kivelson [43] that the observed viscosity behaviour is expected. The theory was applied to the case of vanadyl acetoacetate where a similar phenomenon was observed in organic solvents [44, 45].

The difference between SO_2^- and ClO_2 is immediately explicable: the charge on SO_2^- causes such a strong quenching of molecular rotation that no relaxation can be induced [42].

(ii) The radical ion SO_2^-

It is now well established that the radical SO_2^- which is isoelectronic with chlorine dioxide, is formed when dithionite salts are dissolved in water [42, 46, 47]. That the dithionite ion might readily dissociate was postulated by Dunitz [48] whose X-ray diffraction studies of the ion had revealed an unusually long sulphur–sulphur bond. Hodgson et al. [46] detected a free

Fig. 7.9. Solution spectrum of SO_2^-.

radical in moist dithionite, and recently the high sensitivity of modern spectrometers has been exploited to detect $^{33}SO_2^-$ radicals in natural abundance[42] (Fig. 7.9.). Intensity measurements indicate that each radical contains only one sulphur atom, and the small isotropic hyperfine coupling constant, corresponding to a value for $c_s^2(S)$ of about 0.01 shows that it is a π-radical. Unfortunately the anisotropic part of the hyperfine coupling to ^{33}S could not be measured.

Early solid state spectra obtained from γ-irradiated sodium dithionite[47] consisted of a single structureless line with a g-value of 2.0057 which is close to g_{av} derived from radicals in fluid solution. A similar result was obtained from frozen aqueous solutions[42]. γ-Irradiation of potassium metabisulphite crystals, which contain the ion $^-O_2S-SO_3^-$ gave a single radical having a g-tensor whose principal values, given in Table 7.9, are in good accord with expectation for SO_2^- and are close to those found for chlorine dioxide.

(iii) The ozonide ion, O_3^-

When ozone reacts with powdered alkali-metal hydroxides, orange solids are formed which are quite stable and which readily dissolve in liquid ammonia. These ozonides $(M^+O_3^-)$ are characterized by an intense absorption band with a maximum at about 21,700 cm^{-1} and a single electron spin resonance absorption at $g_{av} \sim 2.012$[49].

The electron spin resonance absorption from the solid showed no marked features which could be assigned to the expected anisotropic g-tensor, but radicals formed in γ-irradiated potassium chlorate and perchlorate and identified as ozonide ions by their electronic absorption spectra[39] had a markedly asymmetric electron spin resonance absorption spectrum at low temperatures. From these spectra were obtained the principal values of the

TABLE 7.9

ELECTRON SPIN RESONANCE AND STRUCTURAL DATA
FOR THE RADICAL ION SO_2^-

Medium	g-Tensor				Hyperfine tensor (gauss)	Reference
	g_{xx}	g_{yy}	g_{zz}	g_{av}	A_{iso}	
$K_2S_2O_5$	2.0018	2.0103	2.0055	2.0059	—	42
$K_2S_2O_4$ aq.				2.0057	14.2	42

$c_s^2 = 0.02$

TABLE 7.10

ELECTRON SPIN RESONANCE DATA FOR THE OZONIDE ION, O_3^-

Medium	g-Tensor				Reference
	g_{xx}	g_{yy}	g_{zz}	g_{av}	
$KClO_3$	2.0025	2.0174	2.0013	2.0104	39

g-tensor listed in Table 7.10. The assignment was arrived at by comparison with the g-tensor for chlorine dioxide, and is in accord with theory.

(iv) The radical ion NO_2^{2-}

A salt having the empirical formula Na_2NO_2 is easily prepared by the addition of sodium nitrite to sodium in liquid ammonia, from which it is precipitated as a bright yellow solid. Magnetic susceptibility results have been interpreted in terms of a monomer–dimer equilibrium

$$2 NO_2^{2-} \rightleftharpoons N_2O_4^{4-} \tag{7.10}$$

the dimer being strongly favoured. Unfortunately the electron spin resonance spectrum of this solid comprised a relatively intense but uninformative single line at $g = 2.003 \pm 0.002$ [47].

Far more useful data have been derived from a radical formed by irradiation of nitrite ions in potassium chloride crystals [50-52] and also by irradiation of potassium nitrate [52,53] (Table 7.11). The average g-value of about 2.007 is not too far removed from that found from $Na_4N_2O_4$ and the total spread of g-values and hyperfine interactions could well be accommodated by the broad singlet of the early studies [47].

It must be stressed that our assignment for NO_2^{2-} is not the same as that of the original workers. Thus Cunningham [53] suggested that the species was nitric oxide, as did Jaccard [50] whilst Schoemaker and Boesman [51] suggested the dioxide as the most probable species.

(a) Since NO_2^{2-} is expected to have the unpaired electron in the $b_1(\pi^*)$ orbital the isotropic coupling to ^{14}N should be small. The value of about 14 gauss is quite usual for such a system, and is far too small for NO_2.

(b) The only hyperfine interaction detected is to one ^{14}N nucleus.

(c) The maximum hyperfine coupling is the parallel value, perpendicular to the plane of the nitrate ions in potassium nitrate. This is expected if the NO_2^{2-} radicals remain in this plane.

TABLE 7.11

ELECTRON SPIN RESONANCE AND STRUCTURAL DATA FOR THE RADICAL ION NO_2^{2-}

Medium	g-Tensor				Hyperfine tensor (gauss)				Reference
	g_{xx}	g_{yy}	g_{zz}	g_{av}	B_{xx}	B_{yy}	B_{zz}	A_{iso}	
KCl[a]	2.0038	2.0099	2.0070	2.0069	16.6	−9.3	−7.3	14.3	50, 52
KCl[b]				2.0069				13.7	51, 52
KNO_3	2.004	2.010	2.008	2.007	19.3	−9.5	−9.5	13.0	53, 52

[a] Similar values found in KBr and KI.
[b] Similar values found in KBr and NaCl.

$c_s^2 = 0.026$
$c_{p_z}^2 = 0.04$
$c_{p_z}^2 = 0.50$

(d) The principal values for the g-tensor are then in good agreement with expectation for a nineteen electron radical.

(e) The p/s ratio of ~ 24 confirms that the electron is a purely π-level, and the distribution of the unpaired electron on to oxygen to the extent of about 40% seems quite reasonable for NO_2^{2-}.

The postulate[50, 51] that the radical under consideration is nitric oxide cannot be ruled out since, so far as we are aware, there are no well-established results for this oxide except for the gas phase. It would be necessary to invoke a major crystal field splitting of the π-levels in order to explain the results obtained, and whilst this is quite possible, it is surprising to us that the g-tensor should then hardly vary as the host crystal is changed. Furthermore, the g-tensor is not at all as expected: for the crystal field parallel to the N–O axis one would certainly expect to observe a marked negative shift in g even in the presence of a crystal field.

(v) The radical ion, SeO_2^-

In the expectation that if formed, the radical SeO_2^- would be recognised both by the electron spin resonance spectra of radicals containing ^{77}Se and by comparison with the results for isostructural radicals such as ClO_2, a variety of selenates and selenites were γ-irradiated and their spectra studied[41]. Powder spectra were enough to show fairly convincingly, that SeO_2^- was indeed formed in several instances[41, 54]. The low value for g_{xx} is surprising because for other radicals in this class values close to 2.0023 have been found, as expected. One possible explanation for the negative shift is that selenium d-orbitals make a slight contribution to the total wave-function. The pertinent orbital would be d_{xz}. This together with the large value of the spin–orbit coupling constant (1688 cm^{-1}) could give rise to a significant negative shift[41] (Table 7.12).

(vi) The radical NF_2

This radical is of particular interest since it exists in equilibrium with its dimer N_2F_4 at normal temperatures. This equilibrium has been extensively studied by Colburn and co-workers[13] who found that the radical contributed only about 0.05% to the mixture at room temperature and pressure, but as much as 90% at 150 °C and 1 mm pressure.

A broad structureless electron spin resonance absorption was obtained from gas-phase studies[55] which, although structurally uninformative, did provide a useful method for counting unpaired electrons. The extreme broad-

TABLE 7.12

ELECTRON SPIN RESONANCE AND STRUCTURAL DATA FOR THE RADICAL ION SeO_2^-

Medium	Temp. (°K)		g-Tensor				Hyperfine tensor (gauss)*				Reference
	a	b	g_{xx}	g_{yy}	g_{zz}	g_{av}	B_{xx}	B_{yy}	B_{zz}	A_{iso}	
Na_2SeO_4	77	77	1.9975	2.0317	2.0066	2.0119					41
	77	300	1.9973	2.0306	2.0068	2.0116					
	300	300	1.9971	2.0301	2.0065	2.0112					
K_2SeO_3 (c)	300	300	1.9986	2.03	2.0090	2.0127	258	−113	−145	33	41
	77	77	1.9976	2.0309	2.0096	2.0131					
	77	300	1.9987	2.0304	2.0102	2.0131					
	300	300	1.9985	2.0297	2.0097	2.0126					
Na_2SeO_3 (c)	300	300	1.9986	2.03	2.0118	2.0108	224	−108	−117	26	41
	77	77	1.9970	2.0305	2.0050	2.0114					
	77	300	1.9974	2.0310	2.0059						
$NaHSeO_3$	77	300	1.9967	2.0268	2.0062	2.0132	219	−115	−114	22	54

Na_2SeO_4 : $c_s^2 = 0.005$ $c_{p_z}^2 = 0.8$ $c_o^2 = 0.2$
K_2SeO_3 : $c_s^2 = 0.007$ $c_{p_z}^2 = 0.9$ $c_o^2 = 0.1$
$NaHSeO_3$: $c_s^2 = 0.004$ $c_{p_z}^2 = 0.86$ $c_o^2 = 0.14$

a Irradiation temperature.
b Measurement temperature.
c g-Tensor measured from hyperfine components.
* Taking the y and z parameters to be −ve.

ness of the line, which had a g-value of 2.010, may be due in part to coupling with rotational motion and partly to the rapid dimerisation.

Whatever the causes of broadening, they are quite suppressed for radicals in certain molecular sieves, since these give rise to well resolved spectra, typical of radicals in solution[13]. Indeed, the situation seems to be quite similar to that discussed in § 7.2a(i) for nitrogen dioxide. The average g-value of 2.009 is in good agreement with that for radicals in the gas phase, and the isotropic hyperfine coupling constants for 16 gauss and 56 gauss for ^{14}N and ^{19}F respectively are reasonable for a radical with the unpaired electron in a $b_1(\pi^*)$-orbital. Even so this is all that these numbers tell us: as yet, attempts to obtain anisotropic values have been unsuccessful. Adrian et al.[31] have reported some preliminary results for NF_2 in an argon matrix, but they were unable to offer any firm identification. At 4.2 °K a strong central line showed clear signs of subsidiary structure, which might have been due to an asymmetric g-tensor. On warming to 22 °K, the centre line became sharper, and two broad wing lines at about 17 gauss from the centre, were also detected. The authors suggested that this triplet was due to ^{14}N in radicals having fluorine nuclei antiparallel. This is in good agreement with the value derived from molecular sieve experiments.

Recently, Farmer et al. have also reported results for NF_2 in both argon and krypton at 4.2 °K[56]. In addition to the central triplet they were able to detect broad triplets to high and low fields which gave an isotropic coupling to ^{19}F of 60 ± 2 gauss. This is close to the 56 gauss found for the freely rotating radical. The g-tensor derived from the spectra at 4.2 °K (Table 7.13) gives an average value of 2.0046, which is in very poor agreement with that found for radicals in the gas phase and on sieves (2.010 and 2.009 respectively). Indeed even their highest g-value of 2.0066 is apparently too low, Reasons for this difference are not obvious at present. Unfortunately. neither of these studies give the desired anisotropic hyperfine parameters

TABLE 7.13

ELECTRON SPIN RESONANCE AND STRUCTURAL DATA
FOR THE RADICAL NF_2

Medium	g-Tensor			Hyperfine tensor (gauss)		Reference
	$g_{\parallel}$	$g_{\perp}$	g_{av}	$A_{iso}^{(F)}$	$A_{iso}^{(N)}$	
Ar, Kr	2.0022	2.0059	2.0047	60	17	56
Sieve			2.009	56	16	13

which could be so helpful in mapping the electron distribution in the b_1-orbital.

(vii) Some related radicals

As in § 7.2a we now turn to radicals which, although no longer nineteen electron triatomic radicals, can nevertheless be thought of as being iso-structural with them in certain respects. We start by considering the amino radical, NH_2 and the mono- and di-sulphonates $NHSO_3^-$ and $N(SO_3)_2^{2-}$. Finally, and less appropriately, we turn to the elusive hydroperoxide radical, HO_2.

The *amino radical* was detected in rare-gas matrices some years ago[57], but although the expected six lines for a tumbling radical were obtained, the pattern of intensities was such that no firm assignment could be made. The spectra of ND_2 and $^{15}NH_2$ were used to differentiate between the two alternatives, thus enabling the parameters listed in Table 7.14 to be derived.

The intensities of the hyperfine lines for NH_2 apparently were anomalous: the nitrogen triplet seemed to have a central line which was too intense and a triplet due to the protons which was too weak. An explanation in terms of a mechanism, which involves the influence of the molecular symmetries on the population of rotational states at low temperatures has been proposed[58]. If the amino radical were effectively stationary then, apart from any anisotropy of the g-value, one would expect a major change in the outer $(m_I = \pm 1)$ lines of the nitrogen triplets but no change in the central line. Similarly, the outer lines of the proton triplets ought to show marked aniso-tropic broadening. The experimental spectrum is that of a radical under-going restricted rotational motion. Hence the outer nitrogen lines are broad-ened, thus accounting for the anomalous intensities for these lines. A similar argument would not explain the reverse effect for the proton lines.

The *radical* $N(SO_3)_2^{2-}$ is interesting inasmuch as that the spin-density on nitrogen, as deduced from the anisotropic hyperfine coupling to ^{14}N, is considerably greater than that for the radical NO_2^{2-} (Table 7.15). In order

TABLE 7.14

ELECTRON SPIN RESONANCE AND STRUCTURAL DATA
FOR THE AMINO RADICAL, NH_2 IN ARGON[57]

$g_{av} = 2.0048$	$A_{iso}^{(N)} = 10.3$ gauss
	$A_{iso}^{(H)} = 23.9$ gauss

TABLE 7.15

ELECTRON SPIN RESONANCE AND STRUCTURAL DATA FOR THE RADICAL IONS $NHSO_3^-$ AND $N(SO_3)_2^{2-}$

Radical	g-Tensor				Hyperfine tensor (gauss)				Reference
	g_{xx}	g_{yy}	g_{zz}	g_{av}	B_{xx}	B_{yy}	B_{zz}	A_{iso}	
$NHSO_3^-$	2.0078	2.0038	2.0037	2.0051	21.3	-9.8	-11.5	13.5	61
$N(SO_3)_2^{2-}$	2.0042	2.0082	2.0025	2.0051	25	-12.5	-12.5	13.2	60

$NHSO_3^-$: $c_s^2 = 0.025$ $c_{p_z}^2 = 0.62$ $c_H^2 = 0.022$
$N(SO_3)_2^{2-}$: $c_s^2 = 0.024$ $c_{p_z}^2 = 0.73$

that the unpaired electron be delocalised on to the SO_3^- groups a molecular orbital must be devised which involves either antibonding levels of the SO_3^- framework, or the sulphur $3d$-levels. The results[59, 60] suggest that neither is of great significance, but it is a pity that interaction with ^{33}S is so difficult to detect for this could give more direct information.

Similar information has been obtained for the radical $HNSO_3^-$ which was obtained by Rowlands[61] by γ-irradiation of single crystals of potassium sulphamate. The results, given in Table 7.15 were obtained at 77 °K. At room temperature the ^{14}N hyperfine tensor was somewhat smaller, and this was interpreted in terms of a twisting motion of the NH_2 group relative to the SO_3^- framework. A similar, but more marked effect had been noted previously[62] for the radical H_2NSO_3 and was similarly interpreted. Rowlands stressed that care must be taken in assigning spin-densities on the basis of comparison with atomic parameters when such motion is possible.

The isotropic proton hyperfine coupling of -23 gauss is identical with that found for α-proton coupling in the methyl radical, but, as expected, the anisotropic tensor was found to be considerably larger than that for the CH_3 group. This was discussed in terms of the combined effects of NH bond length variation and the effective electronegativity of nitrogen in this radical[62]. The results may be compared with the correlations of Fig. 4A.3 in Appendix 4. It is particularly significant that the replacement of an SO_3^- group by a proton on going from $N(SO_3)_2^{2-}$ to $HNSO_3^-$ makes very little difference to the spin-density on nitrogen. This is probably close to unity, since the parameters for ^{14}N are generally found to give low results.

The *hydroperoxyl radical*, HO_2, although expected to be considerably more stable than the hydroxyl radical, has nevertheless proved to be almost as difficult to detect unambiguously. A radical thought to be HO_2 was detected in an early experiment by Livingston, Ghormley and Zeldes[63] who used a cold finger to freeze out the products of an electric discharge through the vapour of water or hydrogen peroxide. A yellow deposit was obtained the electron spin resonance of which consisted of a broad asymmetric single line having the approximate* g-values given in Table 7.16. No proton hyperfine splitting was detected in this or in a subsequent study in which HO_2 was postulated as a secondary product of the photolysis of solution of hydrogen peroxide in various organic solvents at 77 °K[64]. Initially, hydroxyl radicals

---

* These and other g-values estimated from powder spectra in the early days of electron spin resonance are subject to slight correction since they were not always taken from the best features of the spectrum.

TABLE 7.16

ELECTRON SPIN RESONANCE DATA FOR THE
HYDROPEROXYL RADICAL, HO_2

Medium	g-Tensor				Reference
	g_{xx}	g_{yy}	g_{zz}	g_{av}	
H_2O_2 glass	2.0023	2.0065	2.0350	2.015	65
H_2O or H_2O_2	2.0085	2.0085	2.027	2.015	63

attacked the solvent to give organic radicals which remained trapped and were readily detected by electron spin resonance. In the presence of relatively high concentrations of hydrogen peroxide and as the temperature was gradually raised, these spectra gave way to a broad asymmetric triplet quite comparable with that of Livingston *et al.* (Table 7.16).

It was argued that HO_2 radicals would be expected to show such a spectrum, since the electron is expected to be in the π_x^*-level (x being taken as perpendicular to the radical plane and z as the O–O direction) which will be split from the π_y-level by the proton. This is of the same form as that for the superoxide ion, O_2^-, (§ 6.2c (i)) but Δg should be much smaller because of the greater effect of the proton. Thus one would predict qualitatively

$$g_{zz} \gg g_{xx} \sim g_{yy} \sim 2.0023 \qquad (7.11)$$

Furthermore, the unpaired electron will be largely located on the unprotonated oxygen and hence the proton hyperfine coupling should be negative, and very much smaller than the coupling found in, for example, the methyl radical (-23 gauss). This is because hyperconjugative interaction will be zero, so that only spin on the hydroxyl oxygen will contribute.

Recent work by Smith and Wyard[65] has led to resolution, and hence to more accurate g-tensor determination, and to the detection of hyperfine splittings from the proton (Table 7.16). This was achieved by careful annealing of glassy samples at 140 °K.

We tentatively identify 2.0023 as g_{xx}, 2.0065 as g_{yy} and 2.0350 as g_{zz}. The hyperfine data are more difficult to analyse as one does not necessarily expect the g- and hyperfine tensors to refer to the same axes. With the results at present available one can tentatively derive an isotropic coupling of about 13 gauss. This seems very large if the considerations given above are correct, since for a Q value of -23 gauss, this corresponds to a spin-density of about 0.57. This result should be contrasted with that for organic peroxy radicals discussed below. It seems likely that the isotropic term has been considerably over-estimated in this approximation.

Livingston and co-workers[66] using single crystals of hydrogen peroxide have obtained results which are enough to daunt any worker in the field, and might well be taken as casting grave doubt on all of these conclusions. Their results have not yet been reported in detail, but have been fairly complete for many years. In all probability both hydroxyl and hydroperoxyl radicals are formed, and pair-wise trapping, to give an incipiently triplet state species, similar to that found in irradiated persulphates[67] probably plays a major role[66]. A detailed report of their results is eagerly awaited.

It should be mentioned that a subsidiary radical formed in irradiated water–hydrogen peroxide glasses was tentatively identified by Smith and Wyard[65] as HO_3. They report that $g_\perp = 2.0045$ and $g_\parallel = 2.0608$ and that there is the possibility of some poorly resolved hyperfine splitting from the proton. Although this identification is reasonable chemically, it seems surprising that the g-value variation for HO_3 should be far greater than that for its conjugate base, the ozonide ion[39].

It is interesting to consider results for ROO radicals in the context of the radical HO_2. Many radicals of this structure have been postulated in order to explain the appearance of a single asymmetric electron spin resonance band which results when oxygen diffuses into systems containing trapped organic radicals, R. Similarly, in solution, radicals having g-values close to 2.013 are often detected and this can be taken as characteristic of ROO radicals.

Results obtained from the ultraviolet photolysis of hydroperoxides in fluid solution[68] thought to be due to RO radicals formed according to the equation

$$ROOH + h\nu \rightarrow RO\cdot + OH \qquad (7.12)$$

have been reconsidered in terms of the peroxy radicals[32] formed by a secondary reaction

$$RO\cdot + ROOH \rightarrow ROH + ROO\cdot \qquad (7.13)$$

The main reason for this reassignment was that hyperfine coupling to protons in R_2CHO radicals is expected to be of the order of that found in alkyl radicals having β-protons (about 25 gauss). In fact the observed coupling was only about three gauss, which would be reasonable if the radicals were R_2CHOO rather than R_2CHO. This conclusion has recently been strongly reinforced by the results of Ingold and Morton[69]

(c) Twenty-one electron radicals

We know of only one radical in this class, namely F_3^{2-}. This is hardly surprising as such a radical is just one electron short of consisting of three rare-gas atoms; indeed, the surprise is that there is a sufficient gain in energy for the species to have a long life-time.

The *radical* F_3^{2-} was detected by Känzig *et al.*[70] in γ-irradiated lithium fluoride, and identified by its electron spin resonance spectrum. This identification rested primarily on the hyperfine structure, which demonstrated the presence of three fluorine nuclei, two of which were equivalent. The results showed that there was a slight deviation from linearity, the bond angle being about 163°.

Although one would expect such a radical to have its unpaired electron in a σ^*-orbital distributed over all three fluorine atoms, the authors concluded that the levels were inverted by a strong crystal field from a triple vacancy having an effectively negative charge. The resulting postulated structure placed the unpaired electron in the in-plane a_1-orbital. In brief, the evidence cited for this unexpected structure was:

(a) symmetry requires that the central fluorine atom can make no direct $2s$-contribution to the σ^*-orbital whereas a contribution is to be expected for the pseudo π^*-level,

(b) such direct hybridisation will, of course, result in a positive isotropic interaction, whereas core-polarisation would probably contribute a negative component,

(c) the magnitude of the isotropic coupling to the central fluorine atom (probably 534 gauss) was thought to be so large as to rule out a polarisation mechanism.

These conclusions have recently been reconsidered, and the results re-interpreted in terms of a σ^*-structure[71]. First, it is stressed that there is considerable uncertainty concerning the processing of the actual data. As indicated in Table 7.17, there are a variety of seemingly reasonable ways in which the data can be treated, but it will transpire that the most satisfactory treatment is that given as (i) in the Table. This gives 534 gauss for the isotropic hyperfine coupling to the central atom, which, although large numerically, nevertheless corresponds to only 3% $2s$-character. Then, using set (i), we find the $2p/2s$ ratio to be about 18, which is far too large to correspond to any appreciable hybridisation. There seems to be little basis in the suggestion[70] that polarisation will give a negative isotropic coupling. Indeed, the

TABLE 7.17

ELECTRON SPIN RESONANCE AND STRUCTURAL DATA
FOR THE RADICAL ION F_3^{2-} [70, 71]

		Hyperfine tensor (gauss)				Orbital populations			
		B_{xx}	B_{yy}	B_{zz}	A_{iso}	c_s^2	$c_{p_x}^2$	$c_{p_y}^2$	$c_{p_z}^2$
Inner F	(i)	-322	-266	588	534	0.031	0.035		0.57
	(ii)	-143	-623	767	355	0.021		0.30	0.86
	(iii)	-605	-125	729	393	0.023	0.22		0.82
	(iv)	-426	-482	908	214	0.012		0.035	0.86
Outer F	(i)	-58	-120	178	200	0.012		0.039	0.18
	(ii)	-5	-227	231	147	0.008		0.14	0.28
	(iii)	-247	-25	273	105	0.006	0.14		0.32
	(iv)	-194	-132	326	52	0.003	0.10		0.26

isotropic coupling for F_2^-, discussed in § 6.2d (ii) is almost certainly positive and is of a similar magnitude.

The main reason for preferring set (i) to the other sets given in Table 7.17 can be seen in the calculated spin populations recorded there. Set (i) gives a total of 1.0 for the spin-density, whilst the next best, set (ii) gives a total of 2.0. The remainder are even less satisfactory. Since a similar summation for F_2^- gave 1.02, there seems to be good reason for accepting this analysis, even though overlap effects would adjust the totals slightly.

In accord with our usual practice, the unsymmetrical anisotropic tensor values were split into two, each with axial symmetry. This gave, for the central fluorine atom, a small contribution from spin in the π_y^*-level, and for the outer fluorine atoms, a similar minor contribution from spin in the π_y^*-level [71]. Had the molecule been strictly linear then these minor contributions would necessarily have been equal for the x and y directions, the net result being a tensor which would reduce the magnitude of the p_z-tensor.

It is a pity that the g-tensor for this radical was not recorded, since it would probably have enabled a choice to be made between the x and y directions. Nevertheless, independently of this unknown we can deduce that the unpaired electron is located more on the central atom (56%) than on the outer atoms (22% each). This result is in accord with the general trends observed for other radicals.

References

1 A. D. WALSH, *J. Chem. Soc.*, 1953, 2266.
2 A. D. WALSH, *Discussions Faraday Soc.*, 1963, *35*, 218.
3 R. S. MULLIKEN, *Can. J. Chem.*, 1958, *36*, 10.
4 R. K. RITCHIE, A. D. WALSH AND P. A. WARSOP, *Inst. Petrol. Symp. Spectry.*, 1962, 289.
5 J. B. COON AND ORTIZ, *J. Mol. Spectry.*, 1957, *1*, 10.
6 SCHMIDTKE AND H. PREUSS, *Z. Naturforsch.*, 1961, *16a*, 790.
7 SCHMIDTKE, *Z. Naturforsch.*, 1962, *179*, 121.
8 C. A. COULSON AND A. H. NEILSON, *Discussions Faraday Soc.*, 1963, *35*, 71.
9 J. G. CASTLE AND R. BERINGER, *Phys. Rev.*, 1950, *80*, 114.
10 G. R. BIRD, J. C. BAIRD AND R. B. WILLIAMS, *J. Chem. Phys.*, 1958, *28*, 738.
11 P. W. ATKINS, N. KEEN AND M. C. R. SYMONS, *J. Chem. Soc.*, 1962, 2873.
12 G. B. COLBURN, R. ETTINGER AND F. A. JOHNSON, *Inorg. Chem.*, 1963, *2*, 1311.
13 R. ETTINGER AND C. B. COLBURN, *Inorg. Chem.*, 1963, *2*, 1311.
14 C. K. JEN, S. N. FONER, E. L. COCHRAN AND V. A. BOWERS, *Phys. Rev.*, 1958, *112*, 1169.
15 J. B. FARMER, C. A. HUTCHINSON AND C. A. McDOWELL, *5th Intern. Symp. on Free Radicals, Uppsala, 1961*.
16 H. ZELDES AND R. LIVINGSTON, *J. Chem. Phys.*, 1961, *35*, 563.
17 W. B. ARD, *J. Chem. Phys.*, 1955, *23*, 1967.
18 B. BLEANEY, W. HAYES AND P. M. LLEWELLYN, *Nature*, 1957, *179*, 140.
19 J. TATENO AND K. GESI, *J. Chem. Phys.*, 1964, *40*, 1317.
20 N. M. ATHERTON, R. N. DIXON AND G. H. KIRBY, *Trans. Faraday Soc.*, 1964, *60*, 1688.
21 D. W. OVENALL AND D. H. WHIFFEN, *Proc. Chem. Soc.*, 1960, 420.
22 J. A. BRIVATI, N. KEEN, M. C. R. SYMONS AND P. A. TREVALION, *Proc. Chem. Soc.*, 1961, 66.
23 D. W. OVENALL AND D. H. WHIFFEN, *Mol. Phys.*, 1961, *4*, 135.
24 S. A. MARSHALL, A. R. REINBERG, R. A. SERWAY AND J. A. HODGES, *Mol. Phys.*, 1964, *8*, 223.
25 G. HERZBERG AND D. A. RAMSEY, *Proc. Roy. Soc.*, 1955, *233A*, 34.
26 J. A. BRIVATI, N. KEEN AND M. C. R. SYMONS, *J. Chem. Soc.*, 1962, 237.
27 F. J. ADRIAN, E. L. COCHRAN AND V. A. BOWERS, *J. Chem. Phys.*, 1962, *36*, 1661.
28 I. MIYAGAWA, Y. KURITA AND W. GORDY, *J. Chem. Phys.*, 1960, *33*, 1599.
29 E. L. COCHRAN, F. J. ADRIAN AND V. A. BOWERS, *J. Chem. Phys.*, 1962, *36*, 1938.
30 F. J. ADRIAN AND E. L. COCHRAN, *6th Intern. Symp. on Free Radicals, Cambridge, 1963*.
31 F. J. ADRIAN, E. L. COCHRAN AND V. A. BOWERS, *Advan. Chem.*, 1962, *36*, 50.
32 M. C. R. SYMONS, *Advan. Phys. Org. Chem.*, 1963, *1*, 284.
33 B. C. GILBERT, R. O. C. NORMAN AND D. C. PRICE, *Proc. Chem. Soc.*, 1964, 234.
34 I. MIYAGAWA AND W. GORDY, *J. Chem. Phys.*, 1959, *30*, 1590.
35 M. C. R. SYMONS, *J. Chem. Soc.*, 1963, 1189; 1965, 2276.
36 J. C. BAIRD AND J. R. THOMAS, *J. Chem. Phys.*, 1961, *35*, 1507.
37 J. R. THOMAS, *J. Am. Chem. Soc.*, 1964, *86*, 1446.
38 J. E. BENNETT AND D. J. E. INGRAM, *Proc. Phys. Soc.*, 1956, *1*, 109.
39 P. W. ATKINS, J. A. BRIVATI, N. KEEN, M. C. R. SYMONS AND P. A. TREVALION, *J. Chem. Soc.*, 1962, 4785.
40 T. COLE, *Proc. Natl. Acad. Sci. U.S.*, 1960, *46*, 506.

41 P. W. Atkins, M. C. R. Symons and H. W. Wardale, *J. Chem. Soc.*, 1964, 5215.
42 P. W. Atkins, A. Horsfield and M. C. R. Symons, *J. Chem. Soc.*, 1964, 5220.
43 P. W. Atkins and D. Kivelson, *J. Chem. Phys.*, 1966, *44*, 169.
44 D. Kivelson and R. Wilson, *J. Chem. Phys.*, 1966, *44*, 163.
45 P. W. Atkins and D. Kivelson, *J. Chem. Phys.*, in press.
46 W. G. Hodgson, A. Neaves and C. A. Parker, *Nature*, 1956, *178*, 489.
47 H. C. Clark, A. Horsfield and M. C. R. Symons, *J. Chem. Soc.*, 1961, 7.
48 J. D. Dunitz, *Acta Cryst.*, 1956, *9*, 579.
49 J. E. Bennett, D. J. E. Ingram, M. C. R. Symons, P. George and J. S. Griffith, *Phil. Mag.*, 1955, *46*, 443.
50 C. Jaccard, *Phys. Rev.*, 1961, *124*, 60.
51 D. Schoemaker and E. Boesman, *Compt. Rend.*, 1961, *252*, 2099.
52 P. W. Atkins and M. C. R. Symons, *J. Chem. Soc.*, 1962, 4794.
53 J. Cunningham, *5th Intern. Symp. on Free Radicals, Uppsala, 1961.*
54 R. J. Cook, J. R. Rowlands and D. H. Whiffen, *Mol. Phys.*, 1964, *8*, 195.
55 L. H. Piette, F. A. Johnson, K. A. Bookman and C. B. Colburn, *J. Chem. Phys.*, 1961, *35*, 1481.
56 J. B. Farmer, M. C. L. Gerry and C. A. McDowell, *Mol. Phys.*, 1964, *8*, 253.
57 S. N. Foner, E. L. Cochran, V. A. Bowers and C. K. Jen, *Phys. Rev. Letters*, 1958, *1*, 91.
58 H. M. McConnell, *J. Chem. Phys.*, 1958, *29*, 1422.
59 S. I. Weissman, J. R. Tuttle and E. de Boer, *J. Phys. Chem.*, 1957, *61*, 28.
60 A. Horsfield, J. R. Morton, J. R. Rowlands and D. H. Whiffen, *Mol. Phys.*, 1962, *5*, 241.
61 J. R. Rowlands, *Mol. Phys.*, 1962, *5*, 565.
62 J. R. Rowlands and D. H. Whiffen, *Nature*, 1962, *193*, 61.
63 R. Livingston, J. Ghormley and H. Zeldes, *J. Chem. Phys.*, 1956, *24*, 483.
64 J. F. Gibson, M. C. R. Symons and M. G. Townsend, *J. Chem. Soc.*, 1959, 269.
65 R. C. Smith and S. J. Wyard, *6th Intern. Symp. on Free Radicals, Cambridge, 1963.*
66 R. Livingston, unpublished results.
67 P. W. Atkins, M. C. R. Symons and P. A. Trevalion, *Proc. Chem. Soc.*, 1963, 222.
68 L. H. Piette and W. C. Landgraf, *J. Chem. Phys.*, 1960, *33*, 1107.
69 K. U. Ingold and J. R. Morton, *J. Am. Chem. Soc.*, 1964, *86*, 3400.
70 M. H. Cohen, W. Känzig and T. O. Woodruff, *J. Phys. Chem. Solids*, 1959, *11*, 120.
71 M. C. R. Symons, *J. Chem. Soc.*, 1963, 570.
72 R. M. Golding and M. Henchman, *6th Intern. Symp. on Free Radicals, Cambridge, 1963; J. Chem. Phys.*, 1964, *40*, 1554.
73 M. Green and J. Linnett, *Trans. Faraday Soc.*, 1961, *57*, 1.

Chapter 8

Tetra-atomic radicals

As before, we start with a consideration of structure and then proceed to an overall view of the expected electron spin resonance spectra for those classes of radicals likely to be encountered experimentally. In the second half of the Chapter case histories are summarised, and the results tabulated and discussed. As in Chapter 7, we interpret the term "tetra-atomic radicals" in the broad sense of those radicals based on the structure AB_3 having A as the central atom of a species which may be planar or pyramidal.

8.1 STRUCTURAL ASPECTS

(a) Planar molecules

Again, we shall use the LCAO–MO scheme and construct molecular orbitals from the relevant s and p-orbitals of A together with the nine p-orbitals of the three ligands (B). We start with the relatively simple case of planar radicals. The molecular orbitals for planar AB_3 molecules are illustrated in Fig. 8.1a where they are classified according to the group D_{3h}.

The first twenty-four electrons will enter the bonding and non-bonding orbitals and, as there is no strain to be relieved by distorting, radicals with less than twenty-five valence electrons ought to be planar. Twenty-three valence electron species (for example NO_3) will have the configuration $...(2e')^4(e'')^4(a_2')^1$, $^2A_2'$. Thus the unpaired electron is confined to a non-bonding level on the ligands.

(b) Pyramidal molecules

Mulliken[1] and Walsh[2] have discussed the structure of AB_3 molecules and the outline in Chapter 7 is readily extended to include them. Fig. 8.1b. illustrates the molecular orbitals in the 90° (pyramidal) AB_3 molecule and a

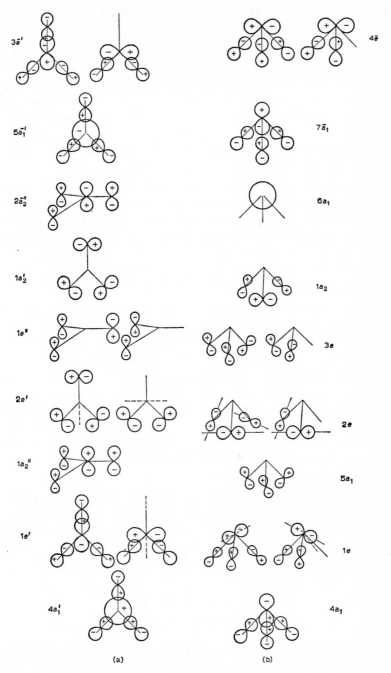

Fig. 8.1. The molecular orbitals in (a) planar and (b) pyramidal AB₃ molecules.

consideration of Walsh's rules (§ 7.1b) leads to the correlation diagram shown in Fig. 8.2. As we discussed in the preceding paragraph the electrons up to the twenty-fourth enter orbitals which are most stable for a planar configuration. The twenty-fifth electron, however, must then enter the anti-bonding $2a_2''$-orbital of the planar molecule. This would acquire s-character and become less antibonding if the molecule were to bend. Thus we expect the molecule to lower its energy on bending and species with more than twenty-four electrons are expected to be pyramidal.

We shall be particularly concerned with twenty-three and twenty-five electron species and the discussion is conveniently divided into these categories. Before discussing their expected electron spin resonance spectra however, we consider the influence of electronegativity on molecular structure.

(c) Electronegativity effects

For twenty-three electron species the electron is confined to the ligand orbitals and hence is unaffected by the electronegativity of A (or B). For twenty-five electron radicals, however, the effect of electronegativity will be marked. In § 7.1c we mentioned the effect of electronegativity on the bond angle and spin-density distribution in seventeen electron AB_2 species; for twenty-five electron AB_3 species the problem is quite analogous and leads to the same conclusions. AB_3 species are in fact implicitly included in Fig. 7.3.

(d) Expected electron spin resonance spectra

(i) Twenty-three electron species

According to the scheme which we have outlined the only hyperfine interaction with the A nucleus would be that due to a polarisation mechanism, or possibly to a dipolar interaction from the electron in the ligand orbitals. It is therefore expected to be very small and nearly isotropic.

The g-tensor is more difficult to discuss but should show axial symmetry and be independent of the spin–orbit coupling on the central atom. The perpendicular value arises from the excitation

$$\cdots (2e')^4 (e'')^3 (a_2')^2, {}^2E'' \leftarrow \cdots (2e')^4 (e'')^4 (a_2')^1, {}^2A_2'$$

and the parallel value (g_{zz}) from the excitation

$$\cdots (2e')^4 (e'')^4 (a_2')^0 (2a_2'')^0 (5a_1')^1, {}^2A_1' \leftarrow \cdots (2e')^4 (e'')^4 (a_2')^1, {}^2A_2'.$$

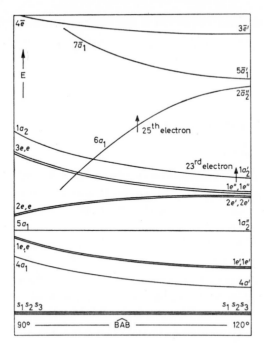

Fig. 8.2.　Correlation diagram for AB_3 radicals.[2]

(These follow from the discussion of Appendix 3, particularly Fig. 3A.1.) From the correlation diagram (Fig. 8.2.) it is apparent that the closest e''-level lies beneath and close to the a_2'-level, whereas the $2a_1'$-level is far above the a_2'-level. Consequently the perpendicular g-value should be much higher than the free-spin value, and the parallel g-value should be much closer and slightly less than the free-spin value.

(ii) Twenty-five electron radicals

The hyperfine interaction tensor should display the axial symmetry of the radical, and since the unpaired electron occupies an a_1-orbital which is essentially built from an sp^n-hybrid on A a large isotropic component is to be expected together with a superimposed anisotropy with the greatest magnitude along the molecular C_3-axis.

The g-tensor would, without due circumspection, perhaps be predicted to have all three principal values lying above the free-spin value. (It will also show axial symmetry.) The g-shift is due to the excitation

$$\cdots (1e)^4 (5a_1)^2 (2e)^3 (3e)^4 (a_2)^2 (6a_1)^2, {}^2E \leftarrow \cdots (2e)^4 (3e)^4 (a_2)^2 (6a_1)^1, {}^2A_1,$$

or

$$\cdots (2e)^4 (3e)^3 (a_2)^2 (6a_1)^2, {}^2E \leftarrow \cdots (2e)^4 (3e)^4 (a_2)^2 (6a_1)^1, {}^2A_1,$$

for the perpendicular direction and

$$\cdots (2e)^4 (3e)^4 (a_2)^1 (6a_1)^2, {}^2A_2 \leftarrow \cdots (2e)^4 (3e)^4 (a_2)^2 (6a_1)^1, {}^2A_1$$

for the parallel direction. Even though the energy difference criterion would predict that $\Delta g_\parallel$ should be larger than $\Delta g_\perp$ (because the e level lies below the a_2 level), because the a_2 orbital is entirely on the ligands and the $6a_1$ orbital is expected to be largely on the central atom, there is little mutual overlap and the energy difference is not the overriding consideration. The sequence $g_\parallel \sim g_\perp \gtrsim 2.0023$ should be expected. To anticipate, this is not always observed and often the g-values are both below the free-spin value. The low value of $g_\perp$ then observed may be due to d-orbital involvement of the type invoked during the discussion for SeO_2^- (§ 7.2b (v)), but as there are no d-orbitals which transform as A_2 in C_{3v} the low value of $g_\parallel$ is still difficult to explain.

8.2 EXPERIMENTAL RESULTS

Only twenty-three and twenty-five electron AB_3 radicals and their analogues are well-characterised. Various radicals derived from borates[3] may well belong to a class having a smaller number of valence electrons, but the results are not yet sufficiently well defined to warrant an attempt at classification.

(a) Twenty-three electron radicals

We only know of two radicals in this class, namely NO_3 and CO_3^-, the former being the better known.

(i) Nitrogen trioxide, NO_3

This radical has long been known in the gas phase, and Chantry et al.[4] have used optical data to support their identification of it in γ-irradiated urea nitrate crystals $[CO(NH_2)_2 HNO_3]$.

As might be expected, NO_3 has also been prepared by irradiating various

TABLE 8.1

ELECTRON SPIN RESONANCE AND STRUCTURAL DATA FOR THE NITROGEN TRIOXIDE, NO_3

Medium	g-Tensor				Hyperfine tensor (gauss)				Reference
	g_{xx}	g_{yy}	g_{zz}	g_{av}	B_{xx}	B_{yy}	B_{zz}	A_{iso}	
$CO(NH_2)_2HNO_3$	2.0203	2.014	2.0066	2.0128					4
$Pb(NO_3)_2$	2.029	2.029	1.998	2.019	0.7	0.7	−1.3	−1.7	37
KNO_3	2.025	2.025	2.005	2.018				−4.5	5, 6
	2.0232	2.0232	2.0031	2.0165	0.28	0.28	−0.57	−3.74	7

crystals containing nitrate ions[5-7]. Results are summarised in Table 8.1. We must point out that the radical studied by Cunningham and co-workers[5] was identified by them as NO_3^{2-}. Also, the radical identified by Boesman and Schoemaker as NO_3[8] is discussed in § 8.2b (iv) below in terms of the more probable structure NO_3^{2-}.

There can be little doubt that the radical obtained on nitrate irradiation is NO_3. We have chosen negative signs for the ^{14}N hyperfine tensor principal values on the grounds that the spin is expected to be confined to the in-plane p-orbitals of the oxygens, the ground state being $^2A_2'$. This gives a dipolar interaction of the form $(-2\beta, \beta, \beta)$ and is also likely to give rise to a small and probably negative isotropic coupling through polarisation of the s-electrons.

The small values for the isotropic coupling are certainly quite reasonable for this structure, so also is the magnitude of the dipolar coupling. Chantry et al.[4] made an approximate calculation for the dipolar interaction in the case of the analogous radical CO_3^-. Using this method, but substituting the parameters for ^{14}N, we calculate a coupling of $(-)1.5$ gauss which is very close to that found. An additional term to allow for spin-polarisation in the $2p_x$ and $2p_y$ orbitals on nitrogen also contributes to the anisotropy, but the accuracy of the results does not warrant its inclusion.

Chantry and co-workers[4] were unable to resolve any hyperfine couplings to ^{14}N, but the single line was unusually broad. We suggest that the distortion giving rise to the marked asymmetry in the g-tensor may also have been the cause of this line-broadening with a consequent blurring of the hyperfine structure.

(ii) The radical ion CO_3^-

This radical which is prepared by the γ-irradiation of single crystals of potassium bicarbonate[4] was identified by the ^{13}C hyperfine structure which appeared in spectra of samples containing 56% of this isotope. This enrichment was necessary as the splitting was very small, as expected, and the lines from $^{13}CO_3^-$ radicals in natural abundance were hidden beneath the central lines from the $^{12}CO_3^-$ radicals.

Apart from the prediction that HCO_3^- would suffer loss of hydrogen on irradiation, identification was based both upon the similarity of the optical spectrum of this radical to that of NO_3 in urea nitrate, and upon the form of the hyperfine tensor (Table 8.2). This was analysed in the same manner as that used for NO_3 on the assumption that the anisotropic coupling must

TABLE 8.2

ELECTRON SPIN RESONANCE DATA[4] FOR THE RADICAL ION CO_3^-

Medium	g-Tensor			Hyperfine tensor (gauss)		
	$g_\parallel$	$g_\perp$	g_{av}	$B_\parallel$	$B_\perp$	A_{iso}
$KHCO_3$	2.0086	2.0184	2.0066	-2	1	-11

necessarily be of the form $(-2\beta, \beta, \beta)$ and that the isotropic coupling should be negative. It is remarkable that if one scales these data by the appropriate atomic parameters for ^{13}C and ^{14}N in order to compare them with those for NO_3, the results are very close indeed to those of Livingston and Zeldes both for the isotropic and the anisotropic components[7]. This internal consistency certainly lends considerable weight to both identifications.

Whiffen and his co-workers drew particular attention to the departure from axial symmetry found in the interaction tensors of both CO_3^- and NO_3 [4]. They stressed that this would not be expected for planar radicals with D_{3h} symmetry, but could well result if the symmetry were reduced to C_{2v} by some distortion, such as in-plane opening or closing of one of the $O\hat{C}O$ angles. The reason advanced for such a distortion was based upon theoretical considerations of the isolated radicals[4]. Briefly, an in-plane distortion of the type envisaged is expected to stabilise the doubly occupied $2b_2$ non-bonding level, although the $3b_2$ level becomes de-stabilised. Since the latter level is only half filled the distortion is predicted.

If indeed this were the case then it is hard to understand why the g-tensor for NO_3 radicals in other environments are axially symmetric (Table 8.1). It could be that the distortion is a dynamic one for these other cases, but since the axial symmetry was preserved at low temperatures whereas the asymmetry was found by Chantry et al. even at room temperature this explanation does not seem to be satisfactory.

It is tempting to suggest that the distortion is favoured in these radicals but is slight in the absence of any strong environmental factors. This being so, one could postulate strong residual hydrogen bonding both for CO_3^- radicals in $KHCO_3$ and for NO_3 radicals in urea nitrate. These interactions could then be responsible for freezing the distortion in one of the three equivalent forms in a manner similar to that suggested to explain the asymmetric structure for the hydrated vanadyl ion[9]. It must, however, be admitted that if asymmetric hydrogen bonding is invoked, and it is very likely to occur in both crystals under consideration, then this alone could cause the observed asymmetry in the g-tensors; there would then be no compelling reason for invoking any intrinsic electronic requirement.

Before leaving this radical we should perhaps record that a second radical was formed in high abundance when potassium bicarbonate crystals were irradiated at room temperature[4]. This radical was found to have hyperfine and g-tensors closely similar to those for the radical CO_2^-, the only major difference being that there was a very small, nearly isotropic doublet splitting. This could not be accurately monitored as a function of orientation of the crystal, but it was never greater than about 5.2 gauss. The most obvious identification would be the conjugate acid of CO_2^- namely $OC(OH)$. The very minor modification of the CO_2^- parameters and the smallness of the proton interaction suggest, however, that the proton may belong to a neighbouring bicarbonate ion, linked to the radical by a hydrogen bond.

(b) Twenty-five electron radicals

This is the most prolific class both with respect to simple AB_3 radicals and also their more complex analogues. We start with a consideration of the radical PO_3^{2-} since the results for this are particularly simple. Having given details of the isoelectronic radicals PO_3^{2-}, SO_3^-, ClO_3 we pass on to NO_3^{2-}, SeO_3^- and AsO_3^{2-}. We devote a section to an examination of various interesting trends. This is followed by a brief consideration of radicals containing fluorine ligands after which a somewhat miscellaneous collection of related radicals are discussed briefly.

(i) The radical ion PO_3^{2-}

This radical was detected in a γ-irradiated single crystal of hydrated sodium ortho-phosphite $(Na_2HPO_3 \cdot 5H_2O)$ by Whiffen and his co-workers[10] and in γ-irradiated polycrystalline Na_2HPO_3 by Keen[11] (Table 8.3). The simple form of the powder spectrum, reproduced in Fig. 8.3. was readily analysed by the method indicated in the Figure, and it is particularly satisfactory to note that the principal values for the hyperfine and g-tensors agree closely with those derived from single crystals. Indeed in this particular case the only merit in using crystals would seem to be that the orientation of the radicals relative to the parent ions in the crystal is known. This information is useful in that it helps to show why it is that radicals are frequently trapped in well-defined orientations after formation rather than

TABLE 8.3

ELECTRON SPIN RESONANCE AND STRUCTURAL DATA
FOR THE RADICAL ION PO_3^{2-}

Medium	g-Tensor			Hyperfine tensor (gauss)			Reference
	$g_{\parallel}$	$g_{\perp}$	g_{av}	$B_{\parallel}$	$B_{\perp}$	A_{iso}	
$Na_2HPO_3{\cdot}5H_2O$	1.999	2.001	2.001	106	-53	593	10
$BaHPO_3$	1.998	1.999	1.999	114	-57	578	11

$c_s^2 = 0.16 \quad c_{p_z}^2 = 0.53 \quad \lambda^2 = 3.31 \quad \widehat{OPO} = 110°$

in a random fashion. Thus in this instance it seems that after ejection of the hydrogen atom the PO_3^{2-} fragment remained in almost exactly its original site, there being a minimum re-arrangement to accommodate the absence of hydrogen and the slightly modified geometry. This appears to be a general rule. If there is no well defined preference the radical may rotate randomly as was found for PF_4 (§ 9.2b (i)); otherwise if the trapping site is anisotropic the radical may rotate in some restricted manner as was found for NO_2 (§ 7.2a (i)).

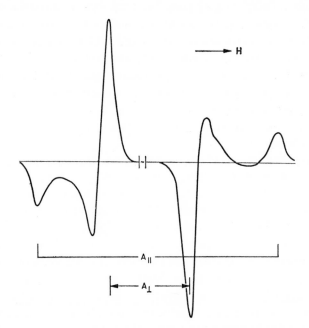

Fig. 8.3.   Electron spin resonance spectrum of PO_3^{2-} in Na_2HPO_3 powder.

The evidence in favour of the identification of the radical under consideration as PO_3^{2-} is primarily the prediction that HPO_3^{2-} could lose a hydrogen atom on irradiation, and the agreement between the molecular parameters derived from the hyperfine coupling tensor and those expected for twenty-five electron AB_3 radicals. The outstanding feature is that the $3p/3s$ ratio is about 4, hence the electron must be in a hybridised orbital with a large s content. The only other radical which might be expected to have a comparable ^{31}P hyperfine tensor is PO_2. This is a less probable product chemically and, unless it undergoes rotation about the O–O axis, is not expected to have axially symmetric hyperfine or g-tensors. The clear relationship between this radical and that identified as ClO_3 in irradiated perchlorates practically eliminates PO_2 [12, 13]. (It is unlikely that ClO_2^+ could be formed and trapped in a perchlorate lattice, so this alternative need not be considered.)

(ii) The radical ion SO_3^-

This radical was more difficult to identify with any certainty because of the very low natural abundance of ^{33}S, the only important isotope of sulphur with a magnetic nucleus. It was found, however, that a particular radical characterised by a single line having a nearly isotropic g-value very close to the free-spin value was formed on irradiation of a number of compounds likely to give SO_3^- [14]. These included sodium dithionate, which contains the ion $^-O_3S–SO_3^-$, potassium methane disulphonate, sulphamic acid and its potassium salt, and potassium amine disulphonate. In all instances it was possible under high gain to detect radicals containing ^{33}S [14]. In one case the resulting hyperfine tensor was estimated and the results were found to fit neatly between those for PO_3^{2-} and ClO_3. This confirms the identification as SO_3^- (Table 8.4).

The identification having been established one can now look at materials

TABLE 8.4

ELECTRON SPIN RESONANCE AND STRUCTURAL DATA
FOR THE RADICAL ION SO_3^- [14]

Medium	g-Tensor (isotropic)	Hyperfine tensor (gauss)		
		$B_\parallel$	$B_\perp$	A_{iso}
$K_2CH_2(SO_3)_2$	2.0036	25	−12	128

$c_s^2 = 0.13$ $c_{p_z}^2 = 0.49$ $\lambda^2 = 3.77$ $\widehat{OSO} = 111°$

which might contain SO_3^- and recognise the radical by its ^{32}S spectrum, without needing to obtain such high concentrations that radicals containing ^{33}S can be detected. This aspect is especially valuable when polycrystalline materials or glassy solids are being studied.

(iii) Chlorine trioxide, ClO_3

The molecule Cl_2O_6 is well known, and is thought to dissociate reversibly into the trioxide. Some preliminary attempts to prepare the trioxide in a solid matrix for study by electron spin resonance were underway[15] when it was found that a radical having magnetic parameters close to those expected for ClO_3 could be formed by irradiating potassium and magnesium per-chlorates[13]. At that time Cole published his results for irradiated single crystals of ammonium perchlorate[12]. Although his treatment of the data was unsatisfactory, the radical was identified as ClO_3, largely by a process of elimination. The results are collected in Table 8.5.

Comparison of these results with those for the isoelectronic radical PO_3^{2-}, together with the argument that no other chemically reasonable oxy-radical of chlorine could have an unpaired electron in an orbital with large s-character on chlorine was evidence enough: the difficult task of isolating the chemically prepared trioxide was therefore abandoned.

Before discussing the results for PO_3^{2-}, SO_3^- and ClO_3 further, we will consider briefly the preparation and identification of three other trioxides: NO_3^{2-}, AsO_3^{2-} and SeO_3^-. The first is distinct from the rest in that it is a first-row radical and might be expected to differ from the others, especially

TABLE 8.5

ELECTRON SPIN RESONANCE AND STRUCTURAL DATA
FOR CHLORINE TRIOXIDE, ClO_3

Medium	g-Tensor			Hyperfine tensor (gauss)			Reference
	$g_\parallel$	$g_\perp$	g_{av}	$B_\parallel$	$B_\perp$	A_{iso}	
NH_4ClO_4	2.007	2.008	2.008	25	-13	128	12, 13
$KClO_4$	2.0066	2.0132	2.0110	29	-15	122	13
$Mg(ClO_4)_2$	2.0069	2.0103	2.0092	33	-17	133	13

	c_s^2	$c_{p_z}^2$	λ^2	$\widehat{OClO}$
$KClO_4$	0.076	0.34	4.47	$112°$
$Mg(ClO_4)_2$	0.083	0.39	4.70	112
NH_4ClO_4	0.080	0.29	3.63	112

with respect to its bond angle. The others are third-row radicals, and here participation of appropriate d-orbitals may be more pronounced.

(iv) The radical ion NO_3^{2-}

This seems to have been prepared by Cunningham[5] by irradiation of potassium nitrate, and by Jaccard[16] and by Boesman and Schoemaker[8] in doped potassium chloride. Cunningham argued that the radical involved was NO_2^{2-}, having identified the radical, discussed above in terms of NO_3, as NO_3^{2-}. Boesman and Schoemaker[8] suggested NO_3 but Jaccard favoured NO_3^{2-}. The results shown in Table 8.6 seem to us to be best assigned to NO_3^{2-} [6]. The $2p/2s$ ratio of about 9, although considerably greater than that for PO_3^{2-} is quite reasonable for NO_3^{2-} as one would expect a smaller deviation from planarity for steric reasons. The estimated bond angle of 116°, corresponding to a deviation of about 13° from planarity, seems quite reasonable. The alternatives, for reasons given above, are not expected to have properties at all resembling those listed in Table 8.6.

One of the major arguments presented in favour of the other identifications is mechanistic. Thus, for example, optical bleaching of F-centres in the host crystal corresponds to a release of electrons. If a paramagnetic centre were to decay under this treatment then one might reason that the species is electron deficient. If on the other hand, the centre were to develop, then it could be electron-rich. This is a safe approach only if one is certain about the nature of the species originally present in the crystal. For example, a nitrite doped alkali halide crystal containing F-centres would be expected to give NO_2^{2-}

TABLE 8.6

ELECTRON SPIN RESONANCE AND STRUCTURAL DATA
FOR THE RADICAL ION NO_3^{2-}

Medium	g-Tensor			Hyperfine tensor (gauss)			Reference
	$g_\parallel$	$g_\perp$	g_{av}	$B_\parallel$	$B_\perp$	A_{iso}	
KCl[a]	2.0020	2.0068	2.0052	20.7	−10.3	40.8	16, 6
KCl[b]			2.0045			39.5	8, 6
KNO₃	2.002	2.006	2.005	19.3	− 9.7	41.7	5, 6

[a] Similar values observed in KBr and KI.
[b] Similar values observed in KBr and NaCl.

$c_s^2 = 0.074 \quad c_{p_z}^2 = 0.61$

$\lambda^2 = 8.19 \quad \widehat{ONO} = 116°$

TABLE 8.7

ELECTRON SPIN RESONANCE AND STRUCTURAL DATA
FOR THE RADICAL ION SeO_3^- [17]

Medium	g-Tensor			Hyperfine tensor (gauss)		
	$g_\parallel$	$g_\perp$	g_{av}	$B_\parallel$	$B_\perp$	A_{iso}
K_2SeO_4	2.0030	2.0156	2.0114			
	2.0037	2.0150	2.0112	126	-63	490[a]
K_2SeO_3	2.0025	2.0148	2.0107			

[a] g-Tensor obtained from hyperfine components.

$c_s^2 = 0.10$ $c_{p_z}^2 = 0.47$

$\lambda^2 = 4.7$ $\widehat{OSeO} = 112°$

on bleaching with F-centre light. The trouble with the doped potassium chloride experiment is that the nature of the initial products was not known, except that they gave no detectable electron spin resonance absorption. We therefore favour the structural arguments used here, provided there is not a complete contradiction with the mechanistic evidence.

(v) The radical ion SeO_3^-

A radical thought to be SeO_3^- has been detected recently in γ-irradiated potassium selenate and selenite[17]. Identification was based upon an analysis of the hyperfine spectrum due to radicals containing ^{77}Se. The axially symmetric hyperfine tensor could be linked to the atomic 4s- and 4p-character on selenium, the results being in good agreement with expectation for SeO_3^- (Table 8.7). Indeed, these data are remarkably close to those for SO_3^-, but the value of $g_\perp$ for SeO_3^- (2.0156) is considerably greater than that for SO_3^- (2.0036). This is partly a result of the greater spin–orbit coupling constant for Se. It may also reflect a greater participation of d-levels, but since the hyperfine tensor has axial symmetry nothing can be deduced with any conviction about this.

(vi) The radical ion AsO_3^{2-}

The results reported by Horsfield for this radical[18] are given in Table 8.8 and derived molecular parameters are compared with those of other radicals in this class in Fig. 10.1. There can be little doubt concerning the correctness of this identification since the results fit in so nicely with the others. Lin and

TABLE 8.8

ELECTRON SPIN RESONANCE AND STRUCTURAL DATA
FOR THE RADICAL ION AsO_3^{2-}

Medium	g-Tensor			Hyperfine tensor (gauss)			Reference
	$g_\parallel$	$g_\perp$	g_{av}	$B_\parallel$	$B_\perp$	A_{iso}	
K_3AsO_4	1.999	1.992	1.997	110	−55	627	18
Na_2HAsO_4	2.004	2.005	2.005	107.2	−53.6	617.1	19

$c_s^2 = 0.18 \quad c_{p_z}^2 = 0.60 \quad \lambda^2 = 3.3 \quad O\widehat{As}O = 110°$

McDowell[19] have also studied this radical in single crystals of disodium arsenate and their results are also given in Table 8.8.

(c) Reactivity

Although our prime concern is with structure, nevertheless it would perhaps be of interest if some implications regarding reactivity were outlined. This seems to be an appropriate place to compare the series of dioxides and trioxides with respect both to dimerisation and hydrogen atom addition.

(i) Dimerisation

One generalisation that can be drawn is that dimerisation will be favoured the more strongly the unpaired electron is localised on the central atom. Thus NO_2 dimerises to N_2O_4 reversibly at room temperature, whereas the oxalate ion, $C_2O_4^{2-}$ displays no tendency to dissociate into CO_2^- radicals. Since the change in bond angle is comparable in these dimerisations it would seem that the important factor is the far greater delocalisation of the unpaired electron in NO_2. Similarly, $S_2O_4^{2-}$ dissociates reversibly at room temperature whilst ClO_2 shows no tendency to dimerise. Again, ClO_3 is formed readily from Cl_2O_6 but $S_2O_6^{2-}$ is very stable indeed, and has no tendency to dissociate.

Another important control exerted by the electronic arrangement in the monomer and probed by electron spin resonance studies concerns the relationship between the shape of the dimer and the form of the molecular orbital of the unpaired electron in the monomer. Thus for seventeen electron dioxides and twenty-five electron trioxides the electron, in so far as it is localised on the central atom, is in the best region of space for the formation of a bond extending along the molecular axis and away from the oxygen

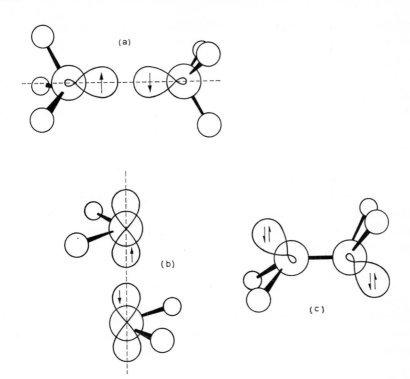

Fig. 8.4.   Electronic distributions and dimerisation. (a) Twenty-five electron AB_3
radicals; (b and c) nineteen electron AB_2 radicals.

atoms (Fig. 8.4.). The resulting "linear" molecules are most comfortably
arranged sterically and there is no reason from this point of view why a short,
strong bond should not form.

For the nineteen electron dioxides the situation is different, as has already
been stressed in Chapter 7. Various compromises are possible between the
two extremes of a pure $p–p$ bond, with the oxygen atoms *cis* or *trans*, as
indicated in Fig. 8.4b., and a "linear" arrangement as for the twenty-five
electron trioxides, the lone-pair electrons taking the place of the two missing
oxygen atoms (Fig. 8.4c.).

One example of this compromise is that achieved by the dithionite ion in
crystalline sodium dithionite. The interesting result that the oxygen atoms
adopt a *cis* configuration may be a dictate of the crystal structure, or possibly
an electronic requirement. Dunitz[20] elegantly showed that this arrangement
would be a direct result of any major contribution to the S–S bond by

sulphur d-atomic orbitals. It remains possible that, in view of the very weak S–S bond, there is some residual delocalisation onto the oxygens resulting in a weak oxygen–oxygen interaction.

These factors are thought to explain the differences between SO_2^- and SO_3^- or ClO_2 and ClO_3 with regard to their tendencies to dimerise. In both instances the unpaired electron is more delocalised onto oxygen in the tri-oxides. Nevertheless, these dimerise far more readily because, we think, of the steric factor discussed above.

(ii) Reaction with hydrogen atoms

The problems are somewhat similar, but in addition, tautomeric forms are possible. In accord with the electron distributions, hydrogens atoms add to phosphorus in PO_3^{2-} but to oxygen in SO_3^-. This parallels the difference between CO_2^- (giving HCO_2^-) and NO_2 (giving $NO(OH)$).

(d) Related species

As before, we have collected results for radicals which seem to us, with some stretch of the imagination, to be linked with those discussed above especially in § 8.2b.

(i) The radicals CH_3, NH_3^+ and SiH_3

The *methyl radical*, CH_3 has been the subject of so much discussion[21, 22] that we will not attempt to cover the work, optical, magnetic and theoretical, that has been devoted to this "parent" of organic radicals. Suffice it to say that, because of its size and symmetry, it has usually if not always, been detected in a tumbling state, the electron spin resonance spectra being characteristic of radicals in solution. For this reason, the spectrum of methyl radicals is often quite easy to recognise in the complex of broad lines which is so frequently the result of radical trapping in glassy organic solids. If four narrow, symmetrical lines of relative intensities $1:3:3:1$ centred on the free-spin g-value and separated by about 23 gauss are observed then almost certainly CH_3 is one of the products. For many reasons it is accepted that the isotropic hyperfine coupling of about 23 gauss is negative, and this value forms the basis of McConnell's well-used relationship[23]

$$A_{iso}^{(H)} = Q\rho_c \qquad (8.1)$$

which connects the experimental hyperfine splitting for ring-protons in aromatic π-radicals with the spin-density, ρ_c, on the adjacent ring-carbon atom, Q being equal to -23 gauss.

The *radical ion* NH_3^+ has been detected in γ-irradiated ammonium perchlorate[12] accompanying the radical ClO_3, and also in ammonium perchlorate by Hyde and Freeman[24]. The proton isotropic hyperfine coupling of -25 gauss is close to that for methyl, and the ^{14}N isotropic coupling of 19.5 gauss is very similar to that found for more complicated π-radicals. There can be little doubt that this radical, like methyl, is essentially planar. Although neither groups of workers were able to extract anisotropic parameters, the results of Hyde and Freeman clearly show the onset of restricted rotation. At elevated temperatures the spectrum consisted of the expected triplet of quartets due to the ^{14}N and ^1H hyperfine coupling. As the temperature was lowered, the outer pair of quartets became much broader than the central set and ultimately became too broad to detect; this left the central quartet still well resolved. At still lower temperatures the central pattern became markedly asymmetric, but the outer lines did not reappear.

These changes have been explained in terms of a restricted rotation, the limitation initially being confined to out-of-plane motion. This restriction is expected to be manifest at a far higher temperature than that at which the radical becomes effectively motionless, since very little movement is required for in-plane rotation between equivalent sites.

Such a restricted motion will profoundly modify the triplet from ^{14}N as this has an anisotropic constrisition of 2β for field parallel to the molecular axis, and $-\beta$ for perpendicular fields. The result, neglecting the effect of g-anisotropy which is likely to be small for NH_3^+, will be to broaden the outer lines due to $M_I(^{14}N) = \pm 1$ leaving the central lines stemming from $M_I(^{14}N) = 0$ unaffected.

This situation, fortuitously, does not arise for protons because their anisotropic hyperfine coupling is approximately of the form $0, \pm \beta$ for parallel and perpendicular fields respectively. If rotation in the radical plane is sufficiently rapid, the perpendicular anisotropy will approximately average zero. Thus the net effect of the proton anisotropic coupling will be only a minor line broadening until rotation in the plane of the radical becomes significantly restricted. Results for the *silyl radical*, SiH_3 [25] illustrate this effect quite well. Presumably in this case the g-anisotropy is greater than that for methyl radicals so that line-broadening due to restricted rotation is more apparent. Also of significance is the markedly smaller value of 7.6 gauss for the proton hyperfine coupling, compared with 23 gauss for the protons in CH_3 which has been discussed[26] in terms of the possibility that silyl radicals are slightly pyramidal. This is expected to lead, initially, to a fall in the magnitude of the proton coupling, because as the radical bends a positive contribution sets in which must first oppose the negative coupling of the planar radical. This is discussed in detail in Chapter 2. It is not yet known if the proton coupling in SiH_3 is positive or negative.

(ii) CF_3, SiF_3 and related radicals

Little can be said about these radicals at present, despite the fact that there are several papers purporting to record electron spin resonance data for them. Thus, for example, Adrian et al.[27] have shown a spectrum obtained from radicals prepared by the photolysis of CF_3I in a rare-gas matrix. This was most complicated and no interpretation was offered. Similarly, results for γ-irradiated CF_4 and SiF_4 have been discussed in terms of the radicals CF_3 and SiF_3 but the results[28], which are particularly complicated in the latter instance, have not been analysed satisfactorily.

It might have been expected that an analysis of these envelope spectra would now be possible in the light of the considerations outlined in this book, and especially in the light of the detailed results given by Cook and Whiffen for the radical $\rangle C–F$ [29]. As these are twenty-five electron radicals, they should be pyramidal; their envelope spectra ought therefore to be at least as involved as that of PF_4 (§ 9.2.b (i)) as many different directions are involved for the hyperfine tensors.

(iii) The radicals $ON(SO_3)_2^{2-}$, $HC(SO_3)_2^{2-}$ and $H_2N^+SO_3^-$

This group of radicals are conveniently classed together, and may be compared with the radicals $N(SO_3)_2^{2-}$ and $HNSO_3^-$ discussed in § 7.2b (vii).

The *radical $ON(SO_3)_2^{2-}$* is remarkable for its stability and in the form of its potassium salt, which is commonly called Fremy's salt, has been known for many years. It gives rise to a well resolved $1:1:1$ triplet of lines in aqueous solution which are often used for calibration purposes. It was studied in single crystal form some years ago by Weissman, Tuttle and de Boer[30] who found an anisotropic coupling (2β) of 14 gauss. This gives a $2p/2s$ ratio of 17.4 which shows that this radical, in contrast to NO_3^{2-}, is essentially planar in the ONS frame. Also the extent of delocalisation (48%) is relatively large, being both larger than that for NO_3^{2-} (19%) and that for $N(SO_3)_2^{2-}$ (27%). This is possibly the result of delocalisation on to oxygen in the planar radical, $ON(SO_3)_2^{2-}$ which is considerably reduced in the pyramidal NO_3^{2-}.

The *radical ion* $HC(SO_3)_2^{2-}$ was prepared incidentally in an extensive and successful effort to prepare and characterise the radical SO_3^- by γ-irradiation of potassium methane disulphonate crystals[31]. The radical was clearly identified not only by its proton hyperfine coupling which was typical of α-protons in planar π-radicals, but also by the hyperfine spectrum for radicals containing ^{13}C in natural abundance.

The proton hyperfine spectrum was typical of such radicals, and indicated that there was little delocalisation on to the SO_3^- groups. The anisotropic part of the ^{13}C hyperfine tensor gave a $2p(C)$ spin population of 0.75. This may be compared with results for the radical $CH(CO_2H)_2$ obtained by irradiating single crystals of malonic acid[32]: these showed that the $2p$ spin population on the central carbon is about 0.69. It is interesting that in neither case is delocalisation of the extent implied by the ^{14}N or ^{13}C hyperfine coupling tensor indicated by the isotropic proton hyperfine coupling which is quite comparable with that for methyl radicals. This peculiarity has been discussed elsewhere[33].

Despite these uncertainties, one can conclude that the extent of electron delocalisation onto SO_3^- groups is less than onto $-CO_2H$ groups, and is small in both cases. One interesting feature of the spectrum for $HC(SO_3)_2^{2-}$ radicals is that for certain directions an extra triplet splitting was detected[14]. This was assigned to a dipolar interaction with two equivalent neighbouring protons. This constitutes one of the few examples of such interactions, although line-broadening is frequently known to result from protons in neighbouring molecules. The coupling tensors were traceless, showing that the interaction was purely dipolar, the maximum coupling being about 2 gauss.

The *radical ion* $H_2N^+SO_3^-$ was formed in irradiated sulphamic acid together with the radical SO_3^- [34]. Results, summarised in Table 8.9, are as expected for such a radical. As discussed for the radical $HNSO_3^-$ in § 7.2b (vii) there was also a marked temperature dependence in the ^{14}N hyperfine tensor; this was interpreted in terms of a torsional motion about the N–S bond such that there resulted a partial averaging of the anisotropic coupling. Thus the parallel value for the ^{14}N coupling increased from 37 to 43.5 gauss on cooling from room temperature to 77 °K.

The constancy of c_p^2 for ^{14}N in the radicals $H_2N^+SO_3^-$, $HNSO_3^-$ and $N(SO_3)_2^{2-}$ (when measured at 77 °K) suggests that there is very little de-

TABLE 8.9

ELECTRON SPIN RESONANCE DATA FOR THE RADICAL IONS $NH_2^+SO_3^-$, $CH(SO_3)_2^{2-}$ AND $ON(SO_3)_2^{2-}$

Radical	g-Tensor				Hyperfine tensor (gauss)				Reference
	g_{xx}	g_{yy}	g_{zz}	g_{av}	B_{xx}	B_{yy}	B_{zz}	A_{iso}	
$NH_2^+SO_3^-$	2.0033	2.0025	2.0019	2.0026	-9.3	-9.3	18.6	18.2 (^{14}N)	34
$CH(SO_3)_2^{2-}$					-23	-25	48	45 (^{13}C)	31
					1	-12	11	-21 (^{1}H)	
$ON(SO_3)_2^{2-}$					-7	-7	14	13 (^{14}N)	30

TABLE 8.10

ELECTRON SPIN RESONANCE AND STRUCTURAL DATA FOR THE RADICAL ION HPO_2^-

Medium	g-Tensor			Hyperfine tensor (gauss)			Reference
	$g_{\parallel}$	$g_{\perp}$	g_{av}	$B_{\parallel}$	$B_{\perp}$	A_{iso}	
$Mg(H_2PO_2)_2$	2.0020	2.0035	2.0030	121.4	-60.7	520.7 (^{31}P)	11
$NH_4H_2PO_2$	2.0019	2.0035, 2.0037	2.0030	112	-56	495 (^{31}P)	35
				$(2.9, -1.1, -2.0)$		82.5 (^{1}H)	

$c_s^2(P) = 0.15 \quad c_{p_z}^2 = 0.61 \quad c_s^2(H) = 0.16 \quad \lambda^2 = 4.07 \quad \widehat{OPO} = 111°$

localisation on to SO_3^- groups, and that the apparent reduction in spin populations may largely be due to many approximations involved in their computation.

(iv) The radical ion HPO_2^-

This radical was identified by Morton[35] in γ-irradiated single crystals of ammonium hypophosphite, $NH_4H_2PO_2$, and independently by Keen[11] in the γ-irradiated magnesium, calcium and sodium salts. Morton also detected the NH_3^+ radical and a secondary species thought to be $O_2P-PHO_2^{2-}$. The latter is discussed in § 8.2e (v). Results are given in Table 8.10 and the powder spectrum, together with the analysis used, is shown in Fig. 8.5. The strongly anisotropic hyperfine tensor was assigned to ^{31}P and the smaller and almost

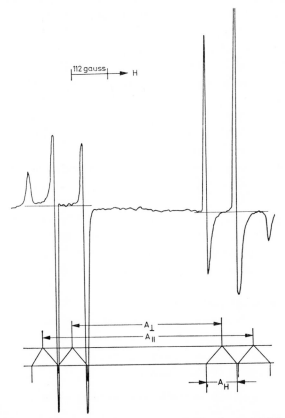

Fig. 8.5.   Electron spin resonance spectrum of HPO_2^- in $Mg(H_2PO_2)_2$ powder.

isotropic tensor to a proton. The latter assignment was confirmed by using deuterated material.

The results justify the interpretation of this powder spectrum (Fig. 8.5.) as HPO_2^-. Nevertheless, had the proton coupling been strongly anisotropic this treatment would have been incorrect because the g-tensor and the hyperfine tensor would refer to principal axes which were not the principal axes of the proton coupling tensor.

Two features are of particular interest: one is the very large proton coupling, and the other is the marked increase in the $3p/3s$ ratio compared with that for the radical PO_3^{2-} (§ 8.2b (i)). The latter result, which suggests that the HPO_2^- radical is somewhat closer to planarity than PO_3^{2-}, is as expected. This may be seen by contrasting NH_3^+, which is planar, to NO_3^{2-} which is pyramidal ($\phi = 116°$). Although PH_3^+ is unknown (all attempts to prepare it have failed), the silyl radical, discussed in § 8.2e (i) is expected to deviate from planarity only to a minor extent, whereas PO_3^{2-} is strongly pyramidal with $\phi = 110°$. Thus a mean angle of about $112°$ deduced from the $3p/3s$ ratio of 4.07 is not unreasonable for HPO_2^-.

This structure, in which the unpaired electron occupies an a_1 orbital similar to that in PO_3^{2-}, is confirmed by a very large proton hyperfine coupling of about 90 gauss. The structural problem is analogous to that for the formyl radical, HCO, discussed in § 7.2a (iii) and has been considered from a theoretical viewpoint[11].

Morton has suggested that the large proton hyperfine coupling is a consequence of a very weak P–H bond: the valence-bond structure $(\dot{H} + PO_2^-)$ being of considerable importance. A similar argument was used by Adrian et al.[36] to explain the results for HCO. In the light of our considerations of the structure of such radicals, it seems that the reverse argument is more fundamental: we could say that the weak P–H bond is a consequence of the electronic structure which is likely to be a general feature of such radicals.

(v) The radical ion $O_2PPHO_2^{2-}$

This radical has been tentatively identified as a secondary product of the γ-radiolysis of a single crystal of ammonium hypophosphite[35]. The first product is HPO_2^- which is thought to react further with a neighbouring $H_2PO_2^-$ ion according to the reaction:

$$H_2PO_2^- + HPO_2^- \rightarrow O_2PPHO_2^{2-} + H_2 \qquad (8.2)$$

The results, given in Table 8.11, are as would be expected if the $^{31}P_{(a)}$

TABLE 8.11

ELECTRON SPIN RESONANCE AND STRUCTURAL DATA
FOR THE RADICAL ION $O_2PPHO_2{}^{2-}$ [35]

Medium	g-Tensor				Hyperfine tensor (gauss)			
	g_{xx}	g_{yy}	g_{zz}	g_{av}	B_{xx}	B_{yy}	B_{zz}	A_{iso}
$NH_4H_2PO_2$	2.0035	2.0051	2.0047	2.0044	-55.5	-47.3	103.8	384.4 $^{31}P_{(a)}$
					-19.3	-20.4	39.6	148.6 $^{31}P_{(b)}$
							32	^1H

$c_s{}^2(P_{(a)}) = 0.11 \quad c_{p_z}{}^2(P_{(a)}) = 0.54 \quad \lambda^2 = 4.91 \quad \widehat{OPO} \sim 113°$

coupling were due to a pyramidal phosphorus having two oxygen atoms and a $-PHO_2^-$ group attached, with the unpaired electron occupying an orbital similar to that for PO_3^{2-} or HPO_2^- (§ 8.2e (iv)). That the small isotropic doublet splitting was due to the proton rather than ^{31}P was confirmed by deuteration [35].

 - The angle between the density axis of the orbital on $P_{(a)}$ and the direction of the P–P bond was estimated as $108° \pm 5°$ from the principal directions of the two hyperfine tensors.

Since the $3p/3s$ ratio for $P_{(a)}$ is about 5, the radical is considerably flatter than either PO_3^{2-} or HPO_2^-. This may, in part, be a consequence of steric interactions between the two oxygen atoms and the bulky $-PHO_2^-$ group. The second phosphorus atom ($P_{(b)}$) has a very large spin-density of about 24%; this resides in the σ-bonding orbital which has a $3p/3s$ ratio of about 4.7. This σ-delocalisation is comparable with that found in HPO_2^- where the spin-density on the proton was found to be about 16%. Furthermore, the alteration within the σ-framework is not very great, since the isotropic coupling to the proton is only about 0.4 times that for the radical HPO_2^-. If Morton's identification is correct, which seems probable, these results are of considerable interest as they monitor the delocalisation of the un-paired electron through the σ-framework.

References

1 R. S. MULLIKEN, Rev. Mod. Phys., 1942, 14, 204.
2 A. D. WALSH, J. Chem. Soc., 1953, 2296.
3 S. LEE AND P. J. BRAY, J. Chem. Phys., 1963, 39, 2863.

4 G. W. CHANTRY, A. HORSFIELD, J. R. MORTON AND D. H. WHIFFEN, *Mol. Phys.*, 1962, *5*, 589.
5 J. CUNNINGHAM, *5th Intern. Symp. on Free Radicals, Uppsala, 1961.*
6 P. W. ATKINS AND M. C. R. SYMONS, *J. Chem. Soc.*, 1962, 4794.
7 R. LIVINGSTON AND H. ZELDES, *J. Chem. Phys.*, 1964, *41*, 4011.
8 E. BOESMAN AND D. SCHOEMAKER, *Compt. Rend.*, 1961, *252*, 2865.
9 R. N. ROGERS AND G. E. PAKE, *J. Chem. Phys.*, 1960, *33*, 1107.
10 A. HORSFIELD, J. R. MORTON AND D. H. WHIFFEN, *Mol. Phys.*, 1961, *4*, 475.
11 N. KEEN, *Ph. D. Thesis*, Leicester, 1963.
12 T. COLE, *J. Chem. Phys.*, 1961, *35*, 1169.
13 P. W. ATKINS, J. A. BRIVATI, N. KEEN, M. C. R. SYMONS AND P. A. TREVALION, *J. Chem. Soc.*, 1962, 4785.
14 G. W. CHANTRY, A. HORSFIELD, J. R. MORTON AND D. H. WHIFFEN, *Mol. Phys.*, 1962, *5*, 233.
15 P. A. TREVALION, *Ph. D. Thesis*, Southampton, 1962.
16 C. JACCARD, *Phys. Rev.*, 1961, *124*, 60.
17 P. W. ATKINS, M. C. R. SYMONS AND H. W. WARDALE, *J. Chem. Soc.*, 1964, 5215.
18 A. HORSFIELD, private communication, 1963.
19 W. C. LIN AND C. A. McDOWELL, *Mol. Phys.*, 1964, *7*, 223.
20 J. DUNITZ, *Acta Cryst.*, 1956, *9*, 579.
21 T. COLE, H. O. PRICHARD, N. R. DAVIDSON AND H. M. McCONNELL, *Mol. Phys.*, 1958, *1*, 406.
22 M. C. R. SYMONS, *Ann. Rept. Progr. Chem.*, 1960, *57*, 68.
23 H. M. McCONNELL, *J. Chem. Phys.*, 1956, *24*, 762; *Ann. Rev. Phys. Chem.*, 1957, *8*, 105.
24 J. S. HYDE AND E. S. FREEMAN, *J. Phys. Chem.*, 1961, *65*, 1636.
25 E. L. COCHRAN, *4th Intern. Symp. on Free Radicals, Washington, 1959.*
26 M. C. R. SYMONS, *Advan. Chem.*, 1962, *36*, 76.
27 F. J. ADRIAN, E. L. COCHRAN AND V. A. BOWERS, *Advan. Chem.*, 1962, *36*, 50.
28 R. E. FLORIN, D. W. BROWN AND L. A. WALL, *5th Intern. Symp. on Free Radicals, Uppsala, 1961.*
29 R. S. COOK, D. H. WHIFFEN AND J. R. ROWLANDS, *Mol. Phys.*, 1963, 7, 31.
30 S. I. WEISSMAN, T. R. TUTTLE AND E. DE BOER, *J. Phys. Chem.*, 1957, *61*, 28.
31 A. HORSFIELD, J. R. MORTON, J. R. ROWLANDS AND D. H. WHIFFEN, *Mol. Phys.*, 1962, *5*, 241.
32 H. M. McCONNELL, H. M. HELLER, T. COLE AND R. W. FESSENDEN, *J. Am. Chem. Soc.*, 1960, *82*, 766.
33 M. C. R. SYMONS, *Tetrahedron*, 1962, *18*, 333.
34 J. R. ROWLANDS, *Mol. Phys.*, 1962, *5*, 565.
35 J. R. MORTON, *Mol. Phys.*, 1962, *5*, 217.
36 F. J. ADRIAN, E. L. COCHRAN AND V. A. BOWERS, *J. Chem. Phys.*, 1962, *36*, 1661.
37 R. M. GOLDING AND M. HENCHMAN, *6th Intern. Symp. on Free Radicals, Cambridge, 1963; J. Chem. Phys.*, 1964, *40*, 1554.

Chapter 9

Penta-atomic radicals

The term "penta-atomic" is intended to imply the species AB_4, where A is the central atom of the molecule and the ligands B are either arranged tetrahedrally or are somewhat distorted from truly tetrahedral symmetry. In particular we are concerned with the thirty-one and thirty-three valence electron species.

9.1 STRUCTURAL ASPECTS

(a) Tetrahedral molecules

Let us consider the molecular orbitals of a tetrahedral complex as being built from s- and p-atomic orbitals of the central atom and the p-atomic orbitals of the ligand atoms. From these sixteen atomic orbitals (Fig. 9.1.) we can construct as many molecular orbitals, each labelled according to the irreducible representation of the molecular symmetry group (T_d). The orbital of lowest energy (Fig. 9.2.) may be either $1t_2$ or $1a_1$; the former is a bonding π-orbital with respect to each A–B axis whereas the latter, built largely from the s-atomic orbital of the central atom, is of σ-symmetry with respect to each of these axes. The corresponding antibonding orbitals we designate $3t_2$ and $2a_1$. We have chosen to use the language of group theory to classify the orbitals because it proves less clumsy than the alternative hybridisation language. The two are, of course, implicitly entirely equivalent, the sp^n-hybridised picture being obtained merely by combining the a_1 and t_2 orbitals. The relative order of the levels is obscure: on a simple view it would seem that the order is $... 1t_2 1a_1 ...$ for the bonding levels[1] but we shall return to this point later.

There are three sets of non-bonding orbitals: these are designated e_1, t_1 and $2t_2$, the e_1-level being doubly degenerate and the t_1- and t_2-levels triply degenerate. These orbitals are confined to the ligand atoms unless there are low-lying d-orbitals on the central atom with the necessary symmetry. It is

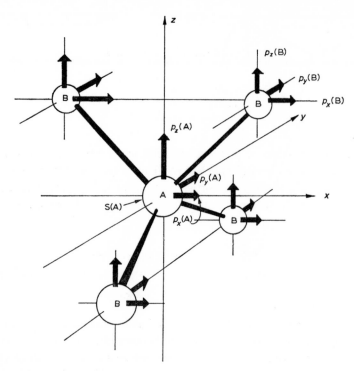

Fig. 9.1. The atomic orbitals employed to construct molecular orbitals in AB_4 molecules.

generally taken that the uppermost level is t_1, partly because it is strictly non-bonding on the ligands; consequently, thirty-one electron species are expected to have a $^2T_1$ ground state with the electron entirely confined to the ligands. A thirty-three electron species should have its unpaired electron in either the $2a_1$- or $3t_2$ orbital, whichever is the lower. The resulting radical would then be either $^2A_1$ or $^2T_2$.

(b) Distortions

A radical may distort from tetrahedral symmetry for a variety of reasons. The $^2T_1$ and $^2T_2$ tetrahedral spatial configurations are intrinsically unstable, according to the Jahn–Teller theorem. We should, therefore, not expect to observe the truly tetrahedral species: indeed, none of the AB_4 species so far prepared have a strictly tetrahedral configuration. Although this distortion

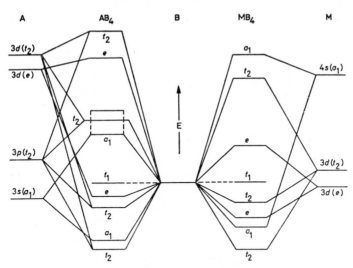

Fig. 9.2.   Energy-level scheme for AB$_4$ and MB$_4$ molecules (M is a transition metal and A a non-metal).

could follow from the Jahn–Teller theorem it could also be imposed by an unsymmetrical environment such as a non-spherical distribution of adjacent cations. If, for example, there were two cations, each equally close to a ligand atom, the effective symmetry of the molecule would be reduced from T_d to C_{2v} with the implication that the molecular orbitals be relabelled with respect to the latter symmetry. A correlation diagram for the reduction in symmetry from T_d to C_{2v} and C_{3v} is shown in Fig. 9.3. Thus, if the tetrahedral molecule were in a $^2T_2$ state, the effect of an unsymmetric environment (C_{2v} say) or of a distortion which resulted in a C_{2v} molecule, would be to give a molecular state which was $^2A_1$, $^2B_1$, or $^2B_2$. In contrast, if the ground state of a tetrahedral radical were $^2A_1$ one would not expect any intrinsic distortion of the Jahn–Teller type. There remains, however, the possibility of a distortion of the sort envisaged by Whiffen and his co-workers for nitrogen trioxide and which is discussed in Chapter 8.

The structure of thirty-three electron species is especially difficult to predict because there is uncertainty concerning the ground state even if the molecule were to be perfectly tetrahedral. Both possibilities ($^2A_1$ or $^2T_2$) have the unpaired electron in a strongly antibonding orbital. The energy of the $^2A_1$ state should be lowered by an admixture of the $(n+1)s$-orbitals of the central atom; other admixtures are not possible unless the molecule were to distort, in which case appropriate p-orbitals could contribute. This might have the favourable effect of removing the electron from the internuclear axis region and so of removing its antibonding character. Alternatively if the $^2T_2$ level of the tetrahedral radical were the lower, the orbital degeneracy would be removed by the expected Jahn–Teller distortion. If this were to result in a molecule of C_{2v} symmetry the $^2T_2$ state would separate as described in the preceding paragraph and the resulting $^2A_1$ state could mix strongly with the original $2a_1$ orbital together, of course, with the outer s-electrons of the central atom. The net effect would be a distorted molecule in a $^2A_1$ configuration identical to that envisaged above. Given that the molecule is distorted, a major problem would be the extent to which the a_1 and t_2 orbitals of the tetrahedral molecule contribute to the final distorted state. This problem can in principle be elucidated by an electron spin resonance investigation in the manner described in § 9.1c and illustrated in § 9.2b (i).

It should be noted that thirty-three electron AB_4 species provide a point of contact with the corresponding transition metal tetroxides; this important point will be developed in § 9.2b (ii).

(c) Expected electron spin resonance spectra

(i) Thirty-one electron species

As has already been remarked, in these species the unpaired electron is expected to be confined to the ligand atoms in a non-bonding t_1-orbital. Consequently, only a very small interaction with the nucleus of the central atom is to be expected and that which does arise must be due to either configuration interaction or a polarisation mechanism. The nearly spherical distribution of the electrons in slightly distorted tetrahedral radicals is such that dipolar interactions with the central atom are averaged to a very small value which is zero in the limiting case of the undistorted molecule.

There is a considerable orbital angular momentum in the undistorted species because the t_1-level is triply degenerate. Such a radical would therefore have a strong coupling between the spin and orbital angular momenta and also between the orbital momentum and the lattice. The resulting spin–lattice interaction would then be considerable and hence the species would be characterised by a very fast relaxation time. In such a situation it is unlikely that any spectrum would be observed except at very low temperatures.

When the molecule is distorted the t_1-orbital splits into orbitals of a_2, b_1

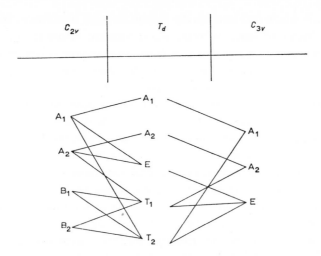

Fig. 9.3.   Correlation of T_d symmetry with C_{2v} and C_{3v} symmetries.

and b_2 symmetry under a C_{2v} distortion or into orbitals of a_2 and e symmetry under a C_{3v} distortion (Fig. 9.3). The g-tensor is then characteristic of either a C_{2v} or C_{3v} radical in the manner discussed in Chapter 7 and Chapter 8. Because of the smallness of the deviation from a state with high angular momentum at least one of the principal values of the tensor will be much larger than the free-spin value.

In summary we may say that a thirty-one valence electron AB_4 radical will have a spectrum characterised by a small hyperfine interaction with the central nucleus and a g-tensor which exhibits a considerable anisotropy and which is generally greater than the free-spin value. The spectrum is likely to be particularly sensitive to both temperature and environment.

(ii) Thirty-three electron radicals

In the corresponding sections of the foregoing chapters we have confined our main attention to the expected forms of the hyperfine tensor associated with the central atom. The outer (ligand) atoms have been treated as non-interacting since in nearly all actual examples they have had non-magnetic nuclei. In the few instances in which this has not been the case (for example NF_2, which was discussed in § 7.2b (vi)) a discussion of the hyperfine inter-action with the outer atoms has been given in the special case of the radical concerned. The only thirty-three electron radical so far discovered is PF_4

and hyperfine interaction with the ligand fluorine nuclei is considerable. It might therefore seem arbitrary if we were to continue our previous practice, and so we include in this section a brief outline of our expectations for the hyperfine coupling to both the central and the ligand atoms.

The hyperfine tensor for the central atom ought to provide a clear distinction between the various possible antibonding orbitals occupied by the electron. If, for example, our expectations of § 9.1a are correct, the electron will be in an a_1 orbital which will have considerable s-character on the central atom. Any anisotropy in the interaction will then be a measure of the distortion from a purely tetrahedral structure because it will reflect the presence of p-orbital character in the molecular orbital.

A distortion will also be reflected in anisotropy of the g-tensor: for a tetrahedral molecule this tensor should be isotropic. In the tetrahedral molecule deviation from the free-spin g-tensor would depend upon the mixing of some t_1-orbital character into the $2a_1$-orbital of the ground state by the spin–orbit interaction (L transforms as T_1 in T_d). Since the only t_1-orbitals available are the non-bonding ligand orbitals, which necessarily lie below the $2a_1$-orbital, the g-shift by this mechanism would be positive. If the molecule were to distort to C_{2v} symmetry, the spin–orbit coupling would have non-vanishing matrix elements to orbitals of symmetry a_2, b_1 and b_2 (see Appendix 3) because, as discussed above, the distortion splits the t_2-orbital into a_1, b_1 and b_2 orbitals with the a_1 the lowest. The predominant coupling is therefore between the a_1-orbital and the higher but close b_1- and b_2-orbitals. The overall effect is a shift to low g-values. The situation is illustrated in Fig. 9.4.

The form of the hyperfine coupling to the nuclei of the outer atoms is far more complicated, whether or not the molecule is strongly distorted. For any one atom the electron can be treated as occupying a σ-orbital with an axis of symmetry along the particular A–B bond direction. The major ligand atomic orbital involved would be $mp(\sigma)$, but there should be a real, though probably small, contribution from the ms-level. For a purely tetrahedral radical each ligand would interact equally with the electron, but as the individual tensor axes are tetrahedrally disposed relative to each other the spectrum of a single crystal would, for an arbitrary direction, correspond to hyperfine interactions with four inequivalent nuclei. In particular orientations two, three, two pairs and four nuclei would become magnetically equivalent.

For a distorted molecule, however, not only would there be a deviation

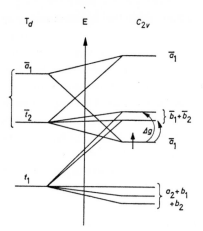

Fig. 9.4.   Effect of molecular distortion on the g-tensor of an AB_4 thirty-three electron species.

from such equivalences, but also the spin-distribution would no longer necessarily be equal. Furthermore, superimposed on the four sets of directions for the hyperfine tensors of the outer atoms there would be the effect of the now anisotropic g- and hyperfine tensors of the central atom. These would have yet different orientations.

Even so, the problem ought to be soluble if oriented radicals in single crystals were available. For the particular case of PF_4, however, all attempts to obtain oriented radicals have failed so far. The task of extracting information from the powder spectrum although formidable was greatly aided by the fact that the isotropic parameters were obtainable from tumbling radicals at room temperature. The situation is discussed in greater detail in § 9.2b (i).

9.2 EXPERIMENTAL RESULTS

The number of radicals known in this class is very small, being confined as far as we know, to a few thirty-one electron tetroxides and the thirty-three electron phosphorus tetrafluoride, PF_4.

We begin by summarising the somewhat sparse and confused field of the thirty-one electron tetroxides.

(a) Thirty-one electron radicals

There is some evidence for the formation of the radical PO_4^{2-} and related species in various irradiated crystalline phosphates, and these will be our first consideration. Thence we pass to a discussion of the properties of the SO_4^- radical and in particular, to the effect of ultraviolet light and γ-irradiation upon crystalline persulphates. At this point we digress for a brief discussion of the changes in the magnetic spectra of radicals which can be effected by trapping them in pairs. We end with a brief consideration of a radical thought to be SeO_4^- which can be detected in certain γ-irradiated selenate crystals.

(i) The radical ion PO_4^{2-}

A general property of γ-irradiated phosphates, both complex and simple, is that they contain radicals whose magnetic properties are close to those expected for PO_4^{2-} radicals distorted slightly either intrinsically or by their immediate environment[2] (Table 9.1). This agreement between expectation and observation cannot be taken as constituting proof and, indeed, there are a variety of alternative radicals which cannot be eliminated. These are substituted phosphates, for example XPO_3 or X_2PO_2, etc., in which the unpaired electron is still largely confined to a non-bonding orbital on oxygen. The other alternative is the as yet unknown trioxide PO_3. Here also the unpaired electron is expected to be confined to a non-bonding level on oxygen and so to have an electron spin resonance spectrum closely similar to that for distorted PO_4^{2-}.

The best documented results are those for irradiated single crystals of KH_2PO_4 and KD_2PO_4[3] which followed some earlier work by Jeffers et al.[4]. Two rather similar centres were observed, the results being given in Table 9.1. The anisotropic doublet was the predominant spectrum from crystals lightly irradiated with low-energy X-rays[3] whilst the isotropic doublet dominated the spectrum of crystals more heavily irradiated with higher energy X-rays or electrons.

The only evidence of proton interaction was that the line-widths were reduced by a factor of about two on deuteration. Thus if either of the radicals were simply $HOPO_3^-$ formed by loss of a hydrogen atom we must conclude that the spin-density on the hydroxyl oxygen is extremely small. This is not an unexpected result since the effective electron-affinity of this oxygen is far higher than that of the other three, and hence the hole should be confined to the latter. Such a structure, however, would necessarily confer considerable anisotropy on the hyperfine and g-tensors, and the former is reported to be isotropic for both species.

The suggestion made by Hughes and Moulton[3] that the electron is essentially confined to a 2p-orbital on just one of the oxygens is equally difficult to reconcile with the results. Thus again there should be an easily measurable anisotropy in the hyperfine coupling to phosphorus, whereas none was reported. The postulate is otherwise an attractive one, for the large g-value of 2.046 was found to lie at only 14° to one of the P–O bond directions. For an electron confined to a single $2p(\pi)$-oxygen orbital one would expect a strong coupling with the other, filled $2p(\pi)$-level for fields along the relevant P–O direction, whereas the other two values should not deviate far from the free-spin value: this was in fact found (Table 9.1).

It is noteworthy that the hyperfine coupling to ^{31}P is almost identical for the two radicals detected and, further that the g-value of 2.015 found for the isotropic doublet is close to g_{av} for the other radical. Attention was called to this similarity by Kohin and Ovenall[5] who suggested that the isotropic lines were due simply to PO_4^{2-} radicals undergoing rapid tumbling. The latter results however, show clearly that this simple explanation is untenable since different energy radiations give rise to different relative concentrations of the two species and, also, the isotropic doublet remains unaffected on cooling the crystals to 4.2 °K [3].

With the present data there seems to be no way of discovering with any certainty the true nature of these two radicals. Of the various possibilities the simple tetroxide, PO_4^{2-} seems to be the most attractive because if distortion from tetrahedral symmetry is not too great, both the hyperfine and g-tensors

TABLE 9.1

ELECTRON SPIN RESONANCE DATA FOR
IRRADIATED PHOSPHATES AND PYROPHOSPHATES

Medium	g-Tensor				Hyperfine tensor (gauss)	Reference
	g_{xx}	g_{yy}	g_{zz}	g_{av}	A_{iso}	
KD_2PO_4	2.004	2.007	2.046	2.0019	32	3
				2.02	50	4
Li_3PO_4				2.028	28.5	2
$Na_4P_2O_7$	2.0072	2.0072	2.0213	2.0119	34.4	2
$Na_3HP_2O_7$	2.0029	2.0029	2.0180	2.0079	36.0	2

ought to be nearly isotropic, as we have stressed in § 9.1c (i). Quite how this radical could be formed in KH_2PO_4 is not clear. If the anisotropic radical is $HOPO_3^-$ then PO_4^{2-} must be in some special site which is created, presumably, by the higher energy radiation.

The wide range of results for PO_4^{2-}-type radicals found in our studies of irradiated powders (Table 9.1) are thought to reflect various degrees of protonation, hydrogen-bonding and crystal-field effects from neighbouring ions: these result in a variety of distortions or partial localisations. It remains possible, however, that at least one of these radicals is the trioxide, PO_3.

(ii) The radical ion SO_4^-

Because the major isotope ^{32}S is non-magnetic, and because ^{33}S is of very low abundance the hope of ever detecting $^{33}SO_4^-$ radicals in solids is small, unless the specimen is very strongly enriched. Thus all that one can use as a guide for the detection of SO_4^- is the g-tensor (which should be of the same form as that assigned to PO_4^{2-} radicals in the previous section) and chemical insight. The latter seemed to be the most trustworthy in this instance, and so attention was focussed upon persulphates, which have a very weak O–O bond and are known, from kinetic and general mechanistic studies to photolyse to SO_4^- radicals on exposure to ultraviolet light.

The problem that was probed by this experiment was apparent from the start, namely: would it be possible for the two bulky SO_4^- radicals to separate in the crystal or would some kind of back reaction prove to be unavoidable? Results for potassium persulphates exposed to ultraviolet light (2537 Å)[6, 7] showed conclusively that radicals were readily formed but the complex form of the electron spin resonance spectrum was not obviously interpretable in terms of the postulate that only SO_4^- radicals were formed.

The electron spin resonance spectrum for most orientations of the crystal consisted of a major doublet and a central weak singlet. The g-tensors derived for the doublet and the central feature were identical. Furthermore, the separation $(2\Delta H)$ between the components was found to follow a $(3\cos^2\theta - 1)$ curve[6]. Since there are no nuclei with $I = 1/2$ in the crystal this doublet splitting cannot be a hyperfine interaction so it was concluded that pairwise trapping had occurred in a surprisingly specific manner. The data were analysed to give values for the parameter $\mathbf{R}$ in the equation

$$\Delta H = (g\beta S/\mathbf{R}^3)(3\cos^2\theta - 1) \tag{9.1}$$

This is the equation for a pair of interacting point-dipoles separated by a distance R, θ being the angle between the external field and the distance vector R: this expression is valid for small values of ΔH.

Preliminary analysis gave $R \doteqdot 13$ Å, and it was tentatively concluded that SO_4^- radicals were trapped in pairs, by a mechanism which always led to a separation of 13 Å. Furthermore, the distance vectors joining in pairs had to be parallel to each other[6].

A consideration of the crystal structure of potassium persulphate[8] gave a possible clue to the reason for such unexpected specificity. The first formed persulphate radicals are so close to one particular neighbour that one or both can react without any major rearrangement of the other ions, somewhat in the manner depicted in Fig. 9.5. The resulting radicals are thereby mechanically insulated from each other and, provided that such a displacement is only possible for "hot" primary radicals, they now remain trapped in their specific sites. A measure of the sulphur distance, assuming no major movement of the groups involved, is 11.4 Å for one displacement, and 19 Å for two. The nearness of these values to those originally deduced from the spectra lends weight to the postulate. It seemed reasonable that the majority of radicals that became trapped required one such interaction, and that in a far smaller number of instances both hot SO_4^- radicals interacted with their persulphate

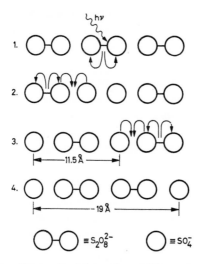

Fig. 9.5.   Possible mode of formation of SO_4^- pairs in $K_2S_2O_8$.

neighbours. The low intensity central line was then assigned to radicals which had become even further separated from their partners.

In principle, since these units are triplet species, a $\Delta M = \pm 2$ transition in the half-field region might be expected. Nevertheless, the predicted intensity of such a transition is so small that it is not surprising that no absorption was detected.

A more recent extensive study of potassium persulphate crystals exposed to 3650 Å light has revealed that initially, only the two major components of the spectrum can be detected, the weak central line being the result of secondary thermal processes[7]. Careful analysis of the single crystal data gave a value of 15.8 Å for the separation between the electrons. This result is almost mid-way between the single and double displacements of Fig. 9.5 and thus casts doubt upon the earlier assignment to SO_4^- radicals. However, the general concept of a pair of radicals formed along the lines of $S_2O_8^{2-}$ ions present in the crystal was confirmed since, within experimental error, this was the parallel direction of **R** (Table 9.2).

A further hint that the radical pairs were probably *not* SO_4^- radicals came from the fact that narrow lines were obtained and yet a very careful search revealed no trace of hyperfine satellites from radicals containing ^{33}S. This set an upper limit of about 3 gauss to this interaction at any orientation. Comparison with the splitting of about 30 gauss found for PO_4^{2-}-type radicals[2, 3] suggests that an isotropic hyperfine coupling of around 8 gauss ought to be detected for SO_4^- radicals or others of this type having the

TABLE 9.2

ELECTRON SPIN RESONANCE RESULTS FOR THE RADICAL PAIR
IN ULTRAVIOLET IRRADIATED POTASSIUM PERSULPHATE

Principal g-values (doublet centre)

	g_1	g_2	g_3
Powder	2.0307	2.0086	2.0056
Crystal	2.0310	2.0082	2.0064

Maximum doublet separation	13.8 gauss
Radical separation (**R**)	15.8 Å
	(Calculated using eq. (9.1))

Orientation of the line joining radical pairs relative to the crystal axes. The orientation of the lines of $S_2O_8^{2-}$ ions is given in parentheses.
$a = 84° (84°)$ $b = 56° (58°)$ $c = 35° (33°)$

unpaired electron confined to one or more oxygen atoms directly bonded to sulphur.

The intermediate distance, the undetectable hyperfine interaction and indeed the form and directions of the g-tensor can all be accommodated if it is supposed that the first formed SO_4^- radicals attack their neighbours to give peroxide radicals, O_3SOO^- rather than a second set of SO_4^- radicals. In other words we now suggest that the displacement

$$SO_4^- + {}^-O_3SOOSO_3^- \rightarrow {}^-O_3SOSO^-{}_3 + OOSO_3^-$$

is energetically favourable. This seems to be reasonable in view of the known stability of peroxide radicals and the very high reactivity of SO_4^- radicals. The trapped SO_5^- radicals adjust their orientations to fit in best with the crystal structure and especially the field from neighbouring cations, and hence the g-tensor, which should have its maximum value along the O–O bond, is oriented nearly at right-angles to the separation vector. The close agreement between the g-tensor for the radical-pair and for known peroxy-radicals can be seen from results given in Table 9.2. The electron separation should then be about 15 Å in good agreement with experiment.

This digression on pairwise trapping is significant in the sense that it may often occur in photolyses or radiolyses, leading either to a marked line-broadening if the trapping distance is variable, or to discrete structure if it is precise.

We are, however not further advanced in our quest for SO_4^- radicals. It is possible that they are formed and trapped as such in γ-irradiated persulphate crystals, but an analysis of the results as yet is incomplete.

Radicals with g-tensors similar to that for the radicals formed in γ-irradiated potassium persulphate have been detected in a variety of irradiated sulphates[9, 10] and are probably also radicals of the same class. Absence of hyperfine coupling, however, puts serious limitations upon their identification which must, therefore, remain tentative.

(iii) The radical ion SeO_4^-

As has been discussed in Chapters 7 and 8, γ-irradiation of various selenates at room temperature gave good yields of SeO_2^- and SeO_3^- radicals[11, 12]. Irradiation of potassium selenate at 77 °K followed by measurement at this temperature gave a new radical, g-tensor of which is given in Table 9.3, and is seen to be as expected for distorted SeO_4^- radicals[11]. On warming to room temperature, these radicals were irreversibly lost, but

TABLE 9.3

ELECTRON SPIN RESONANCE DATA FOR
THE RADICAL ION SeO_4^- [11]

Medium	g-Tensor			
	g_{xx}	g_{yy}	g_{zz}	g_{av}
K_2SeO_4	2.0021	2.0452	2.0072	2.0182
Na_2SeO_4		2.0436		

prior to their destruction marked line-broadening was observed. These properties are again quite reasonable for SeO_4^- as also is the fact that no hyperfine structure from $^{77}SeO_4^-$ radicals could be detected under any conditions[11].

The g-value variation is considerably greater than that observed for PO_4^{2-} and SO_4^- radicals. This may be associated with the greater spin–orbit coupling constant for selenium, but since the unpaired electron is thought to be in a non-bonding orbital confined to oxygen it is more probably a reflection of greater distortion from T_d symmetry.

In summary we can say that thirty-one electron AB_4 radicals have probably been formed in a variety of crystals, but that their properties, although in agreement with expectation, are nevertheless such that identification remains somewhat tentative. That such radicals appear to be formed in host crystals of the parent thirty-two electron ions is at first sight surprising since, by electron-transfer they might be expected to be mobile, or in the physicist's language, AB_4 in a lattice of AB_4^- ions is a mobile hole level. Self-trapping by distortion may be responsible for the well-defined radicals actually obtained, or possibly there is a weak covalent interaction with a neighbouring XO_4^- ion of the sort responsible for the stabilisation of halogen atoms in alkali halides.

(b) Thirty-three electron radicals

(i) Phosphorus tetrafluoride, PF_4

Initial attempts to prepare radicals of this class centred on the possibility of adding one electron to the perchlorate ion to give ClO_4^{2-}. Interest in such a species was especially strong as it could be compared directly with the manganate ion MnO_4^{2-}, which has been extensively studied by electron spin resonance methods[13]. All attempts to prepare ClO_4^{2-} were fruitless and other non-metal oxyions appeared to be even less capable of accepting an outer electron. Nevertheless, Morton solved the problem by γ-irradiating ammonium hexafluorophosphate and thereby forming the thirty-three electron phosphorus tetrafluoride. This radical which is isoelectronic with PO_4^{4-} and hence also with ClO_4^{2-} was found to be tumbling rapidly in the host crystal at room temperature, and so only the isotropic part of the hyperfine tensors were reported. Because of the special interest in this radical, we have endeavoured to glean extra information from low temperature studies[1]. This was bedevilled by two almost insurmountable problems: one being that only envelope spectra could be obtained at low temperatures, since the nearly spherically symmetric and neutral radicals had no preferred orientation in the crystal; the other being the presence of other radicals.

Morton detected a radical in ammonium hexafluorophosphate which he took to be PF^+ or PF^- [14]; this we have discussed briefly in § 6.2b (iii). He also found another species which is thought to be fluorine atoms[14]. The same species, with the exception of the fluorine atoms, have also been observed in potassium hexafluorophosphate[1].

Before giving an outline of the way in which useful information was extracted from the low temperature spectrum, two features of the spectra at higher temperatures ought to be mentioned. These are illustrated in Fig. 9.6. where it will be seen that the spectrum assigned to PF_4 at room temperature consists of many more lines than first-order theory would predict whilst that at 210 °K is so broadened as to be almost undetectable.

First order theory would predict a doublet splitting from ^{31}P and a quintet from ^{19}F, the relation intensities of the latter being $1:4:6:4:1$. Although the outermost lines of each set are indeed single lines, the others are separated into doublets for the next set and triplets for the central features. This second order splitting, which is only found when the hyperfine coupling is very large, has been discussed extensively by Fessenden[15] and others[16] and is well understood (see Appendix 5). No extra structural information is forthcoming, but this effect adds further to the already extensive complication of the envelope spectrum at 77 °K (Fig. 9.6.).

The difficulty of interpreting this spectrum stems primarily from the extreme complexity of overlapping lines. It is noteworthy, however, that the outermost parts of the spectrum are still relatively simple, and are hardly shifted at all relative to the outer lines of the room temperature spectrum. The significance of this observation can best be understood by considering the type of spectrum that one would expect to find for the tetrahedral radical[1].

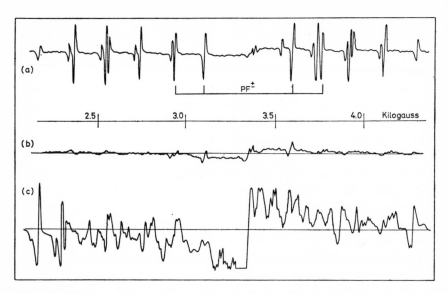

Fig. 9.6. Electron spin resonance spectrum from γ-irradiated KPF$_6$ powder at (a) 300° K, (b) 210° K, (c) 77° K.

We consider first a rotation about an axis perpendicular to a threefold axis and such that two B ligands are always equivalent (Fig. 9.7.). Let the applied magnetic field be perpendicular to this axis, then one obtains a spectrum, one half of which is illustrated in Fig. 9.8. (To calculate this spectrum it was assumed that the hyperfine coupling tensor to the nuclei was of the form $(-\beta, -\beta, 2\beta)$ with the positive coupling along the particular C_3-axis of the tetrahedron. Furthermore, it was assumed that the ratio of the isotropic to the minor anisotropic splitting (β) was $5:1$. Thus the model taken was that of an electron in an a_1-orbital built from an sp^n-hybrid on each ligand atom and on ns-orbital on the central atom.) During this rotation positions are reached such that two, two pairs, three and four ligand nuclei become equivalent; these positions are indicated by the peripheral numbers in Fig. 9.7. and are manifest as cross-over points in Fig. 9.8. Attention is drawn to these points of equivalence for at them the second order effect will set in if the magnitude of the hyperfine coupling parameter is sufficiently large. The effect (Appendix 5) removes some of the degeneracy of the transitions which contribute to a multiplet spectrum and, for example, at the position where four equivalent ligand nuclei are observed the expected half-

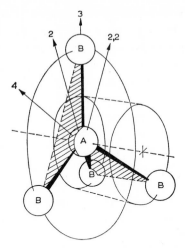

Fig. 9.7.   Typical rotation used in order to reconstruct the powder spectrum of PF_4.

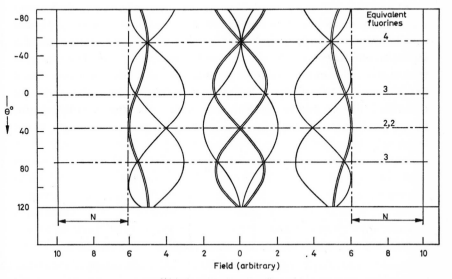

Fig. 9.8.   One half of the calculated spectrum of PF_4 as the molecule is rotated in the manner shown in Fig. 9.7.

References p. 207

spectrum of a 1:4:6:4:1 multiplet is split into a 1:1;3:1;3;2:1;3:1 multiplet, where the colons represent splittings of a magnitude $\sim A_{iso}^{(F)}$ and the semi-colons represent splittings of magnitude $\sim (A_{iso}^{(F)})^2/H$, H being the applied field. Such effects complicate the spectrum considerably but our main point can be made without considering them; and particular reference will be deferred until later and Appendix 5.

Other rotations give rise to quite similar diagrams, and it is always found that the anisotropic spectrum will not extend beyond the range of the isotropic spectrum provided that $\beta \leqslant \frac{3}{2}A_{iso}^{(F)}$. This is easily satisfied for PF_4, since for β to exceed $A_{iso}^{(F)}$ an impossibly large $2p$-population would be required. It is of particular importance that this analysis also shows that there must be a region between the outermost lines and the next pair which always remains clear. This region is marked N in Fig. 9.9. and may be shown to extend over $(A_{iso}^{(F)} - \beta)$ gauss.

As a result of the second order effects, shoulders should be found on the low-field side of the outer lines the maximum shift corresponding to orientations having two pairs of equivalent fluorine nuclei. These shoulders are indicated approximately in Fig. 9.9.

Comparison of Fig. 9.9. with the actual spectrum of Fig. 9.6. shows that these predictions are broadly fulfilled[1]. This enables us to estimate β as about 40 gauss, which is equivalent to 0.07 fluorine $2p$-character. More careful scrutiny reveals several unaccommodated features: clearly the outer shoulders are not due to second order splitting as they are too large, and, for the high-field outermost line, on the wrong side of the main line. Also the spectrum is not quite contained within the isotropic spectrum. These discrepancies, despite the fact that they are small, strongly suggest that the molecule is distorted from tetrahedral symmetry. We stress that this distortion must, nevertheless be quite small.

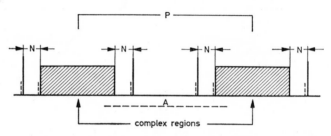

Fig. 9.9. Schematic powder spectrum due to a hypothetical tetrahedral PF_4 radical.

A distortion to give C_{2v} symmetry has been considered in § 9.1c (ii) above, and the way to which the T_d orbitals are modified was depicted in Fig. 9.4. Two effects will strongly influence the form of the electron spin resonance spectrum: the resulting anisotropy in the ^{31}P hyperfine coupling and the g-tensors. These anisotropies would combine to give shoulders on the outer-most lines such as those actually observed. The effect is so small, however, that any attempt to estimate them quantitatively seems to be unwarranted.

This same distortion would adequately account for the low value of g_{av} found for the room temperature spectrum. As stressed in § 9.1c (ii), a shift to high g-values would have been anticipated for the purely tetrahedral species but to low g-values for the distorted species.

We favour a C_{2v} distortion because this is the type found to a far more marked extent, in the thirty-four electron molecule SF_4. Chantry and Ewing[17] found that this molecule undergoes rapid inversions of the type shown in Fig. 9.10. The actual inversion will be a coupled form of the two modes A and B illustrated, but mode B makes the fluorines appear equivalent. It is presumably this inversion which occurring rapidly at room temperature, makes all the fluorines appear to be equivalent in a molecule whose low g-value indicates the presence of a distortion which makes the fluorines non-equivalent. This inversion provides a ready explanation of the marked line-broadening found in the 210 °K region (Fig. 9.6.). Here, presumably, the inversion rate is equivalent to the hyperfine splitting frequency and a rapid relaxation is induced[1].

The calculated electron populations are given in Table 9.4. If one assumes a tetrahedral structure and no contribution from the outer 4s-level on

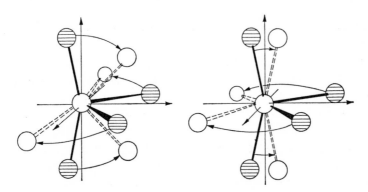

Fig. 9. 10. Inversion modes of the PF₄ radical.

TABLE 9.4

ELECTRON SPIN RESONANCE AND STRUCTURAL DATA
FOR PHOSPHORUS TETRAFLUORIDE, PF_4

	Hyperfine tensor (gauss)			Reference
	$B_\perp$	$B_\parallel$	A_{iso}	
g_{av} = 1.9985 ^{19}F	−40	80	196	1
^{31}P			1346	14

$c_s^2(P) = 0.37 \quad c_{p_z}^2(F) = 0.07 \quad c_s^2(F) = 0.011$

phosphorus, then the whole contribution is from the 3s-level: this gives 0.37 for the total spin-density on phosphorus. The sum of the 2s- and $2p(\sigma)$-contribution from fluorine is then 0.32, giving a total close to 0.7. In view of the approximation involved in summations of this sort this is a satisfactory answer for a penta-atomic radical. Nevertheless, it is clear from the low temperature spectrum that there is some anisotropic contribution from phosphorus. Also, even slight admixture of the outer (4s)-phosphorus level would be enough to account for the missing 30%. Little more can be said at this stage of refinement except to call attention to the fairly low 2p/2s ratio of about 7 found for the fluorine σ-orbital. This is small enough to indicate a real hybridisation, being very close to the ratio found by Schulman and Sugano for the σ-fluorine orbitals in transition metal fluorides[18].

As we anticipated, the radical PF_4 has indeed many features of interest which warrant a comparison with the tetroxides or fluorides of the transition metals. We conclude this Chapter with a brief outline of this meeting ground.

(ii) Comparison of thirty-three electron radicals with d-transition metal tetroxides

For convenience, we select the species PF_4^+, PF_4 and PF_4^- for comparison with MnO_4^-, MnO_4^{2-} and MnO_4^{3-} [13]. One or two outer electrons in the former series are found to induce a distortion from tetrahedral symmetry. This is relatively small for PF_4, the orbital stemming from the lowest anti-bonding σ-level of the parent PF_4^+, but is large for PF_4^-, the two electrons being paired in an orbital which has lost some anti-bonding character and gained non-bonding character as a result of the distortion. The latter series, however, is undistorted apart from a possible Jahn–Teller distortion in manganate. The two electrons in hypomanganate, MnO_4^{3-}, are unpaired in a degenerate *e*-level which has predominantly 3*d*-character on manganese. The relative bonding schemes are indicated in Fig. 9.2.[1]. One significant aspect of these schemes is that the outer *d*-level on phosphorus is so far removed that it hardly contributes to the task of accommodating the outer electrons, whereas, for the transition metal complexes, the electrons can be readily accommodated in these orbitals.

References

1 P. W. ATKINS AND M. C. R. SYMONS, *J. Chem. Soc.*, 1964, 4363.
2 P. W. ATKINS, *Ph. D. Thesis*, Leicester, 1964.
3 E. HUGHES AND W. G. MOULTON, *J. Chem. Phys.*, 1963, *39*, 1359.
4 F. JEFFERS, P. F. WIGEN AND J. A. COWEN, *Bull. Am. Phys. Soc.*, 1961, *6*, 118.
5 R. P. KOHIN AND D. W. OVENALL, *Bull. Am. Phys. Soc.*, 1963, *8*, 343.
6 P. W. ATKINS, J. A. BRIVATI, A. HORSFIELD, M. C. R. SYMONS AND P. A. TREVALION, *6th Intern. Symp. on Free Radicals, Cambridge, 1963*.
7 P. W. ATKINS, M. C. R. SYMONS AND P. A. TREVALION, *Proc. Chem. Soc.*, 1963, 222.
8 R. KEEN, *Z. Krist.*, 1935, *91*, 129.
9 N. A. KEEN, *Ph. D. Thesis*, Southampton, 1962.
10 P. A. TREVALION, *Ph. D. Thesis*, Southampton, 1963.
11 P. W. ATKINS, M. C. R. SYMONS AND H. W. WARDALE, *J. Chem. Soc.*, 1964, 5215.
12 R. J. COOK, S. R. ROWLAND AND D. H. WHIFFIN, *Mol. Phys.*, 1964, *8*, 195.
13 A. CARRINGTON AND M. C. R. SYMONS, *Chem. Rev.*, 1963, *63*, 443.
14 J. R. MORTON, *Can. J. Phys.*, 1963, *41*, 706.
15 R. W. FESSENDEN, *J. Chem. Phys.*, 1962, *37*, 747.
16 E. MACKOR AND E. DE BOER, *Mol. Phys.*, 1962, *5* 493.
17 G. W. CHANTRY AND V. C. EWING, *Mol. Phys.*, 1962, *5*, 210.
18 R. SCHULMAN AND S. SUGANO, *Phys. Rev.*, 1963, *130*, 506.

Chapter 10

Summary and conclusions

In the previous chapters we have reported and commented upon a large number of radicals of which only a few were known until a short time ago. Even those which have been known for a considerable time had not previously been investigated to the degree of intimacy that is obtained by electron spin resonance. It is unfortunate that the interpretation of the spectra has not been capable of a comparable delicacy. Nevertheless the results have been translated into concepts which are meaningful to the chemist and it would be fruitful at this point to review the approximations invoked during this translation. This is also a convenient point from which to review the trends that have been observed: to enquire whether isoelectronic series do indeed conform to the predictions based upon electronegativity arguments and to obtain a broad view of the molecular information that has been obtained.

The story is not yet complete: many problems both of interpretation and understanding remain, and in the final sections of this book we shall, therefore, mention some of them.

10.1 SOME GENERALISATIONS

(a) The applicability of simple theory

Most of the structural information which has been obtained has been from the hyperfine structure of a spectrum. We shall suppose that the tensor has been correctly extracted from the spectrum and all that we shall consider is the interpretation of this in terms of spin-densities on the magnetic nuclei of the radical.

There are a number of major approximations in this important step: it is assumed that the spin-density can be calculated by direct comparison with the hypothetical free-atom hyperfine splitting. The latter values normally have to be calculated and the errors here have already been discussed in § 2.4. But should these atomic values be used? It is possible to think of several reasons why not: the distortion of the atomic orbitals on molecule formation and the inestimable effect of the ligand atoms are among the foremost. Again, the spin-densities have been calculated on the assumption that the electron occupies orbitals of only the valence shell; the contribution from the polarisation of other shells has only been considered when it cannot be avoided, for example, in the so-called π-electron radicals (nineteen-electron AB_2 species). Such contributions cannot normally be distinguished, particularly when they have the same symmetry as the major interactions. Thus, how much of the isotropic interaction in a radical which has been ascribed to occupancy of an ns-orbital is really due to spin in the $(n-1)s$, $(n-2)s$, ... orbitals? Perhaps a guide to this is that the ns spin-density due to polarisation caused by unit occupation of an np-orbital is generally of the order of 1%, whereas typical direct spin-densities are a magnitude greater than this.

Not only are ns-orbital populations impossible to resolve precisely, but it is as yet impossible to separate the contribution from spin in d-orbitals from that in p-orbitals. So often are d-orbitals invoked to explain anomalies in such parameters as bond strengths, lengths and angles that information about the true extent of their involvement would be welcome. An anomaly in the g-tensor of SeO_2^- yielded what may be information on this problem, but there are considerable and severe approximations implicit in the calculation so that little significance can be put on the result.

It is seemingly optimistic to try to estimate spin-densities on non-magnetic neighbouring nuclei if the spin-density on one atom is known. The major question is the effect of overlap: what should the true sum of spin-density on the nuclei be, and what is the contribution of the overlap density? Should the density sum to something of the order $(1 \pm S_{AB}^2)^{-1}$?

What of bond angles? The major approximation is that which supposes the bond angle to be determined by the hybridisation of the central atom. It is not known just how precisely the orbital following is; in other words it is not known to what extent the bonds themselves are bent. Nor is it strictly true that the hybridisation of the bonds is determined only by the hybridisation of the orbital occupied by the unpaired electron.

It is, therefore, with something akin to surprise that we compare the electron spin resonance results with those of other measurements and observe remarkable agreement. The trends with electronegativity will be discussed in the following section but here we may mention the calculated bond angle of

NO_2 (133°) whereas the value observed by rotational spectroscopy is 134°. Further, the sum of spin-densities in the homonuclear diatomics that have been investigated is always very close to unity. Such direct comparisons are infrequent and more are really required before the methods are truly ratified but further confirmation *is* forthcoming when the expected trends of properties as calculated by these routes are in fact observed. To this topic we now turn.

(b) Trends in isoelectronic series

(i) Spin-density distributions

In § 6.1e it was remarked that spin-density on an atom in a radical ought to decrease with increasing electronegativity if the unpaired electron were antibonding in character. In Fig. 10.1. the total spin-density $(c_s^2 + c_p^2)$ on the central atom for seventeen, nineteen and twenty-five electron species are plotted against the atom's electronegativity and it is seen that the results strikingly conform to this prediction. No attempt has been made to distinguish between the seventeen and nineteen electron dioxides but some difference in dependence is expected because the orbitals of the former include some *s*-character. Also, both seventeen electron dioxides and twenty-five electron trioxides respond to changes in spin-density by bending: thus the precise dependence of spin-density on electronegativity would be difficult to predict.

The only species which is notably removed from the lines drawn in Fig. 10.1. is NO_3^{2-}, but this links with the final point made in the preceding paragraph: NO_3^{2-} is not expected to lie on the same line as its analogues formed from second and third row elements because of its considerably flatter shape. The latter is dictated by the steric difficulty of attaching three oxygen atoms to the relatively small nitrogen atom.

So far, then, all the results of spin-density distributions follow the predictions of a simple application of the concept of electronegativity to molecules of similar shape.

(ii) Bond angles

In § 7.1c the relationship between bond angle and electronegativity was developed with the conclusion that the former should increase as the latter increased unless there was any counteracting steric effect. Just this tendency is observed along the sequence AsO_3^{2-}, PO_3^{2-}, SO_3^-, SeO_3^- and ClO_3 whereas the corresponding fluorine compounds AsF_3, PF_3 and NF_3 do not change

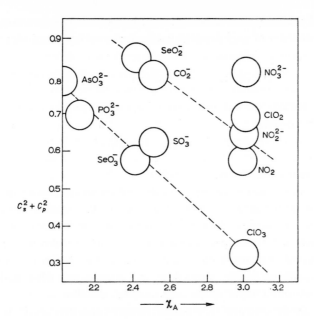

Fig. 10.1. Variation of electron spin-density on the central atom with its electro-negativity in AB_2 and AB_3 radicals.

from the already considerably distorted AsF_3. This is quite analogous to the situation discussed in § 7.1c and illustrated in Fig. 7.3. Although the flatness of NO_3^{2-} is a steric effect ($ON(SO_3)_2^{2-}$ being planar, § 8.2d (ii)), the trend along the second row elements is unlikely to be accounted for by this mechanism.

The replacement of oxygen by hydrogen is illustrated in § 8.2d (iv) where HPO_2^- is discussed: the effect of the substitution is to increase the planarity of the radical, possibly because of the smaller size of the hydrogen atom.

Many of the radicals which have been considered have shown some type of distortion and it would be of interest to know whether this has occurred as a Jahn–Teller effect or in response to the demands of the environment. There is, of course, no ambiguity when the molecule is linear (for example, ClO, HO). For non-linear radicals a constancy of the distortion on going from one crystal to another would support a Jahn–Teller explanation. But the distinction is not really meaningful, only gas-phase measurements would reveal the presence of a purely Jahn–Teller type of distortion. It might be remarked here, however, that the very presence of a distortion, particularly in those species which have been formed by electron ejection, is a source of stability for the centre: the hole is trapped at a site by the distortion.

(c) Identification of radicals in irradiated solids

That the pattern for identification of magnetic centres by electron spin resonance is now fairly well established has been illustrated in the foregoing pages. In summary the process may be rationalised in the following way. Initially there is *chemical expectation*. Gain or loss of electrons or loss of hydrogen are typical of such anticipations, but every case poses specific problems. Care must be taken at this point as the technique is extremely sensitive: so much so that on low dosages particularly, trace impurities may dominate. A typical example of this is the case of X-irradiated beryllium oxide which contained a paramagnetic centre which proved to be associated with a fluoride ion impurity[2]. It is unlikely that impurities in very low concentration would suffer direct damage but quite probable that they could act directly, for example, as electron sources or sinks.

The next stage is to analyse the electron spin resonance spectrum, possibly with the help of single crystals or two instruments operating at different frequencies so that g- and hyperfine tensors can be derived. These are then compared with the predictions for the various fragments that might be formed and hence all but one can usually be eliminated. If this is not possible or if confirmation is necessary, *isotopic substitution* is frequently possible, and may well resolve any ambiguity. The use of ENDOR techniques will generally provide greater resolution or distinguish between different contributing nuclei. For example, by this technique the hyperfine splitting detected in irradiated fluorophosphates (§ 5.5) was shown to arise from ^{19}F rather than ^{31}P nuclei.

Great care must be exercised in ensuring that the radical is really *stationary* when hyperfine data are extracted. If the radicals are tumbling in a restricted fashion, considerable confusion may result, as is well illustrated by the discussion of early studies of nitrogen dioxide trapped in rare-gas matrices (§ 7.2a (i)).

If a variety of magnetic centres contribute to the spectrum, it helps to distinguish their contributions. This can sometimes be accomplished by increasing the microwave power in the hope that one centre will saturate before the other. Under these circumstances there will be a selective broadening of the lines from this centre, leaving the other narrow. Alternatively, one centre may be destroyed by bleaching with suitable ultraviolet or visible light and then its contribution to the total spectrum can be extricated by subtraction. This is well illustrated by the studies of γ-irradiated alkali metal hydroxide hydrates[3]. In a similar way, it is sometimes found that one centre is lost thermally at a lower temperature than that which permits mobility of the other. This is perhaps the least general since very frequently all centres remain trapped until the melting or softening point is reached at which point all centres are rapidly lost.

Once a consistent formulation for the centre has been derived, it may be possible to carry out more detailed calculations to check the postulate or the theory depending upon one's predilections. When sufficient results have been amassed trends in various properties can be established, and results for unknown related species can then be predicted with considerable accuracy.

Despite the successes, many failures and uncertainties remain. Whilst it would be impossible to catalogue all of these, large numbers being unpublished or filed away in obscure reports, we conclude this Chapter, perhaps appropriately, by giving brief outlines of a few such studies.

10.2 SOME UNRESOLVED PROBLEMS

Several instances in which uncertainty still shrouds the proper interpretation of results for paramagnetic centres have already been outlined. For example, what is the true nature of the paramagnetic species formed in irradiated ice or in irradiated potassium hydrogen phosphate? Here we outline briefly some results for irradiated borates, silicon and for various radical species associated with sulphur.

(a) Radicals in irradiated borates

Yasaitis and Smaller detected a four-line spectrum in irradiated glasses containing boron and attributed the structure to hyperfine interaction with ^{11}B nuclei[4]. Since then, Lee and Bray have carried out extensive studies of these and related centres[5] in a wide variety of alkali borate and borosilicate glasses which had been exposed to γ-rays or thermal neutrons. Various centres were detected, but we will confine our attention to a well defined centre, having the properties summarised in Table 10.1, that was frequently encountered in very many of the glasses studied.

TABLE 10.1

ELECTRON SPIN RESONANCE DATA FOR A CENTRE
IN γ-IRRADIATED BORATES [5]

g-Tensor			^{11}B-Hyperfine tensor (gauss)		
$g_{\parallel}$	$g_{\perp}$	g_{av}	$B_{\parallel}$	$B_{\perp}$	A_{iso}
2.0121	2.0024	2.0056	$\begin{cases} \pm 2 \\ \mp 20.7 \end{cases}$	$\begin{matrix} \mp 1 \\ \pm 10.4 \end{matrix}$	$\begin{matrix} \pm 15 \\ \pm 3.7 \end{matrix} \Big\} $ alternatives

That the hyperfine structure is indeed due to coupling with the ^{11}B nuclei rather than with another having $\frac{3}{2}$ spin was shown by using material enriched with ^{10}B, in which case the spectrum was modified in exactly the manner expected. The g- and hyperfine anisotropies were unravelled for the rather complex powder spectra by comparing results obtained at 9.2 KMc/s with those obtained at 23.2 KMc/s[5]. The unpaired electron is thought to be at one of the BO_4 tetrahedra in the glass[4], and is probably trapped on one of the oxygen atoms which is not associated with a second boron atom, since there is no indication of hyperfine interaction with a second boron nucleus.

Of the four alternatives for the isotropic and anisotropic hyperfine interactions with boron given in Table 10.1, all are physically possible, and in the absence of further data, little more can be said about the structure of this centre.

It is interesting that another paramagnetic centre involving one boron nucleus has recently been detected in irradiated single crystals of beryllium oxide[6]. This centre differs markedly from that studied by Lee and Bray, the hyperfine coupling being very large and indicative of an electron strongly associated with boron rather than with oxygen. Nevertheless the simple postulate of a B^{2+} ion in a Be^{2+} site is unsatisfactory since as deduced from the hyperfine parameters the $2p$-character is far larger than the $2s$-character.

(b) Radicals in irradiated silicon

The effect of high-energy radiation on single crystals of silicon has been studied extensively by Watkins, Corbett and their co-workers[7]. The results are extremely involved, and by 1961, at least five distinct paramagnetic centres had been detected and their electron spin resonance spectra documented.

TABLE 10.2

ELECTRON SPIN RESONANCE DATA FOR CENTRES IN
IRRADIATED SILICON [7]

	g-Tensor				^{29}Si-Hyperfine tensor (gauss)		
	g_1	g_2	g_3	g_{av}	$B_\parallel$	$B_\perp$	A_{iso}
A	2.0092	2.0026	2.0033	2.0050	17	− 8.5	146
B	2.0026	2.0085	2.0107	2.0073	42	−21	97
C	2.0012	2.0135	2.0150	2.0099	12	− 5.5	68
E	2.0005	2.0112	2.0096	2.0071	38	−18.5	124
J	2.0004	2.0020	2.0041	2.0022	20	−10	53

All these results have been discussed by Watkins and Corbett[7] in terms of unpaired electrons in "broken bonds", that are associated with various kinds of vacancy. A situation is envisaged whereby "dangling orbitals" remain directed into a given vacancy. In previous discussions we have always envisaged a situation in which radicals formed by bond-breaking processes relax in the crystalline host to a new shape dictated primarily by the new electronic requirements of the radical and only slightly by the crystal. The situation in silicon appears to be quite the reverse, if the interpretation of Watkins and Corbett is correct: the removal of one silicon from the lattice results only in a minor relaxation of the surrounding silicon atoms, so that the orbital of an unpaired electron localised on one of them retains considerable 3s-character. Some typical results are summarised in Table 10.2.

(c) Sulphur radicals

A variety of electron spin resonance studies of radicals derived from sulphur have been reported. In no instance has information from ^{33}S hyperfine coupling been forthcoming and hence structural information can only be derived from the g-tensor.

(i) Radicals in molten sulphur

That S_8 rings open and polymerise when sulphur is heated has been appreciated for many years. The postulate[8] that the strong resonance band found at $g = 2.024$ is due to unpaired electrons on the ends of such radicals is thus chemically very reasonable. Whilst one can theorise at length about the expected form of the molecular orbital for these electrons, the data are of little use in this respect. They do, however, enable one to estimate the stationary concentration of radicals, and Fraenkel and his co-workers have also estimated rates of dimerisation from variations in line-width with temperature[8].

(ii) Sulphur deposits from the gas phase

Deposits of sulphur formed by condensing the heated vapours on to a cold-finger have colours ranging from lime-green to purple depending upon the temperature prior to deposition[9]. All these forms have a weak electron spin resonance spectrum, the intensity increasing as the temperature increases, being greatest for the purple variety. In all cases a single line flanked by well defined shoulders was obtained, the results being as given in Table 10.3. The highest concentration of spins being about one per 500 sulphur atoms.

Radford and Rice supposed that at least two radicals were present, one being responsible for the peak at $g = 2.025$ and the other for the shoulders at $g = 2.039$ and $g = 2.000$. They do not, apparently, obtain any spectra from which the central peak is absent, and it seems more reasonable to suppose that just one species is responsible for all three features. This assignment is implicit in the data given in Table 10.3.

They assign the spectra to polymeric radicals built up from S_2 molecules but having sufficient chain lengths to separate the electrons from each other to a distance great enough to prevent appreciable spin–spin interaction.

(iii) Sulphur in oleum

Dissolution of sulphur in 65% oleum results in a clear blue solution which

TABLE 10.3

ELECTRON SPIN RESONANCE DATA FOR SULPHUR RADICALS
PREPARED FROM THE ELEMENT

Medium	*g-Tensor*				*Reference*
	g_1	g_2	g_3	g_{av}	
Molten S				2.024	8
Deposited	2.000	2.025	2.039	2.0213	9
Oleum (i)	2.025	2.025	2.032	2.027	11
(ii)	2.003	2.018	2.018	2.014	11
Amines	2.003	2.035	2.055	2.030	12

although largely diamagnetic[10] contains radicals in low concentration which are characterised by a single electron spin resonance peak having a $g = 2.013$[11]. At 77 °K this absorption is modified in the manner expected for a radical having an axially symmetric g-tensor, the derived parameters being $g_\parallel = 2.003$ and $g_\perp = 2.018$[11].

It is not certain if the blue colour is a property of these radicals, although this does seem quite probable. All that can be said about the structure of the radical is that it has a g-tensor of form found for linear σ^*-radicals such as Cl_2^-. The corresponding sulphur radical would be S_2^{3-} which is clearly outside the bounds of possibility in 65% oleum. At present we know of no good explanation for the structure of this well defined radical, many otherwise reasonable postulates being eliminated by the results for other sulphur radicals described in the other sections.

In dilute oleums, before sulphur is precipitated, a green-yellow solution which is probably a colloid is formed. The electron spin resonance spectrum at room temperature consists of two lines, one being due to the radicals found in 65% oleum, and the other, having a g-value of about 2.02 may well be a polymeric sulphur radical similar to those found in liquid sulphur. At 90 °K this second radical also shows a marked g-value variation, the principal values of the g-tensor being as quoted in Table 10.3[11].

(iv) Sulphur in amines

Sulphur dissolves in a variety of amines to form intensely coloured solutions, the most usual colours being orange and red. These solutions have been shown by electron spin resonance spectroscopy[12] to contain radicals in low concentration. In fluid solutions these have a g-value of 2.030 ± 0.001 but at 77 °K two well defined shoulders are apparent, from which the g-tensor given in Table 10.3 was obtained. That only one type of radical is involved is shown by the agreement between the average of these three g-values and the solution value, and it is noteworthy that the g-tensor is independent of the amine used.

Hodgson *et al.*[12] suggest that N,N'-polythiobisamines are formed by a series of nucleophilic displacements, and that the relatively weak sulphur-sulphur bonds therein can break reversibly if the chain is long.

(v) Structure of sulphur radicals

Apart from the results for sulphur in 65% oleum, a pattern of g-values is apparent. One g-value of 2.0033 is close to that for the free spin and could be taken as corresponding to a direction parallel to the density axes of p-orbitals comprising a π-level containing the unpaired electron. Then there is another g-value considerably greater than this, and corresponding to a considerable mixing with a filled level. The third g-value falls between these.

Of the radicals discussed in this book, perhaps the nineteen electron radicals such as ClO_2, come closest to having a g-tensor of this form. Purely by analogy, the anion S_3^- would be expected to have such a similar g-tensor but with larger values for Δg because of the greater spin–orbit coupling constant for sulphur, although energy level separations play a significant role. Although S_3^- is improbable, perhaps HS_3 or HO_3S-S_3 might be responsible for the spectra. In S_3^- we imagine complete delocalisation of the unpaired electron in the π^*-level. Protonation or sulphonation would obviously upset the distribution but would not be expected to exclude the unpaired electron totally from one of the sulphur atoms.

There is clearly no need to confine the sulphur chain to three atoms. This raises the interesting problem of delocalisation. If the sulphur chain were to remain in one plane, then, for the radical S_n^- the unpaired electron would surely be delocalised as in S_3^-. Such coplanarity would be most improbable for long chains, but might well be the rule for $n=4$ or even $n=5$.

Clearly, much more experimental information is required. By far the most informative single experiment would be to label radicals with ^{33}S. Such experiments are currently underway and preliminary indications are that the species probably contains two equivalent sulphur atoms[13]. Solid-state spectra may be sufficiently clear to enable a reasonable guess to be made regarding the structure of this species.

References

1 M. C. R. SYMONS, J. Chem. Soc., 1963, 570.
2 Z. ŠRONBEK, L. NOVÁK AND K. ŽĎANSKÝ, Phys. Stat. Sol., 1964, 6, 173.
3 M. J. BLANDAMER, L. SHIELDS AND M. C. R. SYMONS, J. Chem. Soc., 1964, 4352.
4 E. L. YASAITIS AND B. SMALLER, Phys. Rev., 1953, 92, 1068.
5 S. LEE AND P. J. BRAY, J. Chem. Phys., 1963, 39, 2863.
6 A. R. REINBERG, J. Chem. Phys., 1964, 41, 850.
7 G. D. WATKINS AND I. W. CORBETT, Discussions Faraday Soc., 1961, 31, 86.
8 D. M. GARDNER AND G. K. FRAENKEL, J. Am. Chem. Soc., 1956, 78, 3279.
9 H. E. RADFORD AND F. O. RICE, J. Chem. Phys., 1960, 33, 774.
10 M. C. R. SYMONS, J. Chem. Soc., 1957, 2440.
11 D. J. E. INGRAM AND M. C. R. SYMONS, J. Chem. Soc., 1957, 2437.
12 W. G. HODGSON, S. A. BUCKLAR AND G. PETERS, J. Am. Chem. Soc., 1963, 85, 543.
13 D. A. C. McNEIL, personal communication.

The language of group theory

1A.1 DEFINITIONS

We present here a superficial description of the language, content and application of group theory. The only reason for including it here is to enable those unconversant with its language to understand some of the significance of the symbolism that we have employed in the body of this book. This account will be quite informal; for more formal and lengthier accounts the reader is referred to the books by Jaffe and Orchin[1], Cotton[2], Heine[3] and Tinkham[4].

The groups with which we are concerned are the groups of *symmetry operations* of molecules. A symmetry operation is an operation on the molecule *(inversion, rotation, reflection)* such that the initial and final states are indistinguishable. For example, the rotation of the nitrogen dioxide molecule by 180° about the OÑO bisector is a symmetry operation; the rotation by 90° is not. We are not concerned with *translations* and so we consider only the *point groups*, not the *space groups*. The latter must be considered in crystals but the former refer to all those symmetry operations which leave one point fixed (invariant). For completeness the symmetry group must contain the *identity* operation, denoted by E. When this operates on a function it leaves it unchanged. Thus we can write

$$\psi' \equiv E\psi = \psi \tag{1A.1}$$

If we were to operate on a wave-function with an operator other than the identity then, in general, the wave-function generated is a sum of wave-functions:

$$\psi' = R\psi = \sum_i c_i \psi_i \tag{1A.2}$$

Where R is the symmetry operation and the c_i are coefficients. For example, the operation of rotating the NO_2 molecule by 180° about the OÑO bisector, the operation denoted by C_2, has the following effect on the nitrogen p_x-orbital:

$$R p_x = - p_x \tag{1A.3}$$

TABLE 1A.1

C_{2v}			E	C_2	σ_v	σ_v'
(x^2, y^2, z^2)	z	A_1	1	1	1	1
xy	R_z	A_2	1	1	-1	-1
xz	R_y, x	B_1	1	-1	-1	1
yz	R_x, y	B_2	1	-1	1	-1

C_{3v}			E	$2C_3$	$3\sigma_v$
$(x^2 + y^2, z^2)$	z	A_1	1	1	1
	R_z	A_2	1	1	-1
$(x^2 - y^2, xy)$	(x, y)				
(xz, yz)	(R_x, R_y)	E	2	-1	0

C_{4v}			E	C_2	$2C_4$	$2\sigma_v$	$2\sigma_d$
$(x^2 + y^2, z^2)$	z	A_1	1	1	1	1	1
	R_z	A_2	1	1	1	-1	-1
$x^2 - y^2$		B_1	1	1	-1	1	-1
xy		B_2	1	1	-1	-1	1
(xz, yz)	(x, y)	E	2	-2	0	0	0
	(R_x, R_y)						

$D_{3h} = D_3 \times \sigma_n$			E	σ_n	$2C_3$	$2S_3$	$3C_2'$	$3\sigma_v$
$(x^2 + y^2, z^2)$		A_1'	1	1	1	1	1	1
	R_z	A_2'	1	1	1	1	-1	-1
		A_1''	1	-1	1	-1	1	-1
	z	A_2''	1	-1	1	-1	-1	1
$(x^2 - y^2, xy)$	(x, y)	E'	2	2	-1	-1	0	0
(xz, yz)	(R_x, R_y)	E''	2	-2	-1	1	0	0

O			E	$8C_3$	$3C_2 = 3C_4^2$	$6C_2$	$6C_4$
		A_1	1	1	1	1	1
		A_2	1	1	1	-1	-1
$(x^2 - y^2, 3z^2 - r^2)$		E	2	-1	2	0	0
(R_x, R_y, R_z)							
(x, y, z)		T_1	3	0	-1	-1	1
(xy, yz, zx)		T_2	3	0	-1	1	-1
$O_h = O \times i$							

T_d		E	$8C_3$	$3C_2$	$6\sigma_d$	$6S_4$
	A_1	1	1	1	1	1
	A_2	1	1	1	-1	-1
(x^2-y^2, z^2)	E	2	-1	2	0	0
(R_x, R_y, R_z)	T_1	3	0	-1	-1	1
(x, y, z) $\Big\}$	T_2	3	0	-1	1	-1
(xy, yz, zx)						

$C_{\infty v}$				E	$2C_\phi$	σ_v
$(x^2 + y^2, z^2)$	z		$A_1(\Sigma^+)$	1	1	1
	R_z		$A_2(\Sigma^-)$	1	1	-1
(xz, yz)	(x, y) $\Big\}$		$E_1(\Pi)$	2	$2\cos\phi$	0
	(R_x, R_y)					
$(x^2 - y^2, xy)$			$E_2(\Delta)$	2	$2\cos 2\phi$	0
			. . . . . .		. . . . . .	
			etc.		etc.	

In general, therefore, we ought to represent the effect of R by a matrix **R**. For example, if we consider a set of orbitals $\{p_x, p_y, p_z\}$ and take R to be the positive 90° rotation about the z-axis, the effect of R is to produce the following transformations:

$$R p_z = p_z; \quad R p_x = p_y; \quad R p_y = - p_x \tag{1A.4}$$

This result is also obtained by introducing the 3×3 matrix

$$\mathbf{R} = \begin{pmatrix} 0 & 1 & 0 \\ -1 & 0 & 0 \\ 0 & 0 & 1 \end{pmatrix} \tag{1A.5}$$

and the column matrix

$$\begin{pmatrix} p_x \\ p_y \\ p_z \end{pmatrix}$$

since

$$\begin{pmatrix} p_y \\ -p_x \\ p_z \end{pmatrix} = \begin{pmatrix} 0 & 1 & 0 \\ -1 & 0 & 0 \\ 0 & 0 & 1 \end{pmatrix} \begin{pmatrix} p_x \\ p_y \\ p_z \end{pmatrix} \tag{1A.6}$$

Such a matrix is called a *representative* of the operation and depends for its form on the *basis* chosen. For example we need not have chosen the basis $\{p_x, p_y, p_z\}$; another basis would require a different representative for the same operation. The sum of the diagonal elements of a representative matrix is independent of the basis, thus we can talk of the *character* (χ) of an operation. The character of an operation is the sum of the diagonal elements of the matrix representing the operation. As it is independent of the basis it is a valuable property; rarely do we need the actual matrices for the characters are normally sufficient. Tables of characters for different symmetries have been calculated and a few are given in Table 1A.1. We shall explain and employ them later.

We have remarked that a group is the set of *all* symmetry operations R. A *representation* is then the set of all matrices which represent the operations. Once a particular matrix has been assigned to an operation then there is a restriction on the matrices representing the other operations of the group: the multiplication of any two matrices gives the matrix corresponding to the consecutive application of the operators which the original matrices represented. Thus the rule

$$R^{(i)}R^{(j)} = R^{(k)} \qquad (1A.7)$$

must be obeyed by both operators and matrices. A trivial example is for all operations to be represented by 1: the multiplications are then obviously mirrored in the multiplication of these 1×1 matrices, each with $\chi = 1$.

If we look at the following representation:

$$\begin{pmatrix} a & 0 & 0 \\ 0 & a_1 & a_2 \\ 0 & a_3 & a_4 \end{pmatrix} \begin{pmatrix} b & 0 & 0 \\ 0 & b_1 & b_2 \\ 0 & b_3 & b_4 \end{pmatrix} \begin{pmatrix} c & 0 & 0 \\ 0 & c_1 & c_2 \\ 0 & c_3 & c_4 \end{pmatrix}$$

we see that all the matrices are of the form

When a matrix can be put in this form it is said to be *reducible*; when it cannot be so arranged it is said to be *irreducible*. Thus the above matrices are each reducible into a 1-dimensional and 2-dimensional matrix. When we have a representation such that the matrices representing *all* the operations of the group can simultaneously be put into block-diagonal form, the representation is said to be reducible. When this is not possible we have an *irreducible representation.* There are only a finite number of irreducible representations for groups with a finite number of elements (operations). If the order of a group (number of elements) be h, and l_i be the dimension of the ith representation (Γ_i) then

$$\sum_i l_i^2 = h \qquad (1A.8)$$

The physical significance of the concept of irreducibility may be gathered by considering a simple example: that of the set of p_x, p_y and p_z orbitals of the central atom in a triangular pyramidal (C_{3v}) molecule. It is obvious that no symmetry operation of the molecule can transform p_z into a combination of p_x and p_y, whereas p_x and p_y are readily scrambled amongst themselves. Thus the operations of the group C_{3v} with $\{p_x p_y p_z\}$ as the basis, span a 1-dimensional representation and a 2-dimensional representation. There are six operations in the C_{3v} group (the identity, rotation by 120°, rotation by 240°, and three reflections, Fig. 1A.1a.); therefore $h=6$. Since we have already found that there is one 1-dimensional representation we see from eqn. (1A.8) that the only other irreducible representation must be 1-dimensional, because

$$2^2 + 1^2 + 1^2 = 6 \cdot \qquad (1A.9)$$

A very useful property of representations is their orthogonality, which can be expressed in the form

$$\sum_R \Gamma_i(R)^*_{\mu\nu} \Gamma_j(R)_{\alpha\beta} = \left(\frac{h}{l_i}\right) \delta_{ij} \delta_{\mu\alpha} \delta_{\nu\beta} \qquad (1A.10)$$

where $\Gamma_i(R)_{\mu\nu}$ is the $\mu\nu$th element of the matrix in the ith representation of

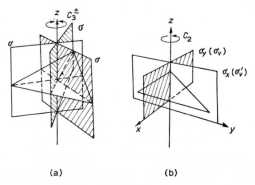

(a)   (b)

Fig. 1A.1.   Symmetry operations of the group C_{3v} (a) and C_{2v} (b).

the Rth operation of the group. A less general form of this, but one that is more useful to us, is a similar statement for the characters:

$$\sum_R \chi^{(i)}(R)^* \chi^{(j)}(R) = h\delta_{ij} \qquad (1A.11)$$

where $\chi^{(i)}(R)$ is the character in the ith representation of the Rth operation. This expression can be used to answer the important question of how any given representation reduces. If the character of the given (possibly reducible) representation be $\chi(R)$ for a particular operation, then in terms of the characters of the irreducible representations

$$\chi(R) = \sum_i c_i \chi^{(i)}(R) \qquad (1A.12)$$

Using eqn. (1A.11) we obtain that

$$c_i = \frac{1}{h}\sum_R \chi^{(i)}(R)^* \chi(R) \qquad (1A.13)$$

We are now in a position to apply some of these results, but first let us explain the labelling of the rows and columns of the character tables, and of the tables themselves.

1A.2 SYMBOLS

(a) The operations

E = the identity operation.
C_n = a rotation by $2\pi/n$.
σ_v = a reflection in the plane including the major symmetry axis.
σ_h = a reflection in the plane perpendicular to the major symmetry axis.
S_n = a rotation by $2\pi/n$ followed by reflection in a plane perpendicular to the axis of rotation.

(b) The representations

The representations are labelled either by $\Gamma_1, \Gamma_2, \ldots$ or by Roman letters. It is the latter system which we shall employ.

A: refers to a 1-dimensional representation such that the major rotation has a character $\chi = 1$. If a number of these exist then they are distinguished by subscripts, *e.g.* $A_1, A_2, \ldots$

B: denotes a 1-dimensional representation but one which has odd parity (changes sign) under the principal rotation. Distinguishing subscripts are also used.

E: denotes a 2-dimensional representation.

T: denotes a 3-dimensional representation.

A superscript prime *e.g.* A′ denotes that a reflection has character of $+1$ whereas a superscript double prime *e.g.* A″ denotes that the reflection has odd parity.

A subscript g or u indicates that the parity of the representation (on inversion) is even or odd; it is meaningful only when there is a centre of inversion in the molecule.

$\Sigma, \Pi, \Delta \ldots$ are used when the infinite axial rotation group is considered. All except Σ are 2-dimensional representations.

S, P, D, ... are the representations of the infinite groups of spherical rotations. They are 1-, 3-, 5-,... dimensional.

(c) The groups

C_n : contains only a simple n-fold axis.

C_{nv} : contains an n-fold axis and the reflection σ_v.

C_{nh} : contains an n-fold axis and the reflection σ_h.

S_n : contains an n-fold axis of improper rotation.

D_n : contains two n-fold axes perpendicular to the principal C_n axis.

V   : the same as D_2 ("Vierergruppe").

D_{nd} : D_n and diagonal reflection planes (σ_d) bisecting the two minor (two-fold) axes.

D_{nh} : D_n and the reflection σ_h.

T   : the group of the regular tetrahedron (the identity, $3C_2$ and $8C_3$).

T_d : T and reflections $(T + 6\sigma_d + 6S_4)$.

T_h : T and the inversion operation.

O   : the group of operations which takes an octahedron or a cube into itself (24 elements or covering operations).

O_h : O and inversion (48 elements).

$C_{\infty v}$: infinite axial rotation group.

$D_{\infty h}$: σ_j and $2C_2$ anywhere within the σ_h plane.

· *References p. 229*

1A.3 APPLICATIONS

Just as the letters S, P, D, ... are used to label the states (and $s, p, d, ...$ the orbitals) of a system with spherical symmetry (the atom), so too can we label the orbitals or states of systems with lower symmetry if we employ the labels for the representations. $\Sigma, \Pi, \Delta, ...$ is a familiar example: a_1, a_2, e possibly a less familiar one. To put the labelling on a more secure basis than inspection (an approach which is frequently sufficient) we quote a number of rules without proof.

(a) To label an orbital

(a) Select the correct group. (If a group with less symmetry is inadvertently chosen the results will not be wrong, merely less precise than is possible; that is, the full symmetry of the problem will not have been invoked.)

(b) Apply the symmetry operations of the group to all the atomic orbitals from which the molecular orbitals are to be constructed and (i) count $+1$ for each orbital going into itself and (ii) count -1 for each orbital going into its negative.

(c) Sum all the numbers so obtained for each operation.

(d) Apply formula (1A.13) to see which irreducible representations are spanned (or inspect for the same result).

(e) To select the orbital which transforms according to the representation Γ_i apply eqn. (1A.11) to each of the characters for all the atomic orbitals and select those which do not disappear.

(f) If the symmetry combinations are already at hand then use only step (e) to determine the representation to which the representation of the orbital is not orthogonal.

As an example of these rules consider NO_2. The symmetry group is C_{2v}. What orbitals can be constructed from the nitrogen 2s- and 2p-atomic orbitals? Using (b) we construct the following tables

	(A)					(B)			
	E	C_2	$\sigma_v(x)$	$\sigma_v'(y)$		E	C_2	σ_v	σ_v'
s	s	s	s	s		1	1	1	1
p_x	p_x	$-p_x$	$-p_x$	p_x		1	-1	-1	1
p_y	p_y	$-p_y$	p_y	$-p_y$		1	-1	1	-1
p_z	p_z	p_z	p_z	p_z		1	1	1	1
				Sum		4	0	2	2

Table (B) is the result of introducing the ± 1 notation. The sum is the result of applying rule (c). By inspection (rule (d)) we see that the set of numbers

$$(4\ 0\ 2\ 2)$$

can be obtained from the character table of the group by adding the columns of the representations $2A_1 + B_1 + B_2$. To find which orbitals contribute to the a_1 molecular orbital is trivial: they are the orbitals whose characters are not orthogonal to

$$A_1:(1\ \ 1\ \ 1\ \ 1)$$

where the ordering is that of the character table (not that it matters in this case). Obviously the a_1 orbital is constructed from the s and p_z-orbitals, b_1 from the p_x-orbital and b_2 from the p_y-orbital.

(b) To label a state

If we label the molecular orbitals of a molecule as $\gamma_1, \gamma_2, \ldots$ then we can write its configuration as $\gamma_1^2 \gamma_2^2 \ldots \gamma_n^2$, $^1\Gamma_j$ if it is a closed shell species, or $\gamma_1^2 \gamma_2^2 \ldots \gamma_n$, $^2\Gamma_j'$ if it is in a doublet spin state. What should the Γ_j be? By analogy with atomic states which we label S, P, ... etc. it would seem that we could label molecular states in a representation designation. This is indeed the case and arises from the fact that the Hamiltonian for the molecule commutes with all the symmetry operations of the molecular symmetry group and so, by a general theorem for commuting operators, the symmetry designation for a molecule is a good quantum number.

To find the representation according to which the entire molecular state transforms we once again use the characters of the contributing orbitals through the rule that

$$\chi(\Gamma_j) = [\chi(\gamma_1)]^2 [\chi(\gamma_2)]^2 \cdots [\chi(\gamma_{n-1})]^2 \{[\chi(\gamma_n)]^2 \quad \text{or} \quad \chi(\gamma_n)\} \qquad (1A.14)$$

By considering this formula it is apparent that closed shell species are $^1A_1$ whereas doublet state species have a configuration that is decided by the symmetry of the half-filled orbital. Thus the molecule $\ldots b_2^2 b_1^2 a_1^1$ is $^2A_1$ whereas $\ldots b_2^2 b_1$ is $^2B_1$. States which arise from the excitation of an inner electron are labelled similarly. Thus if the half-filled orbitals in an atom are γ_k, γ_j and γ_i, then the character of the total molecular state is

$$\chi_\Gamma(R) = \chi_{\gamma_k}(R) \chi_{\gamma_j}(R) \chi_{\gamma_i}(R) \qquad (1A.15)$$

a product which is performed for each operation of the group. For example, what is the state designation of a C_{2v} molecule with the configuration $\ldots b_1\, b_2^2\, a_1\, a_2$?

$$\chi_{b_1}(R)\chi_{a_1}(R)\chi_{a_2}(R) = (1 \quad -1 \quad -1 \quad 1)(1 \quad 1 \quad 1 \quad 1)(1 \quad 1 \quad -1 \quad -1)$$
$$= (1 \quad -1 \quad 1 \quad -1)$$
$$= \chi_{b_2}(R) \tag{1A.16}$$

Therefore the state is B_2. The notation we have used represents the ordered product of the characters; in this example

$$\chi_{b_1}(R)\chi_{a_1}(R)\chi_{a_2}(R) = \left(\chi_{b_1}(E)\chi_{a_1}(E)\chi_{a_2}(E) \quad \chi_{b_1}(c_2)\chi_{a_1}(c_2)\chi_{a_2}(c_2)\cdots\text{etc.}\right) \tag{1A.17}$$

This is known as the *direct product* and is equivalent to the scalar product in vector analysis. Often the $\chi_\Gamma(R)$ so obtained is a sum of states; a decomposition using eqn. (1A.13) must then be used.

(c) Selection rules

A selection rule is a rule that indicates which of the integrals

$$I \equiv \int \psi_f^*\, \Omega \psi_i\, d\tau \tag{1A.18}$$

vanish, where ψ_i and ψ_f are the initial and final states of the system and Ω is an operator. The integral I may be written in bracket notation as

$$I \equiv \langle f\, |\Omega|\, i \rangle \tag{1A.19}$$

If the states $|f\rangle$ and $|i\rangle$ and the operator Ω transform in the molecular symmetry group as Γ_f, Γ_i and Γ_Ω respectively, then we can also define I as

$$I \equiv \langle \Gamma_f\, |\Gamma_\Omega|\, \Gamma_i \rangle \tag{1A.20}$$

The integral I is non-zero only if the direct product $\Gamma_f \times \Gamma_\Omega \times \Gamma_i$, includes A_1.

As an example, let us calculate which orbitals can be mixed with the a_1 orbital in a C_{2v} molecule by the x-component of the angular momentum. From the character table for C_{2v} we observe that L_x transforms as B_2: therefore we need to find all those orbitals such that the product

$$\Gamma_f \times B_2 \times A_1 \subset A_1 \,(\subset \text{ means ``includes''}) \tag{1A.21}$$

From the character table

$$B_2 \times A_1 = (1 \quad -1 \quad 1 \quad -1)(1 \quad 1 \quad 1 \quad 1) = (1 \quad -1 \quad 1 \quad -1)$$
$$= B_2 \tag{1A.22}$$

Therefore, for $\Gamma_f \times B_2 \subset A_1$ we must have $\Gamma_f = B_2$. Thus the state B_2 is mixed with A_1 by the x-component of the angular momentum. It is just this kind of argument which we have invoked to calculate which states contribute to g-tensors, a point which will be expanded in Appendix 3. For convenience the representations according to which the components of angular momenta (or, more generally, axial vectors) transform are included in the character tables.

References

1 H. H. JAFFÉ AND M. ORCHIN, *Symmetry in Chemistry*, Wiley, 1965.
2 F. A. COTTON, *Chemicals Applications of Group Theory*, Wiley, 1965.
3 V. HEINE, *Group Theory*, Pergamon, 1960.
4 M. TINKHAM, *Group Theory and Quantum Mechanics*, McGraw-Hill, 1964.

The spin Hamiltonian

The account of the relationship between the molecular structure of a radical and its electron spin resonance spectrum will be made more quantitative in these Appendices. It is not intended to present an exhaustive and rigorous derivation of the dependence but it is hoped to show how such spectra can be rationalised in terms of relatively simple concepts.

2A.1 THE SPIN HAMILTONIAN

An electron spin resonance spectrum measures the energy absorbed during the stimulated inversion of an electron spin in a magnetic field; it is therefore natural to discuss the energies of the levels involved as eigenvalues of a Hamiltonian involving spin-operators: we refer to this as the spin Hamiltonian. A more subtle definition will become apparent as we proceed. Let us write the Hamiltonian, $\mathscr{H}$, for a radical in an external magnetic field as

$$\mathscr{H} = \sum_r \mathscr{H}^{(r)} \tag{2A.1}$$

(i) $\mathscr{H}^{(1)}$ is the Hamiltonian representing the electronic kinetic and potential energies in a molecule in the absence of both external fields and spin–orbit coupling.

(ii) $\mathscr{H}^{(2)}$ represents the additional energy due to a crystal field from the environment of the radical. The field need not have the same symmetry as the radical itself.

(iii) $\mathscr{H}^{(3)}$ is the only other electric interaction we shall consider and is that arising from the nucleus which, if it has a spin $I > \frac{1}{2}$, possesses an electric quadrupole moment. Explicitly we may write:

$$\mathscr{H}^{(3)} = Q\left[I_z^2 - \tfrac{1}{3}I(I+1)\right] \tag{2A.2}$$

(iv) $\mathscr{H}^{(4)}$ may be divided into two parts, $\mathscr{H}_1^{(4)}$ and $\mathscr{H}_2^{(4)}$, which represent the hyperfine interaction between the unpaired electron and a magnetic nucleus; the former is the anisotropic (dipolar) coupling term and has the form

$$\mathscr{H}_1^{(4)} = g g_n \beta \beta_n \, r^{-3} \left[\frac{3 (\mathbf{I} \cdot \mathbf{r})(\mathbf{S} \cdot \mathbf{r})}{r^2} - \mathbf{I} \cdot \mathbf{S} \right] \qquad (2A.3)$$

where g and g_n are the electronic and nuclear gyromagnetic ratios and β and β_n are the Bohr and nuclear magnetons respectively. For s-electrons the discussion of § 2.3d showed that an isotropic (contact) interaction must be introduced, this may be written as

$$\mathscr{H}_2^{(4)} = g g_n \beta \beta_n (8\pi/3) \delta (\mathbf{r}_n) \mathbf{S} \cdot \mathbf{I} \qquad (2A.4)$$

$\delta (\mathbf{r}_n)$ is the Dirac δ-function which has the property that

$$\int \delta (\mathbf{r}_n) \psi^2 (\mathbf{r}) \, d\mathbf{r} = \psi^2 (\mathbf{r}_n) \qquad (2A.5)$$

$\mathbf{r}_n$ is a nuclear coordinate.

Since we must consider distributions over, for example, p-orbitals to obtain the actual anisotropic hyperfine interaction, we may integrate over all except spin variables in $\mathscr{H}^{(4)}$ and obtain

$$\langle \psi_{np} | \mathscr{H}_1^{(4)} | \psi_{np} \rangle = \mathbf{S} \cdot \mathbf{B} \cdot \mathbf{I} \cong \tfrac{2}{5} g g_n \beta \beta_n \langle r^{-3} \rangle_{np} (-1, -1, 2) M_I M_S \qquad (2A.6)$$

where the notation $(-1, -1, 2)$ corresponds to the $(-\beta, -\beta, 2\beta)$ of Chapter 2 where

$$\langle r^{-3} \rangle_{np} = \int \psi_{np}^* r^{-3} \psi_{np} \, d\tau \qquad (2A.7)$$

Similarly, for an ns-orbital, ψ_{ns}

$$\langle \psi_{ns} | \mathscr{H}_2^{(4)} | \psi_{ns} \rangle = A_{iso} \mathbf{I} \cdot \mathbf{S} \cong \frac{8\pi}{3} g g_n \beta \beta_n |\psi_{ns}^{(0)}|^2 M_I M_S \qquad (2A.8)$$

Thus, if $\mathbf{A} = \mathbf{B} + \mathbf{A}_{iso}$ we may write

$$\mathscr{H}^{(4)} = \mathbf{S} \cdot \mathbf{A} \cdot \mathbf{I} \qquad (2A.9)$$

(v) $\mathscr{H}^{(5)}$ represents the coupling between the orbital magnetic moment ($\beta \mathbf{L}$) and the external field $\mathbf{H}$ and is

$$\mathscr{H}^{(5)} = \beta \mathbf{L} \cdot \mathbf{H} \qquad (2A.10)$$

(vi) When the electron moves in an electric field $\mathbf{E}$ the spin and orbital angular momenta couple magnetically; this spin–orbit coupling we shall approximate as

$$\mathscr{H}^{(6)} = \lambda \mathbf{L} \cdot \mathbf{S} \qquad (2A.11)$$

(vii) If the nucleus has a magnetic moment its energy will depend on its orientation in an applied magnetic field; the Hamiltonian corresponding to this nuclear Zeeman interaction is

$$\mathscr{H}^{(7)} = - g_n \beta_n \mathbf{I} \cdot \mathbf{H} \tag{2A.12}$$

(viii) The magnetic moment associated with the electron spin couples not only to the orbital magnetic moment but also to the applied field; the orientational energy is expressed by

$$\mathscr{H}^{(8)} = 2\beta \mathbf{H} \cdot \mathbf{S} \tag{2A.13}$$

(ix) If there is more than one unpaired electron in the radical, for example, if it is a triplet state species, there will be an interaction between the electrons represented by

$$\mathscr{H}^{(9)} = g^2 \beta^2 (r_{12})^{-3} \left[\mathbf{S}_1 \cdot \mathbf{S}_2 - 3 \frac{(\mathbf{S}_1 \cdot \mathbf{r}_{12})(\mathbf{S}_2 \cdot \mathbf{r}_{12})}{r_{12}^2} \right] \tag{2A.14}$$

2A.2 APPLICATION OF PERTURBATION THEORY

The energy levels of a radical in a magnetic field are obtained from the eigenvalue equation

$$\mathscr{H} |s, m_s\rangle = \varepsilon_{m_s} |s, m_s\rangle \tag{2A.15}$$

and the solution of this equation can be simplified if one resorts to perturbation theory. For a doublet state radical with no magnetic nuclei

$$\begin{aligned}
\mathscr{H} &= \mathscr{H}^{(1)} + \mathscr{H}^{(2)} + \mathscr{H}^{(5)} + \mathscr{H}^{(6)} + \mathscr{H}^{(8)} \\
&= \mathscr{H}_0 + \beta \mathbf{H} \cdot (\mathbf{L} + 2\mathbf{S}) + \lambda \mathbf{L} \cdot \mathbf{S}
\end{aligned} \tag{2A.16}$$

where $\mathscr{H}_0 = \mathscr{H}^{(1)} + \mathscr{H}^{(2)}$.

The magnitudes of $\mathscr{H}_0$, $\beta \mathbf{H} \cdot (\mathbf{L} + 2\mathbf{S})$, and $\lambda \mathbf{L} \cdot \mathbf{S}$ are of the order of 10^5 cm^{-1}, 1 cm^{-1} and 10^2 cm^{-1} respectively; it is therefore apparent that we can use perturbation theory with the last two terms perturbing the ground state which is taken to be diagonal in $\mathscr{H}_0$.

A further approximation is to suppose that we can express the structure of the radical as a linear combination of atomic orbitals, that is: we can write a molecular orbital $|j\rangle$ as

$$|j\rangle = \sum_i c_{ij} |i\rangle \tag{2A.17}$$

where the $|i\rangle$ are atomic orbitals and $|j\rangle$ is normalised; thus, if we neglect overlap,

$$\sum_i c_{ij}^* c_{ij} = 1 \qquad (2A.18)$$

The orbital energies, ε_j are the eigenvalues of the equation

$$\mathscr{H}_0 |j\rangle = \varepsilon_j |j\rangle \qquad (2A.19)$$

We can now apply the perturbations to the orbitals but first let these be written as the spin orbitals $|j, m_s\rangle$. The matrix elements involving L disappear in the ground state; that is there are no terms $\langle j, m_s | L | j, m_s \rangle$ if the ground state is orbitally non-degenerate, in other words the orbital angular momentum is quenched. The matrix elements of L, however, are not zero in higher order and so we may write a first order wave-function as

$$|\bar{j}, \bar{m}_s\rangle = |j, m_s\rangle + \sum_{m_s'} \sum_{j'} \frac{\langle j', m_s' | \mathscr{H}' | j, m_s \rangle}{\varepsilon_j - \varepsilon_{j'}} |j', m_s'\rangle \qquad (2A.20)$$

It will be recalled (Chapter 2) that the spin–orbit coupling and the effect of the external field are co-operative phenomena, consequently it is immaterial which perturbation is applied first; let us apply $\mathscr{H}^{(5)}$ and so set $\mathscr{H}' = \mathscr{H}^{(5)}$ obtaining:

$$|\bar{j}, \bar{m}_s\rangle = |j, m_s\rangle + \sum_{m_s'} \sum_{j'} \frac{\langle j', m_s' | \beta \, \mathbf{H} \cdot \mathbf{L} | j, m_s \rangle}{\varepsilon_j - \varepsilon_{j'}} |j', m_s'\rangle \qquad (2A.21)$$

$$= |j, m_s\rangle + \sum_{j'} \sum_q \frac{\langle j' | L_q | j \rangle}{\varepsilon_j - \varepsilon_{j'}} |j', m_s\rangle \beta H_q \qquad (2A.22)$$

where $q = x, y, z$ and the perturbation is diagonal in m_s because it is spinless. We can now calculate the matrix elements of $\mathscr{H}^{(6)}$ as

$$\langle \bar{j}, \bar{m}_s | \mathscr{H}^{(6)} | \bar{j}, \bar{m}_s \rangle = \langle j, m_s' | \mathscr{H}^{(6)} | j, m_s \rangle$$
$$+ \lambda \beta \sum_{j'} \sum_{q'q} \frac{H_q \langle m_s' | S_{q'} | m_s \rangle}{\varepsilon_j - \varepsilon_{j'}} \left[\langle j | L_{q'} | j' \rangle \langle j' | L_q | j \rangle + \langle j | L_q | j' \rangle \langle j' | L_{q'} | j \rangle \right]$$

$$(2A.23)$$

Terms to the first order have been retained and it should be recalled that

$$\langle j | L_q | j' \rangle = \langle j' | L_q | j \rangle^* \qquad (2A.24)$$

The first term on the right-hand side is seen to be zero if $\mathscr{H}^{(6)}$ is expanded

into
$$\mathscr{H}^{(6)} = \lambda(L_z S_z + \tfrac{1}{2}L_+ S_- + \tfrac{1}{2}L_- S_+) \tag{2A.25}$$

where $L_\pm = L_x \pm iL_y$ and $S_\pm = S_x \pm iS_y$ have the following properties

$$S_\pm |S, m_S\rangle = [S(S+1) - m_S(m_S \pm 1)]^{\frac{1}{2}} |S, m_S \pm 1\rangle$$
$$L_\pm |L, m_L\rangle = [L(L+1) - m_L(m_L \pm 1)]^{\frac{1}{2}} |L, m_L \pm 1\rangle$$
$$S_z |S, m_S\rangle = m_S |S, m_S\rangle$$
$$L_z |L, m_L\rangle = m_L |L, m_L\rangle \tag{2A.26}$$

in units of $\hbar$.

Realising that this matrix element disappears enables us to combine $\mathscr{H}^{(6)}$ and $\mathscr{H}^{(5)}$ into an effective Hamiltonian $\mathscr{H}_S$ which allows one to calculate matrix elements within the unperturbed ground state $|j, m_s\rangle$:

$$\mathscr{H}_S = \lambda\beta \sum_{q,q'} S_q H_{q'} \sum_{j'} \left[\frac{\langle j|L_q|j'\rangle\langle j'|L_{q'}|j\rangle + \langle j|L_{q'}|j'\rangle\langle j'|L_q|j\rangle}{\varepsilon_j - \varepsilon_{j'}} \right] \tag{2A.27}$$

or, written another way,

$$\mathscr{H}_S = \beta \sum_{q,q'} S_q g'_{qq'} H_{q'} \tag{2A.28}$$

If now the perturbation $\mathscr{H}^{(8)}$ is applied to the state $|j, m_s\rangle$ the interaction *within* the state $|j, m_s\rangle$ may be written

$$\mathscr{H}_S = \beta \sum_{q,q'} S_q g'_{qq'} H_{q'} + \beta 2 S \cdot H$$
$$= \beta S \cdot g \cdot H \tag{2A.29}$$

where $g = i g_{xx} i + j g_{yy} j + k g_{zz} k$ \qquad\qquad (2A.30)

Thus the total Hamiltonian neglecting nuclear spin is

$$\mathscr{H} = \mathscr{H}_0 + \beta H \cdot g \cdot S \tag{2A.31}$$

The point at which we have arrived is one in which the effects not explicitly involving spin have been included in a modification $(g/2) \cdot H$ of the applied field or an equivalent modification of the spin.

Further progress in the simplification of $\mathscr{H}$ may be made when it is realised that the hyperfine interactions are of the order of $10\ cm^{-1}$ so that matrix elements of $\mathscr{H}^{(4)}$ may also be calculated within the manifold of eigenstates in which $\mathscr{H}_0$ is diagonal. Examination of $\mathscr{H}_1^{(4)}$ and $\mathscr{H}_2^{(4)}$ reveals that they are linear in S_q and I_q so that $\mathscr{H}^{(4)}$ may be written as

$$\mathscr{H}^{(4)} = \sum_{q,q'} S_q A_{qq'} I_{q'}$$

$$= \mathbf{S} \cdot \mathbf{A} \cdot \mathbf{I} \qquad (2A.32)$$

where $\mathbf{A} = i A_{xx} \mathbf{i} + j A_{yy} \mathbf{j} + k A_{zz} \mathbf{k}$. $\qquad (2A.33)$

Therefore the spin Hamiltonian for a doublet state radical, neglecting quadrupole terms is

$$\mathscr{H}_S = \beta \mathbf{H} \cdot \mathbf{g} \cdot \mathbf{S} + \mathbf{S} \cdot \mathbf{A} \cdot \mathbf{I} - g_n \beta_n \mathbf{H} \cdot \mathbf{I} \qquad (2A.34)$$

It should be noted that the hyperfine interaction is independent of the magnitude of the applied field.

2A.3 SOLUTION OF THE EIGENVALUE EQUATION

We turn now to the calculation of the spectra for various species in which we assume that we know the g- and A-tensors. The values of $\mathbf{g}$ and $\mathbf{A}$ will be discussed in the following Appendices.

(a) No magnetic nuclei present

$$\mathscr{H}_S = \beta \mathbf{H} \cdot \mathbf{g} \cdot \mathbf{S} \qquad (2A.35)$$

This is the simplest possible form for the spin Hamiltonian; we take $S = \frac{1}{2}$ and so there are just two eigenstates of the operator $\mathbf{g} \cdot \mathbf{S}$; these may be written $|j, \pm \frac{1}{2}\rangle$. For an isotropic g-tensor

$$\varepsilon_{\pm \frac{1}{2}} = \langle j, \pm \tfrac{1}{2} | \beta \mathbf{H} \cdot \mathbf{g} \cdot \mathbf{S} | j, \pm \tfrac{1}{2} \rangle = \pm \tfrac{1}{2} g \beta H \qquad (2A.36)$$

Thus for the spin inversion the energy absorbed is

$$h\nu = \varepsilon_{\frac{1}{2}} - \varepsilon_{-\frac{1}{2}} = g\beta H \qquad (2A.37)$$

For an axially symmetric g-tensor let $g_{zz} = g_{\parallel}$ and $g_{xx} = g_{yy} = g_{\perp}$ then,

$$\mathscr{H}_S = \beta g_{\parallel} H_{\parallel} S_{\parallel} + \beta g_{\perp} H_{\perp} S_{\perp} \qquad (2A.38)$$

for which the solution is

$$h\nu = \varepsilon_{\frac{1}{2}} - \varepsilon_{-\frac{1}{2}} = g(\theta)\beta H \qquad (2A.39)$$

where $g(\theta) = (g_{\parallel}^2 \cos^2 \theta + g_{\perp}^2 \sin^2 \theta)^{\frac{1}{2}}$ $\qquad (2A.40)$

where θ is the angle between the molecular symmetry axis and the direction of the applied field. Thus, at constant microwave frequency, ν, the resonance moves from a field given by $g_{\parallel}\beta H = h\nu$ to one given by $g_{\perp}\beta H = h\nu$.

(b) One spin-$\frac{1}{2}$ nucleus present

$$\mathcal{H}_S = \beta \mathbf{H} \cdot \mathbf{g} \cdot \mathbf{S} + \mathbf{S} \cdot \mathbf{A} \cdot \mathbf{I}, \qquad S = I = \tfrac{1}{2} \tag{2A.41}$$

This is best expanded and written in terms of the shift operators previously introduced:

$$\mathcal{H}_S = \beta g H_z S_z + A_z I_z S_z + A_y I_y S_y + A_x I_x S_x - g_n \beta_n H_z I_z$$
$$= \hbar_1 + \hbar_2 + \hbar_{sec} \tag{2A.42}$$

where

$$\hbar_{sec} = g\beta H_z S_z - g_n \beta_n H_z I_z + A_z S_z I_z$$
$$\hbar_1 = a(S_+ I_- + S_- I_+)$$
$$\hbar_2 = b(S_+ I_+ + S_- I_-)$$
$$4a = A_{xx} + A_{yy}; 4b = A_{xx} - A_{yy} \tag{2A.43}$$

For $S=\frac{1}{2}$ and $I=\frac{1}{2}$ there are four spin states $|\,j, m_s, m_I\rangle$:

$$|j, \tfrac{1}{2}, \tfrac{1}{2}\rangle, \quad |j, \tfrac{1}{2}, -\tfrac{1}{2}\rangle, \quad |j, -\tfrac{1}{2}, -\tfrac{1}{2}\rangle, \quad |j, -\tfrac{1}{2}, \tfrac{1}{2}\rangle \tag{2A.44}$$

The nuclear and electronic spins are coupled through the hyperfine interaction and therefore m_s and m_I are not necessarily good quantum numbers. It is therefore necessary to introduce a new quantum number, F, where $\mathbf{F} = \mathbf{I} + \mathbf{S}$. F necessarily does not reveal the distribution of the angular momentum between the electron and the nucleus. If we operate on these unmixed states with $\mathcal{H}_S$ we obtain

$$\mathcal{H}_S |j, \tfrac{1}{2}, \tfrac{1}{2}\rangle = \tfrac{1}{2}g\beta H |j, \tfrac{1}{2}, \tfrac{1}{2}\rangle - \tfrac{1}{2}g_n\beta_n H \; |j, \tfrac{1}{2}, \tfrac{1}{2}\rangle +$$
$$+ \tfrac{1}{4}A_{zz} |j, \tfrac{1}{2}, \tfrac{1}{2}\rangle + b|j, -\tfrac{1}{2}, -\tfrac{1}{2}\rangle$$
$$\mathcal{H}_S |j, \tfrac{1}{2}, -\tfrac{1}{2}\rangle = \tfrac{1}{2}(g\beta H + g_n\beta_n H - \tfrac{1}{2}A_{zz})|j, \tfrac{1}{2}, -\tfrac{1}{2}\rangle + a|j, -\tfrac{1}{2}, \tfrac{1}{2}\rangle$$
$$\mathcal{H}_S |j, -\tfrac{1}{2}, -\tfrac{1}{2}\rangle = -\tfrac{1}{2}(g\beta H - g_n\beta_n H - \tfrac{1}{2}A_{zz})|j, -\tfrac{1}{2}, -\tfrac{1}{2}\rangle + b|j, \tfrac{1}{2}, \tfrac{1}{2}\rangle$$
$$\mathcal{H}_S |j, -\tfrac{1}{2}, \tfrac{1}{2}\rangle = -\tfrac{1}{2}(g\beta H + g_n\beta_n H + \tfrac{1}{2}A_{zz})|j, -\tfrac{1}{2}, \tfrac{1}{2}\rangle + a|j, \tfrac{1}{2}, -\tfrac{1}{2}\rangle$$
$$\tag{1A.45}$$

The energy matrix is therefore, with $A = A_{zz}$,

$|j, m_s, m_I\rangle$	$|j, \tfrac{1}{2}, \tfrac{1}{2}\rangle$	$|j, \tfrac{1}{2}, -\tfrac{1}{2}\rangle$	$|j, -\tfrac{1}{2}, \tfrac{1}{2}\rangle$	$|j, -\tfrac{1}{2}, -\tfrac{1}{2}\rangle$
$|j, \tfrac{1}{2}, \tfrac{1}{2}\rangle$	$\tfrac{1}{2}(G-N+\tfrac{1}{2}A)$	0	0	b
$|j, \tfrac{1}{2}, -\tfrac{1}{2}\rangle$	0	$\tfrac{1}{2}(G+N-\tfrac{1}{2}A)$	a	0
$|j, -\tfrac{1}{2}, \tfrac{1}{2}\rangle$	0	a	$-\tfrac{1}{2}(G+N+\tfrac{1}{2}A)$	0
$|j, -\tfrac{1}{2}, -\tfrac{1}{2}\rangle$	b	0	0	$-\tfrac{1}{2}(G-N-\tfrac{1}{2}A)$

$$\tag{2A.46}$$

The roots of this matrix, which are the eigenvalues of the system, are

$$\varepsilon_i = (\pm \xi' - A)/4 \qquad i = 1, 2 \tag{2A.47}$$

$$\varepsilon_i = (\pm \xi - A)/4 \qquad i = 3, 4 \tag{2A.48}$$

where

$$\xi^2 = 4H^2 (g\beta + g_n\beta_n)^2 + (A_{xx} + A_{yy})^2 \tag{2A.49}$$

$$\xi'^2 = 4H^2 (g\beta - g_n\beta_n)^2 + (A_{xx} - A_{yy})^2 \tag{2A.50}$$

and the eigenstates which form a diagonal basis under $\mathcal{H}_s$ are

$$
\begin{aligned}
|1\rangle &= \quad\cos\phi\,|j,\tfrac{1}{2},\tfrac{1}{2}\rangle + \sin\phi\;|j,-\tfrac{1}{2},-\tfrac{1}{2}\rangle \\
|2\rangle &= -\,\sin\phi\,|j,\tfrac{1}{2},\tfrac{1}{2}\rangle + \cos\phi\,|j,-\tfrac{1}{2},-\tfrac{1}{2}\rangle \\
|3\rangle &= \quad\cos\theta\,|j,\tfrac{1}{2},-\tfrac{1}{2}\rangle + \sin\theta\,|j,-\tfrac{1}{2},\tfrac{1}{2}\rangle \\
|4\rangle &= -\,\sin\theta\,|j,\tfrac{1}{2},-\tfrac{1}{2}\rangle + \cos\theta\,|j,-\tfrac{1}{2},\tfrac{1}{2}\rangle
\end{aligned}
\tag{2A.51}
$$

where ϕ and θ are defined through

$$\tan 2\phi = \frac{A_{xx} - A_{yy}}{2H(g\beta - g_n\beta_n)} \quad \text{and} \quad \tan 2\theta = \frac{A_{xx} + A_{yy}}{2H(g\beta + g_n\beta_n)} \tag{2A.52}$$

At this stage it seems that there should be six transitions; we must therefore investigate which are allowed. To do so we need to investigate the values of the matrix element $\langle n'|S_x|n\rangle$ because usually the spin transition is induced by an oscillating field in a direction perpendicular to the static field. If the latter is H_z the oscillating field is H_x, which couples with the S_x component of the spin angular momentum; the square of this matrix element is proportional to the transition probability, and since $2S_x = (S_+ + S_-)$ we can see that the transition probabilities are proportional to the quantities $\langle n', n\rangle$ which have the following values:

$$
\begin{aligned}
\langle 1, 2\rangle &= 0 \\
\langle 1, 3\rangle &= \cos^2\phi\,\sin^2\theta + \sin^2\phi\,\cos^2\theta + 2\cos\phi\,\sin\phi\,\cos\theta\,\sin\theta \\
\langle 1, 4\rangle &= \cos^2\phi\,\cos^2\theta + \sin^2\phi\,\sin^2\theta - 2\cos\phi\,\sin\phi\,\cos\theta\,\sin\theta \\
\langle 2, 3\rangle &= \cos^2\phi\,\cos^2\theta + \sin^2\phi\,\sin^2\theta - 2\cos\phi\,\sin\phi\,\cos\theta\,\sin\theta \\
\langle 2, 4\rangle &= \cos^2\phi\,\sin^2\theta + \sin^2\phi\,\cos^2\theta + 2\cos\phi\,\sin\phi\,\cos\theta\,\sin\theta \\
\langle 3, 4\rangle &= 0
\end{aligned}
\tag{2A.53}
$$

Typically $A_{xx} \sim A_{yy} \ll g\beta H$, consequently ϕ and θ are approximately zero so that all the above quantities $\langle n', n\rangle$ are zero except $\langle 1, 4\rangle$ and $\langle 2, 3\rangle$ which are equal. The energies of the two transitions are, therefore,

$$hv = \varepsilon_1 - \varepsilon_4 = \tfrac{1}{2}A + \tfrac{1}{4}\{[4H^2(g\beta - g_n\beta_n)^2 + (A_{xx} - A_{yy})^2]^{\frac{1}{2}} +$$
$$+ [4H^2(g\beta + g_n\beta_n)^2 + (A_{xx} + A_{yy})^2]^{\frac{1}{2}}\} \qquad (2A.54)$$

$$hv = \varepsilon_2 - \varepsilon_3 = -\tfrac{1}{2}A + \tfrac{1}{4}\{[4H^2(g\beta - g_n\beta_n)^2 + (A_{xx} - A_{yy})^2]^{\frac{1}{2}} +$$
$$+ [4H^2(g\beta + g_n\beta_n)^2 + (A_{xx} + A_{yy})^2]^{\frac{1}{2}}\} \qquad (2A.55)$$

When the hyperfine components are very small compared to the applied field the transitions occur at

$$hv = \pm \tfrac{1}{2}A + g\beta H_0 \qquad (2A.56)$$

The spectrum is therefore a doublet symmetrically disposed about the resonance position for a radical with zero nuclear spin (H_0). For a hyperfine interaction of the same order of magnitude as the applied field the quantisation axis is no longer fully determined by the latter and the variation of the energy levels is non-linear in the applied field. The doublet is then unsymmetrically disposed about H_0. Furthermore the parameters $\langle 1, 3 \rangle$ and $\langle 2, 4 \rangle$ are not then very close to zero but the corresponding transitions would be observed only if the microwave frequency were altered to fulfil the condition

$$hv = \tfrac{1}{2}A \pm \tfrac{1}{4}(\xi - \xi') \qquad (2A.57)$$

To obtain the spectrum parameters in the intermediate field situation is a lengthy process involving an iterative solution of the above matrix. We indicate below a solution of the Breit–Rabi equation[1, 2] which is a suitable alternative in some cases.

(c) The Breit–Rabi equation

A suitable form of this equation is

$$\varepsilon_{F=I\pm S} = \frac{-\Delta W}{2(2I+1)} + g_n\beta_n HM_F \pm \frac{\Delta W}{2}\left\{\frac{1 + 4M_F x + x^2}{(2I+1)}\right\}^{\frac{1}{2}} \qquad (2A.58)$$

where $\Delta W = (2I+1)A/2$ and $x = (g-g_n)\beta H/\Delta W$. A simple solution is for the case where $I = \tfrac{1}{2}$ and direct nuclear interactions ($\mathscr{H}^{(7)}$) can be neglected. The equation then becomes

$$\varepsilon_{\frac{1}{2}\pm S} = -A/4 \pm (A/2)(1 + 2M_F x' + x'^2)^{\frac{1}{2}} \qquad (2A.59)$$

where $x' = g\beta H/A$. We saw in § 2A.3b that the electronic and nuclear spins couple to give four states designated by the quantum numbers F and M_F. In the present case we have $F = 1$ and 0; consequently, if we call the energy of the F, M_F state $\varepsilon(F, M_F)$ we have

$$\varepsilon(0,0) = \frac{-A}{4} \frac{-A}{2}(1 + x'^2)^{\frac{1}{2}} \qquad (2A.60)$$

$$\varepsilon(1,-1) = \frac{-A}{4} \frac{+A}{2}(1 - 2x' + x'^2)^{\frac{1}{2}} = \frac{-A}{4} + \frac{A}{2} - \frac{g\beta H}{2} \qquad (2A.61)$$

$$\varepsilon(1,0) = \frac{-A}{4} + \frac{A}{2}(1 + x'^2)^{\frac{1}{2}} \qquad (2A.62)$$

$$\varepsilon(1,1) = \frac{-A}{4} \frac{+A}{2}(1 + 2x' + x'^2)^{\frac{1}{2}} = \frac{-A}{4} \frac{+A}{2} + \frac{g\beta H}{2} \qquad (2A.63)$$

Under the selection rule $\Delta M_F = \pm 1$ there are four transitions, but we have seen that two are of importance at reasonably large fields and their energies are given by

$$h\nu_a = \varepsilon(1,1) - \varepsilon(0,0) = \frac{A}{2} + g\frac{\beta H}{2} + g\frac{\beta H}{2}\left(1 + \frac{1}{x'^2}\right)^{\frac{1}{2}} \qquad (2A.64)$$

$$h\nu_b = \varepsilon(1,0) - \varepsilon(1,-1) = \frac{-A}{2} + g\frac{\beta H}{2} + g\frac{\beta H}{2}\left(1 + \frac{1}{x'^2}\right)^{\frac{1}{2}} \qquad (2A.65)$$

For such fields $(1 + x'^{-2})^{\frac{1}{2}} \sim 1 + (2x'^2)^{-1}$, consequently

$$h\nu_a = g\beta H + A/2 + A^2/4g\beta H \qquad (2A.66)$$

$$h\nu_b = g\beta H - A/2 + A^2/4g\beta H \qquad (2A.67)$$

In a normal experiment ν is kept constant, thus if the resonances occur at H_a and H_b we can combine the pair of equations and obtain

$$A = g\beta(H_b - H_a) - \frac{A^2}{4g\beta}\left(\frac{H_b - H_a}{H_a H_b}\right) \qquad (2A.68)$$

$$A = g\beta(H_b - H_a)f \qquad (2A.69)$$

where f, a correction factor which tends to unity as the hyperfine splitting tends to zero, is given by

$$f = 1 - A^2/4g^2\beta^2 H_a H_b \qquad (2A.70)$$

Similarly, adding the two equations gives

$$h\nu = g\beta\bar{H} + (A^2/4g\beta H_a H_b)\bar{H} \qquad (2A.71)$$

References p. 240

where $2\bar{H} = H_a + H_b$. Thus, if we calculate the g-value from the centre of the spectrum and obtain a value g^*, then the true g-value is

$$g = g^* (f^*)^{-1} \qquad (2A.72)$$

where $f^* = 1 + A^2/4g^2\beta^2 H_a H_b$. $\qquad (2A.73)$

The overall result is that when the hyperfine splitting is not very small compared to the applied field the true hyperfine splitting is less than the distance between absorption lines and the g-value is less than that measured at the centre of gravity of the spectrum.

SUMMARY

In this Appendix we have seen that the features of a spectrum can be desribed in terms of a spin Hamiltonian[3]. In the following Appendices we shall relate the parameters of this Hamiltonian to the molecular structure of particular radical species. The spin Hamiltonian was developed as an operator for the "fictitious spin" of a system, that is the spin which would be present in the absence of spin–orbit coupling. The effect of this latter is absorbed into one of the parameters in the Hamiltonian (the g-tensor).

References

1 G. Breit and I. Rabi, *Phys. Rev.*, 1931, *38*, 2082.
2 J. E. Nafe and E. B. Nelson, *Phys. Rev.*, 1948, *73*, 718.
3 A. Abragam and M. H. L. Pryce, *Proc. Roy. Soc.*, 1951, *199A*, 135.

Appendix 3

Calculation of g-values

3A.1 GENERAL THEORY

Let us recall the definition of g as

$$\mathbf{g} = 2.0023\mathbf{1} + \|g'_{qq'}\| \tag{3A.1}$$

where $\mathbf{1}$ is the unit matrix and $g'_{qq'}$ is as defined in Appendix 2. Thus the shifts in the principal g-values from the free-spin value are

$$\Delta g_{qq'} \equiv g'_{qq'}$$
$$= \sum_{j' \neq j} \frac{\langle j|\mathrm{L}_q\lambda| j'\rangle\langle j'|\mathrm{L}_{q'}| j\rangle + \langle j|\mathrm{L}_{q'}\lambda| j'\rangle\langle j'|\mathrm{L}_q| j\rangle}{\varepsilon_j - \varepsilon_{j'}} \tag{3A.2}$$

which, if we introduce the definition of $|j\rangle$, becomes

$$\Delta g_{qq'} = \sum_{j'}\{[\sum_{ii'} c^*_{ij}c_{i'j'}\lambda_i\langle i|\mathrm{L}_q| i'\rangle][\sum_{ii'} c^*_{i'j'}c_{ij}\langle i'|\mathrm{L}_{q'}| i\rangle] + [h.c.]\}(\varepsilon_j - \varepsilon_{j'})^{-1} \tag{3A.3}$$

where λ_i is the spin–orbit coupling parameter associated with the ith atom and $|i'\rangle$ are the atomic orbitals of the ith atom involved in the mixing molecular orbital $|j'\rangle$. h.c. represents the Hermitian conjugate of the preceding expression.

Let us illustrate the application of this formula: to do so recall that

$$\mathrm{L}_z = \frac{1}{i}\left(x\frac{\partial}{\partial y} - y\frac{\partial}{\partial x}\right)$$

$$\mathrm{L}_y = \frac{1}{i}\left(z\frac{\partial}{\partial x} - x\frac{\partial}{\partial z}\right)$$

$$\mathrm{L}_x = \frac{1}{i}\left(y\frac{\partial}{\partial z} - z\frac{\partial}{\partial y}\right) \tag{3A.4}$$

The cartesian form of the p- and d-orbitals are, neglecting the radial functions,

$$p_x \propto x$$
$$p_y \propto y$$
$$p_z \propto z \tag{3A.5}$$

$$d_{xy} \propto 2xy \qquad d_{z^2} \propto (2z^2 - x^2 - y^2)/\sqrt{3}$$
$$d_{yz} \propto 2yz \qquad d_{x^2-y^2} \propto (x^2 - y^2)$$
$$d_{xz} \propto 2xz \tag{3A.6}$$

Thus, all the matrix elements of L_x, L_y and L_z are zero except

$$\langle p_x |L_y| p_z \rangle = \langle p_y |L_z| p_x \rangle = \langle p_z |L_x| p_y \rangle = i \tag{3A.7}$$

$$\langle d_{xy} |L_z| d_{x^2-y^2} \rangle = 2i \tag{3A.8}$$

$$\langle d_{xz} |L_y| d_{z^2} \rangle = \langle d_{z^2} |L_x| d_{yz} \rangle = \sqrt{3}\,i \tag{3A.9}$$

$$\langle d_{xy} |L_y| d_{yz} \rangle = \langle d_{yz} |L_z| d_{zx} \rangle = \langle d_{zx} |L_x| d_{xy} \rangle$$
$$= \langle d_{x^2-y^2} |L_x| d_{yz} \rangle = \langle d_{x^2-y^2} |L_y| d_{xz} \rangle = i \tag{3A.10}$$

It should be recalled that $\langle i|L_q| i' \rangle = \langle i' |L_q| i \rangle^*$; the subscripts to the d-orbitals have been arranged to illustrate the symmetry of the matrix elements.

We now have sufficient information to enable us to calculate g-values of molecules in their different directions but the task can be greatly facilitated if Group Theory is used. Thus if the orbital $| j \rangle$ transforms according to the irreducible representation $\Gamma_j(G)$ in the symmetry group G of the radical, and if L_q transforms according to the irreducible representation $\Gamma_q(G)$ then all the matrix elements $\langle j' |L_q| j \rangle$ will be zero except those for which

$$\Gamma_q(G) \subset \Gamma_{j'}(G) \overset{s}{\times} \Gamma_j(G) \tag{3A.11}$$

where $\subset$ is the sign of inclusion and $\overset{s}{\times}$ indicates that the symmetrised direct product should be taken if $\Gamma_{j'}(G)$ and $\Gamma_j(G)$ are the same and are not 1-dimensional representations. (In the language of Appendix 1, the symmetrised product has the character $\chi_s(R)$ where

$$\chi_s(R) = \tfrac{1}{2}\left[\chi(R^2) + \chi^2(R)\right] \tag{3A.12}).$$

This condition is represented in Fig. 3A.1 where the symbol $(\Gamma_j)\!-\!\boxed{q}\!-\!(\Gamma_{j'})$

means that the g-shift in the q-direction arises from mixing the states which transform according to the representations Γ_j and $\Gamma_{j'}$. Character tables are shown in Appendix 1 and the co-ordinates refer to those of Fig. 1A.1.

Thus we have greatly reduced the labour necessary in the calculation of g-shifts, in fact the Δg-value may be written

$$\Delta g_{qq} = 2 \sum_{j'} \left\{ \frac{[\sum_i c_{ij}^* c_{i'j'} \lambda_i \langle i' | L_q | i \rangle][\sum_i c_{ij}^* c_{i'j'} \langle i | L_q | i' \rangle] \delta(j'qj)}{(\varepsilon_j - \varepsilon_{j'})} \right\} \tag{3A.13}$$

where $\delta(j'qj)$ is unity if eqn. (3A.11) is satisfied but zero otherwise. For

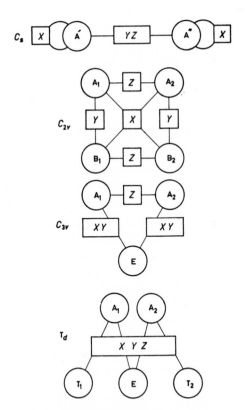

Fig. 3A.1. State-mixing that contributes to the g-tensor in molecules of different symmetry.

References p. 254

p orbitals this reduces to

$$\Delta g_{qq} = 2 \sum_{j'} \left\{ \frac{[\sum_i c_{ij}^* c_{i'j'} \lambda_i][\sum_i c_{ij}^* c_{i'j'}] \delta(j'qj)}{(\varepsilon_j - \varepsilon_{j'})} \right\} \tag{3A.14}$$

where i' refers to the atomic orbital on the ith atom in the orbital $|j'\rangle$; we therefore neglect all neighbouring atom effects in this approximation.

3A.2 EXAMPLES

(a) σ*-radicals

In these radicals the unpaired electron is in a σ^*-orbital, for example the fifteen electron species AB^{n-}. If we consider the bonding sequence of Fig. 3A.2. which refers to the orbitals shown in Fig. 3A.3. then in the simplest terms the σ-orbital energies are solutions of the secular determinant

$$\begin{vmatrix} \alpha_A - \varepsilon & \beta_\sigma \\ \beta_\sigma & \alpha_B - \varepsilon \end{vmatrix} = 0 \tag{3A.15}$$

and the π-orbital energies of the determinant

$$\begin{vmatrix} \alpha_A - \varepsilon & \beta_\pi \\ \beta_\pi & \alpha_B - \varepsilon \end{vmatrix} = 0 \tag{3A.16}$$

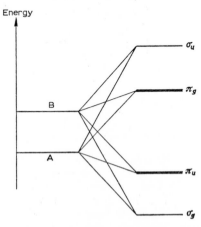

Fig. 3A.2.   Energy level scheme for a diatomic AB-radical. The g, u subscripts apply when A = B.

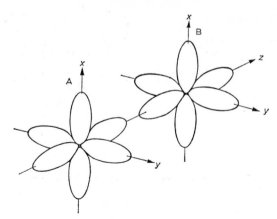

Fig. 3A.3.   Orbitals and axes in diatomic molecules.

where β_σ and β_π are the σ and π resonance integrals, and α_A and α_B are the Coulomb integrals of atoms A and B respectively. Solutions of these determinants are

$$\varepsilon_\eta = \frac{\alpha_A + \alpha_B}{2} \pm \beta_\eta \operatorname{cosec} 2\theta_\eta \, (\eta = \sigma, \pi; \theta_\sigma = \zeta, \theta_\pi = \xi) \quad (3A.17)$$

$$|\sigma_g\rangle = - p_{z_a} \cos \xi + p_{z_b} \sin \xi$$
$$|\sigma_u\rangle = p_{z_a} \sin \xi + p_{z_b} \cos \xi$$
$$\left.\begin{aligned}|\pi_g^{(1)}\rangle &= - p_{x_a} \sin \zeta + p_{x_b} \cos \zeta \\ |\pi_g^{(2)}\rangle &= - p_{y_a} \sin \zeta + p_{y_b} \cos \zeta \end{aligned}\right\}$$
$$\left.\begin{aligned}|\pi_u^{(1)}\rangle &= p_{x_a} \cos \zeta + p_{x_b} \sin \zeta \\ |\pi_u^{(2)}\rangle &= p_{y_a} \cos \zeta + p_{y_b} \sin \zeta \end{aligned}\right\} \quad (3A.18)$$

where the x and y components of the π orbitals have been separated and where

$$\tan 2\theta_\eta = 2\beta_\eta (\alpha_A - \alpha_B)^{-1} \quad (3A.19)$$

Although in $C_{\infty v}$ the g, u subscripts have no significance they do enable us to distinguish the bonding and antibonding orbitals and are obtained by correlation to $D_{\infty h}$.

The character tables of the group $C_{\infty v}$ show that L_x, L_y, L_z transform as Π, Π and Σ^- respectively. Therefore, since $\Pi \overset{s}{\times} \Pi = \Delta + \Sigma^+$ we can construct the mnemonic diagram shown in Fig. 3A.4. The corresponding diagram for

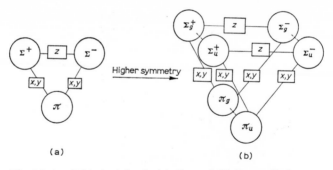

Fig. 3A.4.   Orbital mixing in (a) $C_{\infty v}$ and (b) $D_{\infty h}$ radicals.

$D_{\infty h}$ (homonuclear diatomics) is also included and was constructed similarly.

Thus, since in a homonuclear σ^*, Σ_u^+ radical there are no orbitals which transform as Σ_u^- or Σ_g^-, there are no matrix elements of L_z at all to any other states. Consequently Δg_{zz} is zero. This also applies to heteronuclear diatomics. For the shift in the value of $g_\perp$ we see from the diagrams that the σ_u orbital is mixed with the π_u-orbital in the homonuclear case, yet with both the π-orbitals in the heteronuclear case; this difference arises because the subscripts g and u have no group theoretical significance in the latter case. For the sake of generality we shall consider the heteronuclear case and cast it in such a form that the homonuclear values are also readily obtained. We shall retain the distinction between the two components of a particular π-orbital and denote their energies by $\varepsilon_{\pi_\eta}^{(i)}$, η is g or u and i is 1 or 2 corresponding to the x or the y components respectively.

We find that

$$\langle \sigma_u | L_x \lambda | \pi_g^{(2)} \rangle = \langle \pi_g^{(2)} | L_x \lambda | \sigma_u \rangle^* = \langle \sigma_u | L_y \lambda | \pi_g^{(1)} \rangle^* = \langle \pi_g^{(1)} | L_y \lambda | \sigma_u \rangle$$
$$= -i(\lambda_A \sin \xi \sin \zeta - \lambda_B \cos \xi \cos \zeta) \qquad (3A.20)$$

and

$$\langle \sigma_u | L_y \lambda | \pi_u^{(1)} \rangle = \langle \pi_u^{(1)} | L_y \lambda | \sigma_u \rangle^* = \langle \sigma_u | L_x \lambda | \pi_u^{(2)} \rangle^* = \langle \pi_u^{(2)} | L_x \lambda | \sigma_u \rangle$$
$$= -i(\lambda_A \sin \xi \cos \zeta + \lambda_B \cos \xi \sin \zeta) \qquad (3A.21)$$

Similarly, the matrix elements $\langle \sigma_u | L_q | \theta \neq \sigma_u \rangle$ are based in an identical manner upon the two:

$$\langle \sigma_u | L_x | \pi_g^{(2)} \rangle = +i \cos(\xi + \zeta) \qquad (3A.22)$$

$$\langle \sigma_u | L_y | \pi_u^{(1)} \rangle = -i \sin(\xi + \zeta) \qquad (3A.23)$$

Consequently the g-value shift is obtained by direct substitution of these matrix elements into eqn. (3A.2) or, more straightforwardly, from a direct substitution of the definitions of the orbitals into eqn. (3A.14) with due regard for the $\delta(j'qj)$ rule. We therefore obtain:

$$\Delta g_{xx} = \big[\langle \sigma_u | L_x \lambda | \pi_g^{(2)}\rangle \langle \pi_g^{(2)} | L_x | \sigma_u\rangle +$$
$$+ \langle \pi_g^{(2)} | L_x \lambda | \sigma_u\rangle \langle \sigma_u | L_x | \pi_g^{(2)}\rangle\big]\big(\varepsilon_{\sigma_u} - \varepsilon_{\pi_g}^{(2)}\big)^{-1}$$
$$+ \big[\langle \sigma_u | L_x \lambda | \pi_u^{(2)}\rangle \langle \pi_u^{(2)} | L_x | \sigma_u\rangle +$$
$$+ \langle \pi_u^{(2)} | L_x \lambda | \sigma_u\rangle \langle \sigma_u | L_x | \pi_u^{(2)}\rangle\big]\big(\varepsilon_{\sigma_u} - \varepsilon_{\pi_u}^{(2)}\big)^{-1} \tag{3A.24}$$

$$= 2\big(\lambda_A \sin\xi \sin\zeta' - \lambda_B \cos\xi \cos\zeta'\big)\cos(\xi+\zeta')\big(\varepsilon_{\sigma_u} - \varepsilon_{\pi_g}^{(2)}\big)^{-1}$$
$$+ 2\big(\lambda_A \sin\xi \cos\zeta' + \lambda_B \cos\xi \sin\zeta'\big)\sin(\xi+\zeta')\big(\varepsilon_{\sigma_u} - \varepsilon_{\pi_u}^{(2)}\big)^{-1} \tag{3A.25}$$

$$\Delta g_{yy} = 2\big(\lambda_A \sin\xi \sin\zeta - \lambda_B \cos\xi \cos\zeta\big)\cos(\xi+\zeta)\big(\varepsilon_{\sigma_u} - \varepsilon_{\pi_g}^{(1)}\big)^{-1}$$
$$+ 2\big(\lambda_A \sin\xi \cos\zeta + \lambda_B \cos\xi \sin\zeta\big)\sin(\xi+\zeta)\big(\varepsilon_{\sigma_u} - \varepsilon_{\pi_u}^{(1)}\big)^{-1} \tag{3A.26}$$

$$\Delta g_{zz} = 0 \tag{3A.27}$$

The dependence of the g-shifts on the angles ξ, ζ and ζ' (where the prime is used to indicate the possible inequality of ζ and ζ' if the environment is anisotropic and the $\pi^{(1)}$ and $\pi^{(2)}$-orbitals not truly degenerate) is reflected in the trigonometric functions. For a homonuclear diatomic $\xi = \zeta = \zeta' = \pi/4$, and $\lambda_A = \lambda_B = \lambda$ consequently

$$\Delta g_{xx} = + 2\lambda\big(\varepsilon_{\sigma_u} - \varepsilon_{\pi_u}^{(2)}\big)^{-1} \tag{3A.28}$$

$$\Delta g_{yy} = + 2\lambda\big(\varepsilon_{\sigma_u} - \varepsilon_{\pi_u}^{(1)}\big)^{-1} \tag{3A.29}$$

$$\Delta g_{zz} = 0 \tag{3A.30}$$

This reflects more quantitatively the group theoretical result previously obtained. Since λ and $\varepsilon_{\sigma_u} - \varepsilon_{\pi_u}$ are positive quantities the g-shifts are positive. When the radical is a heteronuclear diatomic the term $\cos(\xi+\zeta)$ is no longer zero and $\sin(\xi+\zeta)$ is less than unity; consequently the mixing of the π_g-levels becomes increasingly important but the g-shifts remain positive (Fig. 3A.5).

(b) π-radicals

The situation is more complex in the case of π- and π^*-radicals because the ground state is degenerate and perturbation theory is not necessarily

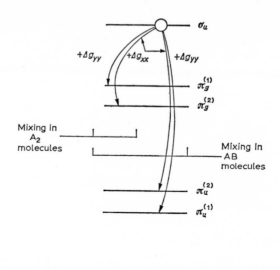

Fig. 3A.5. Orbital mixing and g-values in homonuclear and heteronuclear radicals.

applicable. Känzig and Cohen[1] have given expressions for the g-values of O_2^- in an anisotropic environment and obtain the following results:

$$g_{xx} = g_e\delta - \frac{\lambda}{E}(-\delta' - \delta + 1) \qquad (3A.31)$$

$$g_{yy} = g_e\delta - \frac{\lambda}{E}(+\delta' - \delta - 1) \qquad (3A.32)$$

$$g_{zz} = g_e + 2l\delta' \qquad (3A.33)$$

where

$$\delta^2 = \Delta^2/(\lambda^2 + \Delta^2)$$
$$\delta'^2 = \lambda^2/(\lambda^2 + \Delta^2)$$
$$\Delta = \varepsilon_{\pi g}^{(1)} - \varepsilon_{\pi g}^{(2)}$$
$$E = \varepsilon_{\pi g}^{(1)} - \varepsilon_{\sigma g} \qquad (3A.34)$$

and l is an empirical parameter which allows for the effect of the environment on the orbital angular momentum about the z-axis. It is seen that for no removal of degeneracy

$$g_{xx} = g_{yy} = 0$$
$$g_{zz} = 4 \qquad (3A.35)$$

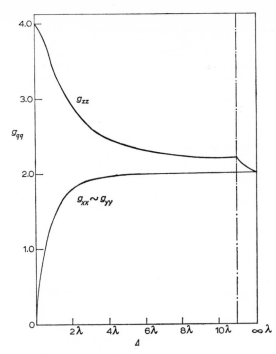

Fig. 3A.6. g-Values in a AB(π)-radical. The diagram has been constructed assuming that $E = 10\ \lambda$.

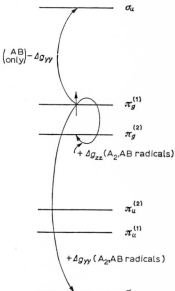

Fig. 3A.7. g-Values in orbitally quenched homonuclear and heteronuclear AB(π)-radicals.

TABLE 3A.1

SYMMETRY COMBINATIONS OF ATOMIC ORBITALS

C_{3v}

Representation	*B-atomic orbitals*	*A-atomic orbitals*
A_1	$\xi_5 = \dfrac{1}{\sqrt{3}}(\eta_1 + \eta_2 + \eta_3)$ $\xi_6 = \dfrac{1}{\sqrt{3}}(\zeta_1 + \zeta_2 + \zeta_3)$	s, p_z, d_{z^2}
A_2	$\xi_7 = \dfrac{1}{\sqrt{3}}(\omega_1 + \omega_2 + \omega_3)$	—
E	$\xi_8 = \dfrac{1}{\sqrt{6}}(2\eta_1 - \eta_2 - \eta_3)$ $\xi_9 = \dfrac{1}{\sqrt{6}}(2\zeta_1 - \zeta_2 - \zeta_3)$ $\xi_{10} = \dfrac{1}{\sqrt{2}}(\omega_2 - \omega_3)$ $\xi_{11} = \dfrac{1}{\sqrt{2}}(\eta_2 - \eta_3)$ $\xi_{12} = \dfrac{1}{\sqrt{2}}(\zeta_2 - \zeta_3)$ $\xi_{13} = \dfrac{1}{\sqrt{6}}(2\omega_1 - \omega_2 - \omega_3)$	$p_x, p_y \, d_{xz}, d_{yz},$ $d_{xy}, d_{x^2-y^2}$
A_1	$\xi_5 = \dfrac{1}{\sqrt{2}}(\omega_{z1} + \omega_{z2})$ $\xi_6 = \dfrac{1}{\sqrt{2}}(\omega_{z3} + \omega_{z4})$ $\xi_7 = \dfrac{1}{\sqrt{2}}(\omega_{x3} - \omega_{x4})$ $\xi_8 = \dfrac{1}{\sqrt{2}}(\omega_{y1} - \omega_{y2})$	$s, p_z, d_{z^2}, d_{x^2-y^2}$

C_{2v}

Representation	B-atomic orbitals	A-atomic orbitals
B_1	$\zeta_9 = \dfrac{1}{\sqrt{2}}(\omega_{z3} - \omega_{z4})$	
	$\zeta_{10} = \dfrac{1}{\sqrt{2}}(\omega_{x1} + \omega_{x2})$	p_x, d_{xz}
	$\zeta_{11} = \dfrac{1}{\sqrt{2}}(\omega_{x3} + \omega_{x4})$	
B_2	$\zeta_{12} = \dfrac{1}{\sqrt{2}}(\omega_{z1} - \omega_{z2})$	
	$\zeta_{13} = \dfrac{1}{\sqrt{2}}(\omega_{y3} + \omega_{y4})$	p_y, d_{yz}
	$\zeta_{14} = \dfrac{1}{\sqrt{2}}(\omega_{y1} + \omega_{y2})$	
A_2	$\zeta_{15} = \dfrac{1}{\sqrt{2}}(\omega_{x1} - \omega_{x2})$	
	$\zeta_{16} = \dfrac{1}{\sqrt{2}}(\omega_{y3} - \omega_{y4})$	d_{xy}

As the value of Δ increases the value of $g_\perp$ increases towards that of the free spin whereas $g_{\parallel}(g_{zz})$ decreases to this value. This is not quite true; what in fact happens is that the above formulae blend into the values given by perturbation theory for large values of Δ; this is illustrated in Fig. 3A.6. Application of Group Theory shows that the scheme in Fig. 3A.7. applies when the degeneracy is removed by a crystal field: it is seen that diatomic π-radicals are particularly susceptible to environmental effects.

(c) AB_n -radicals

It is not intended to enter into the details of the calculation of the g-values for all such radicals; one example of an AB_4 species will be considered in some detail but the application of the preceding equations should, at this stage, be quite straightforward. We must interpolate at this point the explicit forms of the molecular orbitals of AB_n species; these may all be written in the form

$$\psi = \sum_i c_i \xi_i + \sum_i d_i \xi_i' \qquad (3A.36)$$

where ξ corresponds to s- and p- and ξ' corresponds to d-orbitals on the ith atom. Molecular orbitals can be formed from combinations of these orbitals which form bases for the irreducible representations of the molecular symmetry group. Such combinations, the axes to which they refer, and the explicit forms of the orbitals for various molecular symmetries are given in Table 3A.1, Fig. 3A.8. and Table 3A.2 respectively.

Let us calculate the g-tensor for an AB_4 molecule with C_{2v} symmetry. Reference to Fig. 3A.1. shows which states will intermix to give a shift in the g-values for a particular direction. For a $^2A_1$ ground state we must determine the matrix elements $\langle A_2 | L_z | A_1 \rangle$, $\langle B_1 | L_y | A_1 \rangle$ and $\langle B_2 | L_x | A_1 \rangle$ for the values of Δg_z, Δg_y and Δg_x respectively. For simplicity we shall

TABLE 3A.2

EXPLICIT MOLECULAR ORBITALS

1. C_s

$$|A'\rangle = c_1 s + c_2 p_z + c_3 p_x + c_5 \xi_5 + c_6 \xi_6 + c_8 \xi_8 + c_9 \xi_9 + c_{10} \xi_{10} + \psi_d(A')$$

$$|A''\rangle = c_4 p_y + c_{11} \xi_{11} + c_{12} \xi_{12} + c_{13} \xi_{13} + c_7 \xi_7 + \psi_d(A'')$$

$$\psi_d(A') = d_1 d_{z^2} + d_2 d_{x^2-y^2} + d_4 d_{xy}$$

$$\psi_d(A'') = d_3 d_{yz} + d_5 d_{xz}$$

2. C_{3v}

$$|A_1\rangle = c_1 s + c_2 p_z + c_5 \xi_5 + c_6 \xi_6 + \psi_d(A_1)$$

$$|A_2\rangle = \xi_7$$

$$|E\rangle = \begin{cases} c_3 p_x + c_8 \xi_8 + c_9 \xi_9 + c_{10} \xi_{10} + \psi_d^{(1)}(E) \\ c_4 p_y + c_{11} \xi_{11} + c_{12} \xi_{12} + c_{13} \xi_{13} + \psi_d^{(2)}(E) \end{cases}$$

$$\psi_d(A_1) = d_1 d_{z^2}$$

$$\psi_d(E) = d_2 d_{x^2-y^2} + d_3 d_{yz} + d_4 d_{xy} + d_5 d_{xz}$$

3. C_{2v}

$$|A_1\rangle = c_1 s + c_2 p_z + c_5 \xi_5 + c_6 \xi_6 + c_7 \xi_7 + c_8 \xi_8 + \psi_d(A_1)$$

$$|B_1\rangle = c_3 p_x + c_9 \xi_9 + c_{10} \xi_{10} + c_{11} \xi_{11} + \psi_d(B_1)$$

$$|B_2\rangle = c_4 p_y + c_{12} \xi_{12} + c_{13} \xi_{13} + c_{14} \xi_{14} + \psi_d(B_2)$$

$$|A_2\rangle = c_{15} \xi_{15} + c_{16} \xi_{16} + \psi_d(A_2)$$

$$\psi_d(A_1) = d_1 d_{z^2} + d_2 d_{x^2-y^2}$$

$$\psi_d(B_1) = d_5 \psi_{xz}$$

$$\psi_d(B_2) = d_3 \psi_{yz}$$

$$\psi_d(A_2) = d_4 \psi_{xy}$$

For AB_2 molecules C_i ($i = 6, 7, 9, 11, 13, 16$) are zero. The basic atomic functions for C_s and C_{3v} are the same, this is permissible because C_s is a subgroup of C_{3v}

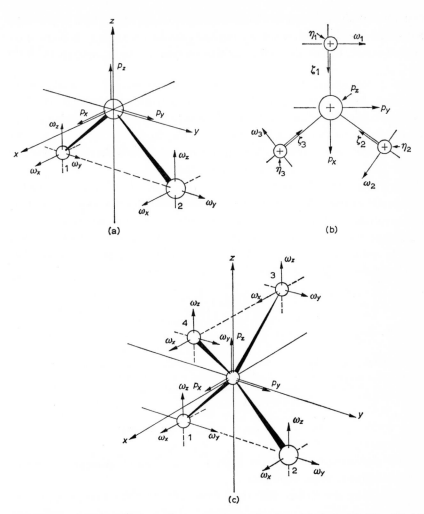

Fig. 3A.8. Atomic orbitals used to construct molecular orbitals in (a) AB_2, (b) AB_3 and (c) AB_4 molecules.

assume that all of these excited states arise from excitation into or from the half-filled a_1-orbital, although a complete calculation ought to include other excited states. Let us also represent the energies of the Γ_j-orbitals by $\varepsilon(\Gamma_j)$

(i) Δg_{zz}:

$$\langle A_2 | L_z \lambda_i | A_1 \rangle =$$

$$= \langle A_2 | L_z \lambda_i | c_1 \psi_s + c_2 \psi_z + c_5 \xi_5 + c_6 \xi_6 + c_7 \xi_7 + c_8 \xi_8 + d_1 d_{z^2} + d_2 d_{x^2-y^2} \rangle$$

$$= \left\langle A_2 \left| \frac{ic_7}{\sqrt{2}} (\omega_{y_3} - \omega_{y_4}) \lambda_B - \frac{ic_8}{\sqrt{2}} (\omega_{x_1} - \omega_{x_2}) \lambda_B + 2i\, d_2 d_{xy} \lambda_A \right. \right\rangle$$

$$= i(c_7 c_{16} \lambda_B - c_8 c_{15} \lambda_B + 2\lambda_A d_2 d_4)$$

$$\Delta g_{zz} = \frac{2(c_7 c_{16} \lambda_B - \lambda_B c_8 c_{15} + 2d_2 d_4 \lambda_A)(c_7 c_{16} - c_8 c_{15} + 2d_2 d_4)}{\varepsilon(A_1) - \varepsilon(A_2)} \tag{3A.37}$$

(ii) Δg_{yy}:

$$\langle B_1 | L_y \lambda_i | A_1 \rangle = i \left[\lambda_A c_2 c_3 + (\sqrt{3}\, d_1 - d_2) d_5 \lambda_A + (c_5 c_{10} + c_6 c_{11} - c_7 c_9) \lambda_B \right]$$

$$\Delta g_{yy} = 2 \left[\frac{\lambda_A (c_2 c_3 + \sqrt{3}\, d_1 d_5 - d_2 d_5) + (c_5 c_{10} + c_6 c_{11} - c_7 c_9) \lambda_B}{\varepsilon(A_1) - \varepsilon(B_1)} \right]$$

$$\times (c_2 c_3 + \sqrt{3}\, d_1 d_5 - d_2 d_5 + c_5 c_{10} + c_6 c_{11} - c_7 c_9) \tag{3A.38}$$

(iii) Δg_{xx}:

$$\Delta g_{xx} = 2 \left[\frac{(c_2 c_4 + \sqrt{3}\, d_1 d_3 + d_2 d_3) \lambda_A + (c_5 c_{14} + c_6 c_{13} - c_8 c_{12}) \lambda_B}{\varepsilon(A_1) - \varepsilon(B_2)} \right]$$

$$\times (c_2 c_4 + \sqrt{3}\, d_1 d_3 + d_2 d_3 + c_5 c_{14} + c_6 c_{13} - c_8 c_{12}) \tag{3A.39}$$

Similar expressions for other radicals may be derived using the coupling diagrams illustrated in Fig. 3A.1.

It should be emphasised that these formulae are difficult to apply: this is because they require a knowledge of both excitation energies and coefficients of excited-state orbitals; it is only rarely that both data are forthcoming. The calculation of g-tensors has been considered in some detail by Stone[2].

References

1 W. KÄNZIG AND M. H. COHEN, *Phys. Rev. Letters*, 1959, *3*, 509.
2 A. J. STONE, *Proc. Roy. Soc.*, 1963, *271A*, 424.

Appendix 4

Determination of spin-density distribution and bond angles

4A.1 POPULATION ANALYSIS

In this Appendix we are concerned with the information which can be obtained from the magnitude of the hyperfine coupling tensor. In Chapter 2 it was pointed out that the spin-density distribution could be determined if the hyperfine coupling constants were known for the pertinent orbitals in the free atoms. The square of the coefficient of that orbital in the molecular orbital of the unpaired electron is then the ratio of the observed splitting to the free-atom splitting. This presupposes at least four major assumptions; that the atom is unaffected by bond formation; that the effect of inner shell polarisation is relatively small; that effects due to overlap populations are ignored and that the free-atom values are known. This is a disconcerting list of requirements but the situation is alleviated if we are mainly interested in trends of population along series of similar species. We shall assume that this is so and therefore just concentrate upon the calculation of the free-atom values.

In § 2A.1 the form of the hyperfine coupling tensors A_{iso} and **B** were shown to depend upon the quantities $|\psi_{ns}(0)|^2$ and $\langle r^{-3} \rangle_{np}$, where the former is the value of $|\psi_{ns}|^2$ at the nucleus and the latter is the mean value of r^{-3} over the np-atomic orbital.

(a) Determination of $\langle r^{-3} \rangle_{np}$

The values of $\langle r^{-3} \rangle_{np}$ are normally calculated directly from the wavefunctions of the free atom by integration. If only hydrogenic orbitals are available $\langle r^{-3} \rangle_{np}$ may be calculated from the expression[1]:

$$\langle nl | r^{-3} | nl \rangle = (Z_{nl}^*)^3 / [n^3 l (l+1)(l+\tfrac{1}{2})] \tag{4A.1}$$

For Slater orbitals:

$$\langle r^{-3} \rangle_{np} = 2 Z_{np}^{*\,3} [n^4 (n-1)(2n-1)]^{-1} \tag{4A.2}$$

where Z_{nl}^* is the effective atomic number for the orbital concerned. An alternative and better method is to use self-consistent field (SCF) wave-functions which may be integrated numerically by standard methods. The results of such calculations[2] are given in Table 2.1.

It is interesting to compare the values of $\langle r^{-3}\rangle_{np}$ as calculated from these two types of functions and attention is drawn to Fig. 4A.1. The considerable divergence between the SCF and hydrogenic $\langle r^{-3}\rangle_{np}$ values emphasises the danger of employing hydrogenic values for the heavier atoms. It should be pointed out, however, that the SCF values may themselves be considerably in error for two major reasons. Firstly, the value of $\langle r^{-3}\rangle_{np}$ is strongly determined by that part of the wave-function that is close to the nucleus, and this is the least accurately determined region. Secondly, it is a property of the variation method that a first order error in the wave-function leads to only a second order error in the energy; the accuracy of the wave-function is less sensitive to variation than that of the energy. One may say it is not necessarily accurate to use wave-functions which have been minimised with respect to the energy. Although this is a difficulty which is not easy to circumvent its effect is minimised if trends are considered as a major consequence of the calculations.

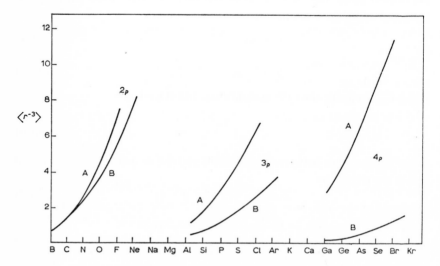

Fig. 4A.1.   Comparison of the values of $\langle r^{-3}\rangle_{np}$ calculated from hydrogenic orbitals with those calculated from SCF orbitals.

(b) Calculation of $|\psi_{ns}(0)|^2$

Values of $|\psi_{ns}(0)|^2$ are calculated directly for Slater or analytic SCF orbitals and by extrapolation of numerical functions. The same difficulties as those discussed in the preceding section obtain here also and SCF values are used wherever possible.

4A.2 DETERMINATION OF BOND ANGLES

We extend here the observation made in § 2.4b that the results of a population analysis may be used for the determination of bond angles if the molecular orbital includes an sp^n-hybrid on a central atom. To do this it is assumed that the orthogonality conditions derived by Coulson[3] are applicable and valid. We consider molecules of symmetry C_{2v} and C_{3v} with a magnetic nucleus in the central atom and define the *hybridisation ratio*, λ, as equal to $(c_p^2/c_s^2)^{\frac{1}{2}}$. The angles between the ith and jth bonds may then be determined from the condition that

$$\lambda_i \lambda_j \cos \phi_{ij} + 1 = 0 \qquad (4A.3)$$

Let us take λ as the hybridisation ratio for the sp^n-hybrid atomic orbital on the central atom, then it may be shown that the BAB angle (ϕ) in a C_{2v} molecule obeys the condition that

$$\lambda = \sec(\phi/2)/\sqrt{-\sec\phi} \qquad (4A.4)$$

whence

$$\phi = 2\cos^{-1}(\lambda^2 + 2)^{-\frac{1}{2}} \qquad (4A.5)$$

For a C_{3v} molecule the orthogonality condition leads to

$$\lambda = \sqrt{\frac{\sec^2\theta - 3}{2}} \qquad (4A.6)$$

where θ is the angle between the AB bond and the sp^n-hybrid orbital. Since θ and ϕ are related by

$$\cos\phi = \tfrac{1}{2}(3\cos^2\theta - 1) \qquad (4A.7)$$

we obtain

$$\phi = \cos^{-1}\left[\frac{1.5}{2\lambda^2 + 3} - \frac{1}{2}\right] \qquad (4A.8)$$

The angles and hybridisation ratios to which these equations refer are shown in Fig. 4A.2.

Fig. 4A.2.   Angles and hybridisation ratios in C_{2v} and C_{3v} molecules.

It is clear, then, that if λ^2 is determined from the orbital populations, substitution into one of these equations leads to the bond angle directly. The variation of bond angle with hybridisation ratio has already been illustrated in Fig. 2.7. Inspection of this diagram indicates that in the regions of importance, the bond angle is moderately insensitive to the hybridisation ratio but is not so insensitive as to be meaningless. Consequently calculated bond angles will be fairly reliable even though the populations may be somewhat in error; also it is important to discuss trends in hybridisation ratios as well as bond angles or some information may be lost. Apart from those already mentioned, important sources of inaccuracy include the complete omission of d-orbitals and the possibility of bent bonds.

4A.3 NEIGHBOURING ATOM INTERACTIONS

Information about spin-densities at a non-magnetic nucleus may also be obtained by a consideration of the interactions (both isotropic and anisotropic) with a neighbouring magnetic nucleus. This is the basis of almost the whole of the analysis of the spin-density distribution in aromatic radicals and radical ions where the π-electron density on a carbon atom (ρ_c) is related to the splitting from an α proton $(A_{iso}^{(H)})$ through the equation

$$A_{iso}^{(H)} = Q_{CH}^{H} \rho_c \qquad (4A.9)$$

The anisotropic dipolar interaction between a π-electron and a proton at a distance R from the atom on which the π-electron is centred has been calculated by McConnell and Strathdee[4] who specifically considered a $2p$

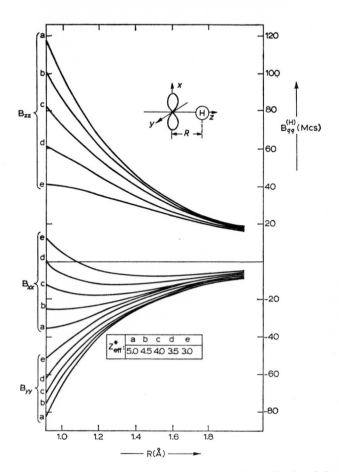

Fig. 4A.3. Variation of α-hydrogen anisotropic coupling with bond length and adjacent effective nuclear charge.

orbital. Their results can be extended to the case of a nucleus at a distance R from an np-orbital[5]. We shall not give details of the calculation here but draw attention to Fig. 4A.3 in which the variation of the principal values (B_{xx}, B_{yy}, B_{zz}) for the anisotropic coupling tensor for a proton at varying distances from an electron entirely in a $2p$ π-orbital is illustrated for various values of Z^* of the other atom. Similarly Fig. 4A.3. reflects the dependence of the tensor on the value of Z^* for various interatomic distances.

It should be emphasised that an anisotropic coupling between an α-nucleus and an *ns*-orbital on the neighbouring atom is to be expected. Attention is drawn here to the work of Derbyshire[6] in which McConnell's and Strathdee's work is extended to the case of a general proton position.

References

1 E. CONDON AND G. SHORTLEY, *Theory of Atomic Spectra*, Cambridge University Press, 1950.
2 J. R. MORTON, J. R. ROWLANDS AND D. H. WHIFFEN, *Natl. Phys. Lab. Circ.*, No. BPR 13.
3 C. A. COULSON, *Volume Commémoratif Victor Henri, Contributions à l'Etude de la Structure Moléculaire*, 1948, p. 15.
4 H. M. McCONNELL AND J. STRATHDEE, *Mol. Phys.*, 1959, *2*, 129.
5 P. W. ATKINS, *Ph. D. Thesis*, Leicester, 1964.
6 W. DERBYSHIRE, *Mol. Phys.*, 1962, *5*, 225.

Appendix 5

Analysis of electron spin resonance spectra

We are concerned in this Appendix with showing how the g- and A-tensors can be obtained from electron spin resonance spectra; we are more concerned with pragmatism than subtlety and it is hoped that the section will help the reader in the task of unravelling a complex spectrum or at least to understand another's interpretation.

To begin we recall that the microwave frequency is kept constant while the magnetic field is swept through the spectrum. The experimental arrangement is such that it is often more convenient to record the first derivative of the absorption than the absorption itself. This is advantageous in several respects, one being that small inflexions in the absorption spectrum are much more obvious in the derivative spectrum. The second derivative spectrum is also occasionally used. The points of measurement and the corresponding shapes of the absorption, first and second derivative curves are shown in Fig. 5A.1.

Information may be increased if spectra are run at different microwave frequencies; those commonly employed are X-band (3 cm wavelength), K-band (1.25 cm) and Q-band (8 mm). Thus by going from low to high frequencies (and therefore to higher magnetic fields) the spectra from different radicals with different g-tensors may be separated and hence the interpretation made easier. A further point is that second order effects which are strong when the external field is comparable in magnitude with the hyperfine interaction, become less prominent as the field is increased and the spectrum is thus progressively simplified. Direct field effects on the nuclei may then become important, however, in which case the complexity will be increased.

The discussion of § 2A.3 showed that parallel transitions could be induced when the hyperfine splitting was sufficiently large but these are more of a confirmatory nature and yield no new information.

At this point let us recall the effects of having a large hyperfine coupling constant (say $\sim 10^2$ gauss). If there is only one equivalent nucleus the A- and

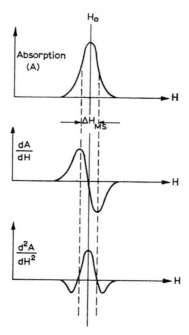

Fig. 5A.1.   An absorption line with its first and second derivatives.

g-tensors will not be measured directly from the line positions but will need correcting in the manner indicated in § 2A.3. If there is more than one equivalent nucleus the expected hyperfine spectrum will show a further sub-division of the multiplet lines. This point was illustrated in § 9.2 but we can be more general here.

Fessenden[1] has shown that in the case of *n*-equivalent spin-$\frac{1}{2}$ nuclei the hyperfine spectrum should be calculated using a Hamiltonian which retains the terms in $S_x I_x$ and $S_y I_y$. The effect of including these off-diagonal terms is two-fold: the degeneracy of some of the transitions is removed so that the normal binomial distribution rule for intensities for spin-$\frac{1}{2}$ nuclei is contra-vened, and the whole spectrum is moved to low field. This is illustrated in Fig. 5A.2 which shows the effect of including the off-diagonal terms for a system with four-equivalent spin-$\frac{1}{2}$ nuclei which, in first order, give a spectrum intensity distribution of $1:4:6:4:1$ and in second order give the distribution $1:1:3:1:3:2:1:3:1$. The magnitude of the shifts to be expected in a number of cases is given in Table 5A.1. This shows the degeneracy (relative intensity) of the possible lines of the spectra for *n*-equivalent spin-$\frac{1}{2}$ nuclei and their

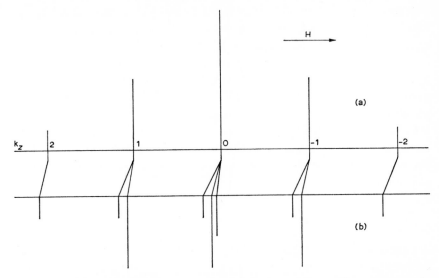

Fig. 5A.2. Effect of off-diagonal elements of the hyperfine coupling tensor on the spectrum. (a) First order spectrum; (b) second order spectrum.

TABLE 5A.1

SECOND ORDER STRUCTURE OF ELECTRON SPIN RESONANCE HYPERFINE SPECTRA[1]

k_z	4	3		2				1				0		
shift	8	22	6	32	16	4	38	22	10	2	40	24	12	4	0
$n = 0$															1
2										1				1	1
4						1			1	3			1	3	2
6			1		1	5		1	5	9		1	5	9	5
8	1	1	7	1	7	20	1	7	20	28	1	7	20	28	14

$2k_z$	9	7		5				3				1		
shift	9	25	7	37	19	5	45	27	13	3	49	31	17	7	1
$n = 1$															1
3										1				1	2
5						1			1	4			1	4	5
7			1		1	6		1	6	14		1	6	14	14
9	1	1	8	1	8	27	1	8	27	48	1	8	27	48	42

displacement from their position of the first order lines in units of $A^2/4g\beta H$. All shifts are to low field, including those for the high-field half of the spectrum (which is not shown in the Table).

Two further points may be added to this discussion. The centres of gravity of the second order groups are all equally shifted to low field, so that the hyperfine splitting constant can be obtained precisely by measuring between the centres of gravity. Nuclei with coupling constants which are equal in magnitude but which are opposite in sign are magnetically inequivalent and therefore do not couple. The appearance of second order splitting is, then, diagnostic of relative sign as well as absolute magnitude of the coupling constants.

5A.1 SOLUTION SPECTRA

A radical in solution takes up all orientations with respect to the external field in a time short compared to the time that an electron exists in a particular energy state; consequently all the anisotropies of the spectrum are averaged to zero. The spectrum is analysed by recording the microwave frequency and the magnetic fields at which the resonances occur. The values of A_{iso} and g_{av} may then be determined either directly from these data or if necessary by the application of the Breit–Rabi equation (§ 2A.3c). Often ambiguities of interpretation arise, particularly in multi-line spectra. For example, it may not be clear whether a line is a hyperfine component or whether it is due to another species. Such ambiguities may be resolved in the following ways.

(i) By isotopic substitution. The new isotope will in general have a different magnetic moment or spin. The spectrum is due to a hyperfine interaction if the new spectrum is changed in accord with these new parameters. If there is no change the spectrum is due to two species.

(ii) By power saturation. If the spectrum is due to two species they will not usually have the same relaxation times. Consequently, if the microwave power is increased sufficiently one of the lines will be saturated before the other. This is shown as a broadening and gradual disappearance of the line. This method is not completely positive because if one of the lines overlaps the spectrum due to a fast relaxing species, relaxation may be enhanced and so the saturation experiment would become less conclusive (see § 5.2). Fortunately, this is not likely to be a common situation.

(iii) By changing the microwave frequency. In Chapter 2 we observed that the hyperfine spectrum is independent of field (to a good approximation).

Thus if we go from X- to Q-band and the splitting between the two lines remains constant, it is due to a hyperfine interaction. If the splitting changes the lines are due to species with different g-values.

If we decide by one or more of these techniques, or merely assume, that the spectrum is due to one species then we can apply the Breit–Rabi equation (if the splitting is large) and the solutions found in § 2A.3c. By taking $A = H_b - H_a$ we can correct A by calculating f with this value of A. The new value of A can then be put into f and the next approximation to f thereby found. Similarly g^* may be calculated from the centre of the spectrum $((H_a + H_b)/2)$ and then corrected to the true g-value, $g = g^* f^*$ with f^* given in § 2A.3c.

A similar procedure may be followed for species with I greater than $\frac{1}{2}$.

5A.2 CRYSTAL SPECTRA

Here we are concerned with two aspects of the study of single crystals, first the ways in which the crystal is aligned in the magnetic field and sets of spectra obtained for a range of orientations, and secondly with ways of processing the wealth of data thereby obtained. We will not discuss the task of obtaining single crystals which are dilute with respect to the paramagnetic species that is being studied. This task is often formidable, and we do stress that a preliminary study of the powder spectrum (§ 5A.3) may either eliminate the need for using single crystals or at least aid in the task of extracting the required parameters from the single crystal data.

Crystals are commonly mounted on a rod which can be rotated in the manner shown in Fig. 5A.3. It is generally time-consuming to attempt to discover by trial and error the particular orientations of the crystal corresponding to the principal directions of the various tensors. The following procedure, due to Schonland[2], has therefore been evolved in order to simplify the task.

The method is based upon the expression for the g-value at a general orientation of the crystal:

$$g^2 = \sum_i l_i G_{ij} l_j \qquad (5A.1)$$

The l_i and l_j are direction cosines which relate that particular general orientation to some chosen system of axes set in the crystal and to which the matrix G refers. The problem is to determine the matrix G and then to

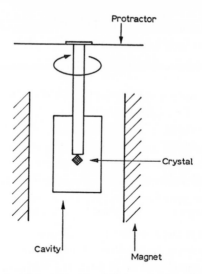

Fig. 5A.3. The experimental arrangement for measuring the spectrum of a single crystal.

diagonalise it: we shall then have determined the principal values of the g-tensor and the orientation of the principal axis relative to the chosen axes. The latter axes are not completely arbitrary but we shall prescribe them below. The diagonalisation of $\mathbf{G}$ is straightforward: the roots λ of the equation

$$\det |\mathbf{G} - \lambda \mathbf{I}| = 0 \qquad (5A.2)$$

must be determined, then the λ_i are the squares of the desired principal values of the g-tensor. Let us then concentrate upon the determination of $\mathbf{G}$.

The most general expression for g is

$$g^2 = \alpha + \beta \cos 2\theta + \gamma \sin 2\theta \qquad (5A.3)$$

where θ is a rotation angle and the α, β, γ are parameters which we must determine. If the maximum value of g during a rotation is denoted by $g^{(+)}$ and occurs at $\theta^{(+)}$, then

$$2\alpha = g^{(+)2} + g^{(-)2} \qquad (5A.4)$$

$$2\beta = (g^{(+)2} - g^{(-)2}) \cos 2\theta^{(+)} \qquad (5.A5)$$

$$2\gamma = (g^{(+)2} - g^{(-)2}) \sin 2\theta^{(+)} \qquad (5A.6)$$

Therefore, if the g-value variation is measured in three planes, nine pieces of information are obtained from which the six independent components of **G** may be both determined and cross-checked. There is an ambiguity in the sign of γ to which we must shortly return for it will lead to two possible sets of principal values.

To determine **G** experimentally select the most sensible set of axes in the crystal. For example, if the crystal is orthorhombic, choose the a, b, c axes; if it is monoclinic choose the a, b axes and an axis orthogonal to these. In any case take measurements in two planes which are mutually perpendicular (the 1,2 and 3,1 planes) and a third which contains the axis 2 and which meets the 3,1 plane in a line making an angle ε with axis 3 (the angle being measured in a positive sense from 3 to 1). These rotation planes are illustrated in Fig. 5A.4.

The crystal is then rotated so that θ is measured from axes 1, 2, 3 in the positive right-handed sense. If the values of the parameters α, β, γ are denoted by a subscript i for a rotation in the jk plane the matrix **G** can be constructed as follows:

$$
\begin{array}{|c|c|c|}
\begin{array}{c}\alpha_3 + \beta_3 \\ \alpha_2 - \beta_2\end{array} & \gamma_3 & \gamma_2 \\
\hline
\gamma_3 & \begin{array}{c}\alpha_3 - \beta_3 \\ \alpha_1 + \beta_1\end{array} & \dfrac{\gamma_1 - \gamma_3 \sin \varepsilon}{\cos \varepsilon} \\
\hline
\gamma_2 & \dfrac{\gamma_1 - \gamma_3 \sin \varepsilon}{\cos \varepsilon} & \alpha_2 + \beta_2
\end{array}
\tag{5A.7}
$$

also $G_{33} \cos^2 \varepsilon + G_{11} \sin^2 \varepsilon + 2G_{31} \sin \varepsilon \cos \varepsilon = \alpha_1 - \beta_1$ (5A.8)

The pairs of values on the diagonals serve as consistency checks. The case when the third rotation plane is perpendicular to the other two is particularly simple, for then $\varepsilon = 0$ and

$$G_{11} = \alpha_2 + \alpha_3 - \alpha_1 \tag{5A.9}$$

$$G_{12} = \pm \left[(\delta_3 + \alpha_1 - \alpha_2)(\delta_3 - \alpha_1 + \alpha_2)\right]^{\frac{1}{2}} \tag{5A.10}$$

where

$$\delta = \tfrac{1}{2}(g^{(+)^2} - g^{(-)^2}) \tag{5A.11}$$

The other components of **G** are generated by cyclic permutation of 1,2 throughout the expression for G_{12}. The sign of G_{12} is that of γ_3; this condition is also cyclic.

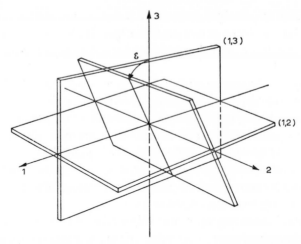

Fig. 5A.4.   Rotation planes used to determine the *g*- and hyperfine tensors of radicals in single crystals.

The ambiguity in the sign of γ must now be resolved. This is obtained either by marking the crystal, or when this fails, for example when different crystals have to be used or when there are several magnetic sites in the crystal, by performing a rotation in a plane other than those three already employed. The results for this rotation may be predicted from the expression

$$g^2 = g_{xx}^2 l^2 + g_{yy}^2 m^2 + g_{zz}^2 n^2 \qquad (5A.12)$$

where the g_{ii}^2 are the principal values of $\mathbf{G}$ and the l, m, n are the direction cosines which specify the rotation with respect to the principal axes of $\mathbf{G}$. It is not always necessary to do a complete rotation to resolve the ambiguity: indeed, measurement for one orientation is normally sufficient.

This account has followed Schonland's presentation very closely: his paper should be consulted for a discussion of the accuracy of the method[2]. Other methods have been devised by Weil and Anderson[3] and Geusic and Carlton Brown[4].

5A.3 POWDER SPECTRA

The powder spectrum is the envelope of the spectrum from all possible orientations of the radical; all that is required is a method of determining the principal values directly from the spectrum for they are present implicitly.

The major loss of information sustained is that the orientation of the radical in the crystal cannot be determined, but this may not be serious. The advantage is that doped single crystals need not be prepared and this frequently saves time.

A number of authors have discussed line-shapes of powder spectra. We shall confine this outline to the results obtained by Kneubühl[5] and will not give any quantitative discussion, such as those of Sands[6] or of Ibers and Swalen[7]. In particular we shall consider radicals with only one magnetic nucleus since otherwise the spectrum becomes particularly complex (§ 9.2, Fig. 9.8.). Furthermore we shall also assume that the principal directions of the g- and A-tensors are coincident. (The problems which arise if this is not the case have been considered in § 9.2.)

Fig. 5A.5a. shows the spectrum to be expected for a species with an axially symmetric g-tensor $(g_\perp, g_\perp, g_\parallel)$. The upper diagram is the absorption, the full line the idealised absorption and the broken line a possible real absorption. The lower curve is the first derivative of the upper curve. The broken line in the lower diagram is the trace normally recorded; the value of $g_\parallel$ is taken from the value of the field at the shoulder, and the value of $g_\perp$ is taken at the point of maximum slope as indicated in the Figure. The slope of the absorption lines is greatest when $g_\parallel$ and $g_\perp$ are close together.

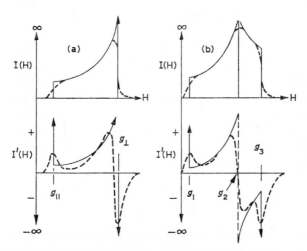

Fig. 5A.5. Absorption and first derivative curves for radicals with a g-tensor that is (a) axially symmetric and (b) anisotropic.

When the species has a fully anisotropic g-tensor the idealised and real absorption and first derivative spectra are as shown in Fig. 5A.5b. The point made in the final sentence of the preceding paragraph is also illustrated in this diagram. It is noticed that g_1 and g_3 are taken from the field at the shoulders and g_2 from the cross-over point of the first derivative curve.

When there is a magnetic nucleus present the spectra are more complicated and a number of ambiguities may be introduced, particularly if $I = \frac{1}{2}$. Some typical situations are illustrated in Figs. 5A.6. and 5A.7. together with possible interpretations. In Fig. 5A.7., which is for a radical having $I = 1$, the ambiguities are seen to be resolved. This is because the features must be self-consistent, that is we must be able to select $2I + 1$ features corresponding to each g-value for a species with nuclear spin I.

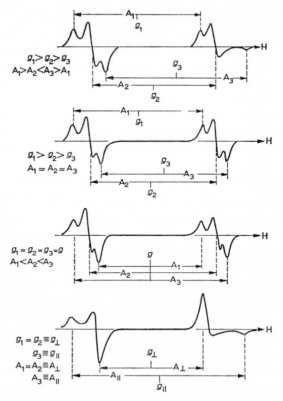

Fig. 5A.6.   Typical powder spectra for radicals with one spin-$\frac{1}{2}$ nucleus.

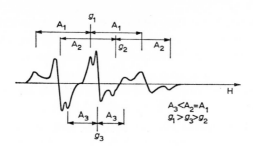

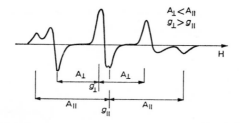

Fig. 5A.7. Typical powder spectra for radicals with one spin-1 nucleus.

Occasionally the species contains a nucleus which has more than one isotope in appreciable natural abundance. The spectrum then consists of the superposition of spectra of which several examples have already been given in the text.

The powder method has many limitations and inaccuracies. Some of the former have been indicated. The latter arise, for example, from the difficulty of precisely locating a shoulder on a line. Also the above diagrams have been calculated for δ-function absorption line-shapes for each individual orientation and have only been estimated for real line-shapes. Kneubühl has investigated the consequences of admitting real line-shapes and concludes that the corrections are only large when $g_{\parallel}$ and $g_{\perp}$ are very close together [5]. Ibers and Swalen have reaffirmed this for the case when the individual line-shapes are Lorentzian and conclude that curves should be computed with formulae which they derive, and then fitted to the experimental curves [7]. Where powder and crystal parameters are both available the agreement is encouraging using the simple procedure outlined above for powders. Thus these corrections do not seem to be necessary unless extreme accuracy is required.

References

1 R. W. FESSENDEN, *J. Chem. Phys.*, 1962, *37*, 747.
2 D. S. SCHONLAND, *Proc. Phys. Soc.*, 1959, *73*, 788.
3 J. A. WEIL AND J. H. ANDERSON, *J. Chem. Phys.*, 1958, *28*, 864.
4 J. E. GEUSIC AND L. CARLTON BROWN, *Phys. Rev.*, 1958, *112*, 64.
5 F. K. KNEUBÜHL, *J. Chem. Phys.*, 1960, *33*, 1074.
6 R. S. SANDS, *Phys. Rev.*, 1955, *99*, 1222.
7 J. A. IBERS AND J. D. SWALEN, *Phy. Rev.*, 1962, *127*, 1914.

Index of data

The following table gives the page on which electron spin resonance data for particular radicals are summarised

[H : 86, 87]

Subject Index